I Used To Be Italian

Thank you dear old
friends for the moral
support throughout this
grinding project. (Emphasis
on _old_)
   Read page 289 first. You
may not want to bother with
the rest of the book.

      Love,
    John V. Rovesti
      4/17/02

I Used To Be Italian

JOHN V. LONERO

PACOLET PINES PUBLISHING
P.O.B. 1047   TRYON, NC 28782

ISBN - 0-9717078-0-4

LCCN 2001135876

Published by
Pacolet Pines Publishing, Tryon, N.C.

Printed in the United States of America by
M.A. Designs, Tryon, N.C.

All artwork, cover and book format design by
John V. Lonero — Author photo by Hedy E. Lonero.

It brings me great pride and honor to dedicate this book to Santa and Pasquale Lonero. Also known as Susie and Pat.

a.k.a. Mamma and Papa

FOREWORD

This book was written by a friend of mine but that doesn't make any difference. I have friends who can't write, can't juggle, can't speak French and hate cats. I still like them. John Lonero happens to be able to write and, even better, can <u>remember.</u> He knows that memory comes through the heart, not the brain.

<u>I Used To Be Italian</u> is about a bright, warm-hearted boy growing up in the Italian ghetto of Cleveland, Ohio in the Thirties. It was a gentler, harder time; there were half as many people on the earth as there are now, and they all weren't trying to get on talk shows. It was a country of flagpole sitters and streetcars and radio. It was a time of wide-eyed exploration, confusion, and first loves.

It was a familial war, fought across America, between the dreams of the New World and the roots of The Old Country.

Lonero, with remarkable humor and openness, takes us through adventures and heartbreaks of those innocent years during the Thirties. Then into the rebellious adolescent years of the Forties, and finally surviving into the maturing and career-development years of the Fifties. Because even as he found the love of his life, even as he became a rising star on Madison Avenue, even through getting his Ph.D. and getting commendations from the state of New York for his contributions to art education, he never forgot either Mamma's hushed admonition, "Don't bring dishonor to your family," or the streetcorner advice of Vinnie Grosso, his life-long buddy, "If someone's gotcha by the short hairs, you grab 'em by the balls. The whole friggin' world is one big friggin' shell game. Forget that and you're as useless as a second-hand suppository."

I Used To Be Italian reminds me of the constructed memoirs of writer-monologist Jean Shepherd, all classics and several of which have been made into movies. Reading John's manuscript made me wish I'd had his childhood.

I can think of no higher compliment.

Billy Kerby, screenwriter
Hollywood, CA

FOR THE READER

"That's a lotta baloney!" my sister Ann managed to say through a mouthful of Cappacola-ham sandwich. "How can your book be fiction? Most of this stuff actually happened. I know, because I was there. Honest t' God!"

And she's right. Most of the stuff in this book actually happened and I embellished here and there. So maybe what you're about to read is creative non-fiction. You decide, after you learn the facts.

The protagonist, Jamie LaBianca, I knew very well. I crawled deep into his mind and skin. There was some embellishment here.

Vinnie Grosso, Jamie's loyal *paesano*, is a composite of some wonderfully wild people I've had the good luck to know in my lifetime. I didn't have to exaggerate much here.

I patterned Mamma and Papa after my own parents to balance the nuttiness in the book with heaps of virtue, integrity, and wisdom. No hyperbole here.

Same for Ric. Baptized Enrico, known as Ric (pronounced Reek) to his family and friends, Henry, to the church community, Andy in school, and "Blackie" in the army during WWII.

Sister Ann, known in her love-of-life childhood years as Anna-Bananna, didn't take much embroidering to make it into the book. Just a little toning-down.

The other important characters, like Jenny Lange, Michael DaFutte and "Frankie the Foot," are composite-characters molded and sculpted from a lot of wonderful people who are locked in my memory.

Then there's Mata. Mata is a four letter word for Hedy, my lifetime wife, my *anima cuore*. Without her, there would be no book. Neither of us typed. I wrote the book long-hand, Hedy taught herself to type, bought a word processor and nurtured me and the book through the torturous months and years it took to learn the craft of writing a novel, and the incredibly convoluted politics of publishing.

The other people who kept the project afloat whenever it got waterlogged and started to sink, were Loretta Hudson, Billy Kerby, Candy Davis, Margaret Henning, Helen Harriss, and Jodi Lashua.

Thank you all, for sharing your patience, hearts, and skills.

My gratuitous gratitude to Sol Stein, who's book, <u>Stein on Writing</u>, taught me more about writing than most of the creative writing courses we all endured through our college-credit-accumulating years.

So, reader, what do you think? Fiction or non-fiction?

Here's what I think. I've been advised that for legal reasons I will make the disclaimer that any resemblance to real people, places, or situations, is purely coincidental. Or as Anna-Bananna put it so succinctly, "It's a lotta baloney!"

John V. Lonero, Ph.D.

TABLE OF CONTENTS

Amicizie sono fabbricate dal fuoco.

ITALIAN PROVERB

Friendships are forged in fire. Each time a family or friends survive a common crisis together, the bond grows stronger. The more catastrophic the crisis, the stronger the bond. War buddies, for instance, are buddies for life.

Chapter I

Now I knew I had to get a gun. I'd avoided making the decision for a long time, but here it was, again, the acrid taste of intuitive, imminent danger.

I drove slowly. All of the landmarks were gone. Just...gone. Replaced by neon sleaze inhabited by a multi-racial subspecies clustered in debris-strewn doorways, and loitered in frozen, unnatural poses, inside, against, and on the roofs of cars, haphazardly parked.

I stopped for a traffic light at an intersection and stared at the street signs attached to the lamppost. The white block letters against the dark green background on one sign read: "Clark Avenue." The other, pointing perpendicular to it read: "Fulton Road." Clark and Fulton! Our hangout corner when we were kids! Ah right! Finally. Something I could relate to. At least I'd found the lamppost and the signs. But nothing else looked even vaguely familiar.

After an absence of 14, maybe 15 years, I'd landed at the Cleveland Airport, rented a new 1965 car, and bumbled my way like a stranger to an area the map on the seat next to me identified as my old neighborhood.

I gawked and craned, waiting for the light to change. A young black man with a bright orange bandanna wrapped around his forehead, slowly pedaled his bicycle into the crosswalk and stopped directly in front of my grille. When our eyes met, he glowered like he had a score to settle.

Suddenly, a body crashed belly-down onto the hood of my car. I never saw where it came from. It seemed to have dropped from above.

"Jesus Christ!" I flailed at the already secured doorlocks.

The bizarre shoes, attached to the legs spread-eagled on the hood, fell over the headlights. The hideous head of the assailant, wrapped with another orange bandanna, landed only inches away from the windshield directly in front of me. I watched with horror as the pursed lips spewed something the color and consistency of mayonnaise onto the glass. Without hesitation, the attacker snapped the wiper back and forth to create an impenetrable fan-shaped smear that covered most of the windshield on my side.

The bicycle rider made his way to the passenger side of the car and like his counterpart, disgorged a mouthful of the same gooey mess onto the other half of the windshield. When he forced the wiper back and forth I couldn't see the street in front of me.

It took a few seconds for my frozen reflexes to respond and recognize a variation of "the blind pigeon" I'd learned on these very streets as a kid. *"Never walk close to a dark doorway or shadows at night in a different neighborhood. If someone drops a bag over your head from behind, you're a blind, maybe dead, pigeon."*

"Holy Christ! Holy Jumpin' Jesus!" With knee jerk action I stomped down hard on the accelerator.

The thug on the hood hit the windshield, screaming as he slid to the pavement. "Honky muth-a-fucker! Lily-white cunt lapper! Ofay bitch-bastard!"

The car leaped forward through a shrieking mob of bloodthirsty Neanderthals who yanked at the door handles

16

and pounded on the raised windows. In the blur, I caught the glint of a knife blade. If I hadn't insisted on air conditioning at the rental agency, the windows would be rolled down and one of these unplugged lunatics would be carving out my pounding heart to hold up to the next full moon.

By turning the traffic light in my favor at exactly the right time, my guardian angels got me through the intersection without my getting hit by crossing traffic.

"God Almighty...Good God Almighty!" My spastic hands seemed to be disconnected from my brain.

When I gathered enough sense to find and press the windshield washer button, it squirted and the damaged wipers cleaned a narrow wedge shape. I frantically maneuvered the car for several blocks, hyperventilating, and looking over my shoulders, when I could, until somehow, I managed to reach my destination.

My eyes, which seemed to be functioning independent of each other, found the sign attached to the high chain-link entrance gate. It read: "Daisy Enterprises, Ltd./By appointment only." The gate and the 10-foot-high fence that enclosed the compound were topped with strands of barbed wire. It looked more like a correctional institution than a lithograph and cardboard die-cut plant.

By the time the security guard slid open the horizontal gate, waved me into the inspection pen and closed the gate behind me, I'd turned down the adrenalin-rush and recovered enough to place my trembling credentials onto his outstretched hand. While he searched for my name on his clipboard, a second member of the security force stepped out of the guard house and paused with his hands on his hips. He stared through his pilot sunglasses in my direction.

"Whatsa matta Wilburn, we got a party crasher here?" Unlike Wilburn, who wore a short-sleeved shirt and trousers, the second man in brown and beige looked like he was made up to play the role of one of the Mexican Federales in the movie *Viva Zapata!* Jodhpurs, brown knee-high leather boots, chest strap from right hip gun holster to left epaulet, topped with a tan officer's hat that sat on top of a full crop of curly black hair. There was a narrow band of forehead showing between the hairline and the thick eyebrows.

"Throw...the...bum...outta...here! *OUT!*" He snapped his thumb over his shoulder like a baseball umpire calling a close play at first base.

This was the final indignity. I collected the residue of terror, helplessness, and humiliation I'd suffered from the corner violation, packed it into a red-hot ball of rage, and stepped out of the car, ready for a high-decibel shouting match.

"Hey! Goombah!" bellowed the Federales impersonator. "Come over here!" He took off his hat, folded his sunglasses into it, and handed the hat to Wilburn. "It's me! Tony Giardello!" He flashed a stained, gap-toothed smile that exposed gold incisors.

I shuddered and let out a grateful-to-God sigh of relief as I sagged against the car fender. I had reached the protective shelter of our old neighborhood eccentric, Tony Giardello. It was Tony, when I was a kid, who assumed the role of mother hen and unobtrusively watched over me, my brother Ric, and my sister Annie, like it was his sworn duty. But, there was a dark side to Tony. His reputation for physical violence was widespread, and he couldn't keep a job because of his hair-trigger temper.

He wrapped his tree-trunk arms around me in a

bear-hug, effortlessly lifted me off my feet, spun me in forward-moving pirouettes, and set me down next to where Wilburn was standing.

"I gotta tell ya somethin', Jamie-Babe," said Tony, "the manager had these guys spiffying-up this place for a week because 'The Big Boss" from New York is comin' down. Whoa! All of a sudden, we got clean toilets, no cigarette butts all over the place, paint splashed around. And Wilburn, here, has been letting in the suits with their tinted-glass shiny cars all morning. They came early to impress...*The...Big...Boss....* They're all up in the boardroom right now eating shrimp and drinkin' wine while they wait for...*The...Big...Boss...*from New Yaw-w-k." Tony let out a shriek and pounded my shoulder, which was a little higher than his head.

"Hey, Wilburn, you know who this guy is? You know who you almost threw out?" He let out another shriek, put his mouth close to Wilburn's ear and in a low voice said, "This tall man in a sweatshirt and blue jeans, in a rented sub-compact car with bird shit all over the windshield is...heh...heh...heh...heh...heh... *The...Big...Boss...from...New...Yor-r-r-k!!!*"

Wilburn put on a non-committal smile that could be easily switched from "I don't get it," to "Pleased to meet you," or, if necessary, "You didn't really think I'd fall for that one, do you?" What he said was, "All the way from New York. Um...m...m...."

"New York my ass," said an animated Tony. "This is Jamie LaBianca. He's one of *us*, Wilburn. He was born and raised right here, in this neighborhood. He started Daisy Enterprises by himself. In a store. Right here. *Here!* Where I'm standin'! From *zero*. ZERO, Wilburn...to zillionaire! How do you like them apples?" He pointed past the row of employee cars lined on the inside of the protective fence. "His mother's house used to be right there, this side of 33rd. Am I right, Jamie?"

"Almost." I took his arm and nudged him away from Wilburn's ears. We strolled down the row of parked cars toward 33rd street.

"Now that you brought it up, Tony, you almost got it right, but not quite. In fact, right here, where we're standing," I said, as I tamped my foot, "there was a storefront where Daisy, the wonderful woman from Tennessee, painted her lampshades. That's where we got the name for our place. On the corner of 33rd street, on that side, was the Texaco Gas Station. Our house was right next to it."

"Jamie," said Tony, "I gotta ask ya something. Tell me if I'm wrong. On the way over here, you come in a cheap car and work clothes so you can blend into the woodwork, but I could see by the looks of the car that the young punks blind-pigeoned you. YOU of all people. Now...ya gotta ask yourself. Why me? Not the car back of you. No. They picked *you*. You know why? Your old-time street smarts would'a worked in the old days. But, no more. Not when a neighborhood gets this bad."

"I came down to give recognition awards to the bottom-line boosters, Tony, but from now on, these execs get flown to New York, as usual. The hell with this crap."

"Jamie," said Tony, "you forgot the plates. Rental car plates tell these young assholes you're a stranger or a lost tourist with luggage, clothes, camera, lots of good stuff to hock. Next time, come with tinted windows. Punks are afraid of black windows. Could be mobsters with guns." He tapped the revolver on his hip. "If you had one of these in your pocket to wave around, you could come see us lots more times."

"I know you're right, Tony, I know. I carry large sums of

money sometimes, and I know I should carry a gun. Matter of fact, I had one for target practice when I was going to college. One day I had an accident with it. Smacked a girl right on the forehead with a spent bullet. Scared the shit out of me and I swore off guns. But...I gotta get realistic."

"These days, goombah, you *better* get realistic," said Tony.

"I know, I know," I said. "Things ain't what they used to be. What happened with those *bastardos* a little while ago scared the shit outta me. Look at this. My hands are still shaking. The gun laws are very strict in New York. Very, very hard to get a license to carry. I hate to do it, but I know now, whatever it takes, I'm gettin' a gun."

"Explain somethin' else to me, Jamie." He flattened the wrinkles on the front of my sweatshirt with the palms of his hands and read aloud, "Blessed Are the Troublemakers." He stared at the message, got a quizzical expression on his face, shrugged his shoulders, and asked, "What the hell is that supposed to mean? You *like* troublemakers?"

I laughed and said, "I was wondering how long it was gonna' take for you to ask. No...no, Tony. It's not like that. I'm not a masochist. It's —"

"Say what?" he asked, with his right ear cocked in my direction, but still wearing the puzzled expression.

"Glutton for punishment. You know...soft in the head...weirdo." He caught that, so I went on. "OK. So now you get my drift. Remember Mike DaFutte?"

"Yeah, yeah. Well, no, I didn't know Mikey too good but I knew his big brother 'Frankie the Foot' really good."

"Well, Mike is a big shot lawyer in New York now and he gave me this sweatshirt. It's like an inside lawyer joke. Without the troublemakers, they'd all be out of work." When it registered, we both laughed as I stroked my chest like I was playing a small accordion.

"Speaking of troublemakers," said Tony, "you still pickin' up after Vinnie Grosso? I hear if it wasn't for you —"

"You know," I interrupted, "I keep hearing that story about me and Vinnie, but Vinnie doesn't owe me anything. If anybody owes, I owe Vinnie. When his mother died —"

"Who's older, you or Vinnie?"

"Vinnie is a year older than me and —"

"Your brother Rico older?"

"Ric is two years older than me."

"Everybody that doesn't know your family thinks all three of you guys are brothers. Damn good lookin' brothers. You could go to Hollywood. You get a face like that, I get a face like this. If I had a face like you guys, I woulda gone after your sister Annie an' you'd be talkin' to your brother-in-law right now." He grinned his gold-incisor grin. "Ann—"

"Wait...wait. Before we leave Vinnie," I said, "*You* brought him up, now listen. Maybe you don't remember, but Vinnie's mother died when he was eight or nine, something like that. OK? His father was never around, so Vinnie spent most of his time at our house, and I gotta tell ya, I learned a lot from Vinnie. A lot. I have a bunch of diplomas that show I earned a formal education, but my best education, how to survive in this world, I got down at the corner of Clark and Fulton. And Vinnie —"

"And Vinnie killed a guy," interjected Tony. "You can't get around it, Jamie. That ain't dippsy-doodle. He blotted-out a guy. Vinnie —"

"No...no, Tony. Vinnie killed in self defense. You just told me a minute ago I had the right to stick the muzzle up that son-of-a-bitch's nostril and blow his head off. That's OK, but not for Vinnie? Right?"

"Ya know Jamie, I remember even your father used to say, '*Vinnie has at least one wobbly wheel.*'"

"Vinnie explored the world and I followed him. You might say he ran interference for me. While he took all the heavy hits, I was Mr. Nice-guy who saved his ass. Bullshit, Tony. If Vinnie hadn't shown me what was available out there, I wouldn't be talkin' to you here, now, I'd be in a church cellar somewhere, folding old clothes for the poor."

"Yeah. Well, I remember, through thick-'n-thin, you guys always used to stick together," said Tony, as he studied the protective barbwire atop the chain-link fence.

"You know..." I said, "the word in the old neighborhood was — 'each time friends or family share and survive a common crisis together, the bond grows stronger.'"

"Say what?"

"Two guys go through hell together, they're gonna be buddies for life," I translated.

"Damn right," said Tony, "if the war is against Krauts, Japs, or even buddy against buddy. Don't matter. You got *that* right, an' you can bet your balls on that. For sure."

"Yeah. Vinnie got into one mess after another...sometimes with me," I said. "A troublemaker? Sure. But a blessed troublemaker. And that, dear Tony, is also for sure."

We stopped at the boundary fencing and turned back toward the main building. Reports to New York indicated that this Cleveland branch was constantly under siege, plagued with vandalism and robberies. When I reviewed the list of applicants for more security, I saw Tony Giardello's name. The only thing noted under his qualifications was a number of years as manager of the White Tower hamburger joint on 25th Street.

I not only hired him long distance, sight unseen, to solve the current problem, I put him in charge. He was security chief for a little over a month when the alarming string of robberies and destruction stopped. No more robberies, no more vandalism. Period.

"I knew if anybody could fix this, it was going to be you," I said. "How did you accomplish this remarkable feat? No break-ins? None?"

"I'm always on the night shift," said Tony. "Couple weeks ago my three German Shepherds corner a kid over by the shipping dock. I cuff 'im and take 'im for a ride on my bike." He pointed the middle fingers on both hands to a squat brown, beige, and chrome Harley-Davidson motorcycle that occupied a parking space we were approaching.

"That's your bike? Jeez, that's a beauty. I was lookin' at it when we walked past it before. I had an Indian when I was in college. Nothin' like this. This is a beautiful machine." I leaned closer to the script-letter chrome and black emblem attached to the front fender-well and read, "Hydra-Glide."

"So you took the kid to the police on this bike?"

"Hell-l-l-l no. That's exactly what that punk would like. Every time one of these assholes spends a night in the can, it's like getting a merit badge for his gang. That's what the security chief before me used to do. No, no. I put a canvas money bag over his head, pull the strings tight, and take 'im for a nice short ride down to Popolizzio's."

"The funeral home? Jesus, Tony, I don't know if I wanna know the rest of this story." Tony shrugged his shoulders.

"OK." I said, "I gotta know. But this is strictly, strictly, off the record. OK? Off the record."

"There's not much to the story," said Tony, "I take 'im to

the shed behind Popolizzio's where they store the coffins, put the cuffed kid in one of the coffin's, an' when I pull the bag off his head, only the top half of the coffin is open. Then I make one of his nostrils bigger with the muzzle of my gun, then I talk to him 'till we have a...a...a understanding, then I turn him loose so he can go tell his other asshole pals what the new deal is around here."

"Jesus H. Christ, Tony," I said, my hands cupping my ears, "I don't want to hear another word. Not another word, do you hear? Do your thing, just don't tell me about it."

"Listen Jamie, I never got to really thank you for this job. I was really starting to scratch there for a while. This was a big break for me and I swear on my mother's grave, goombah, so help me God, you ain't never gonna be sorry. Never." He took my hand and pumped it vigorously.

"Hey, Tony, what are friends for? I did you a favor. Now I need a favor. I've got 25 minutes to get back and change clothes before the board meeting starts. Take me on your buddy-seat to my car to pick up my camera. I wanna get some shots of my real alma-mater...nice shots of the signs down at the corner...nice close-up shots of...." I peered through a viewfinder I made with my fingers. "...Clark and Fulton."

"You got it, boss! Git on."

Chapter II

"Jamie, watch this goddam pile o' bricks and crap comin'
up," said Vinnie Grosso, who was leading the way through the
short-cut he'd discovered through the backyards of our
primarily Italian inner-city neighborhood. Ever since 8-year-
old Vinnie's mother died, he'd learned to express his bitterness
by swearing a lot, but I was glad to have the sound of his voice
to follow as he guided me through the tangle of sharp obstacles
hidden in the dark shadows of a half-moon-lit night.

It was unusually hot and sweaty for late autumn in
Cleveland, Ohio. I was only 7, Vinnie was a year older than me,
and more wise in the ways of the world; both too young to
appreciate that we were in the depths of The Great Depression,
but old enough to know that the best place for free excitement and
entertainment every night, after supper, was at the hangout
corner, Clark and Fulton.

I struggled to keep up with Vinnie who was bigger
than me and had dropped over the fence into the alleyway that
came out near the corner. From this distance we could
hear the undulating commotion and the sporadic clamor coming from the gathered gang in response to something that
was already in progress.

"Goddam it, Jamie," urged Vinnie, in a half whisper, "hurry
up. I think there's a fight going on already. Listen. I think it's
Nunzio and the big Polack."

As Vinnie and I cautiously exited the alley, Nunzio shouted at his opponent facing him under the street light. "How the hell did you get to be so goddam stupid?"

"I used to be Italian."

"Yeah, an' when the maggots ate your brain you automatically became a friggin' Polack," retaliated Nunzio.

"At least we got a whole bunch'a really smart maggot bambinos out of it, you Dago Wop bastard."

"Nah, nah. What'cha got was a bunch'a poor, measly, goddam maggots who don't know no better, dying a horrible, rotten death by Polack poison."

It was as if we'd entered a darkened theatre in the middle of a play and were tip-toeing down the aisle as inconspicuously as possible to find a seat somewhere on the crowded stoops. Bill and Lino waved to us and pointed to the two spots on the steps they'd saved for us.

As we settled into our reserved spaces, Lino filled us in on what was going on and could barely control his enthusiasm when he came to the line he'd been waiting to deliver.

"Like Basil jus' said, this one's gonna be a ball buster."

"What'a ya mean?" I asked.

"Well, Jamie boy, it's like this," he said, in a poor imitation of the wise old wagon master we'd seen in the Tom Mix western Saturday at the Garden. "Somebody under that light is gonna get their balls busted, an' we're about to find out who."

The circle of light cast by the lamppost directly in front of us loosely established an arena on the ground in which the teenage toughs defined the rules by going through the nightly ritual of adjusting the pecking order of our pack.

The swaggering candidates vying for the position of "*Capo,*" usually the largest and most successful at enforcing the rule of the fist, positioned themselves directly under the light of the fluted dark green metal lamppost which was enveloped in clouds of moth-like insects.

"I wouldn't piss on your ass if there were flames shootin' out of it!"

"Oh yeah, Mr. Tough Guy? I'll knock you flatter than a turd from a high cow's ass!" shrieked Nunzio.

"Hot damn, here they go!" said Vinnie, as he leaned forward next to me, "I think this one's going all the way." He had the bloodthirsty look of someone with a ringside seat at the main event of a heavyweight boxing match. As usual, the vulgarity left me gaping and blinking with amazement. In our house, swearing or anything to do with sex, even the *word* sex, was absolutely forbidden. Naturally, as a minnow in this tank of sharks, I was swept up by the intensity of the drama and the potential bloodletting that seemed imminent.

The menacing gestures and the blistering language kept escalating until the shouting rivals' heads were almost touching. If they did, there was no turning back. No interference, no mercy. The last one standing won. To save face, neither brawler wanted to land the first blow for fear he might end up bloodied and battered in the gutter with no sympathy because "he started it." As they cocked their arms ready for the counter punch, the edgy "seconds" on the fringe moved in tighter.

Suddenly, a loud explosion next to me blew me against Lino. Vinnie had unclipped his "hammer-head" from his belt and smacked it against the concrete steps. The tong-shaped cast-iron device with the spring-metal hinge worked on the same principle as a cap gun but was loaded with a "Big Bertha" cap that was ten times louder than the ordinary cap and sounded like a starter's pistol.

Vinnie's intent was to startle the fighters into crossing the line to the point of no return, but his plan succumbed to the law of unintended consequences.

Instead of the reflex punch landing, everyone froze in their tracks, giving the seconds time to physically restrain "their boys" and drag them kicking and screaming into the darkness, in opposite directions.

"Leave 'em alone!" shouted Vinnie, "leave 'em alone, leave 'em alone, goddamit!"

Once a safe distance had been established, the proper verbal abuse required to wind down continued until the squabblers sputtered to a truce and awkwardly drifted toward their designated lamppost positions. I was always relieved when that happened. It was like watching a heart-stopping high-wire act at the circus that courted disaster without a net. When the aerialists completed their routine and successfully cheated death, I stopped pressing my nails into the palms of my hands, and started breathing normally again.

To dampen the potential seriousness of these disturbing situations, Basil DeBenedictis, with his exquisite timing and pacifying instincts, sat on a stoop in the dark fringes with his homemade banjo at the ready. Basil's body was stunted but his ability to take charge was not. He was probably the oldest teenager in the gang, grew a wispy goat beard on his chin, was about three feet tall, three feet wide, and always created a diversion when things started to get out of hand. He served the same vital purpose as the rodeo clowns we saw in the newsreels.

He leaped into the light of the lamppost with his instrument as soon as the musclemen were dragged off into the shadows. The one string banjo was made from a wooden cigar box with an attached movable neck and a taut banjo string. With infinitesimal movements of the neck Basil could alter the pitch on the string to achieve the amazing array of notes necessary to accompany himself. He'd run through an arpeggio on the makeshift banjo and burst on stage with exaggerated gestures and a step-cadence that punctuated the snappy tempo: *"They go wild, simply wild over me / I don't know what it is that they can see / They look at me and sigh / in my arms they want to die /...."*

Basil...the safety net. I always felt especially uneasy on the rare nights when he wasn't standing by, with his banjo.

Others in the group with equal musical ability sang gripping a cappella barbershop quartet songs and still others, yarn spinners, could regale or horrify, at will, with their beguiling tales of sex and violence. But, as entertaining as these preliminary performances were, the highlight of any evening, the stellar act, began when Frankie the Foot, a little older than everyone else, made his nightly appearance. He was a *Capo dei capi.* Revered, trusted, and feared.

Frankie always joined the group late in the evening as the closing act because he worked late every night at Miller's Drug Store. After Mr. Miller had gone home, it was Frankie's duty to prepare the store for the following morning. He wasn't paid for overtime, officially, but he was unofficially compensated for the conscientious job he always did.

The value of the items he pilfered from the store each night was carefully calculated to balance the worth of his overtime and he always shared the booty with the performers and theatre-goers across the street. In order not to create an obvious deficit in any of the drugstore stock, Frankie never took a lot of one thing but prudently took a little from here, and a little from there, with enough variety to please just about every street urchin holding up his begging-bowl.

"Who wants some chocolate-covered cherries?" In one bound we were in the lamplight with our hands extended. Frankie the Foot gave better quality door prizes than they ever gave at the Garden Theatre at Saturday afternoon cliff-hangers.

Many of the things distributed were baffling, but to conceal our ignorance, we accepted everything with grace and without question.

"All right," said Frankie, as he reached into the bag, "who needs some raincoats? Faz? You need any?"

"Yeah, I'll take a couple." Frankie handed Faz a fistful of foil-wrapped condoms.

"Dino? Jo-Jo? Mamaluk, you still goin' with that tub?"

"Yeah, gim'me some," said Mamaluk, "when I put one of these on and slip into that beautiful tub, I'm in heaven! I jus' tie one end of a rope around my belt an' the other end to the radiator so I don't fall in, then I *s-l-i-p* right in." He did a couple of Fred Astaire dance steps as he sang, "Heaven. I'm in heaven, and my heart beats so...hey, Frankie, gim'me a couple more a those. Hey-hey, heaven, I'm in heaven —"

"Tell me something, Frankie," said Jo-Jo, "do I need a raincoat if I use her armpit? I'm goin' out with Dino's sister who likes to do it in the armpit an' I don't wanna catch cooties or the clap." A remark like that guaranteed a hot, pounding pursuit into the darkness.

"Better leave my sister out of this you son-of-a-bitch!"

"OK, Dino! OK! I'm sorry, OK?" came the response from out of the darkness. "I'm not takin' out your sister, OK? *I'm takin' out your brother!*"

"Here man. I got somethin' for you to take out. Here! Come an' git it, man! Right here!"

"A vulture shit on a rock an' the sun hatched it. Welcome

to the human race, you dickless wonder!"

The surplus condoms were often distributed evenly among us younger boys who week after week accepted them with gratitude and ignorance, and stuffed them into our pockets.

Although my inventory of raincoats kept growing, I had no idea what these tin-foil wrapped balloons were for, exactly. With all the crotch-grabbing, I knew it had something to do with the weenie, and women, and the armpit. But what? Were raincoats for keeping your weenie dry when you were in the tub like Mamaluk? For peeing underwater? I knew they'd hold water because I'd experimented with that, and I knew they were some kind'a mortal sin because of the way everybody hid them whenever older people started to come near. I dun'no. I would love to know, but I wasn't about to risk eternal humiliation by exposing my monumental stupidity. If anybody finds out I don't get it, I'm *really* gonna get it.

The one thing Frankie never shared with the wee ones were cigarettes. Generally, the adolescents rolled their own, so it was always a treat when Frankie offered them coveted Camel or Lucky Strike cigarettes, courtesy of Miller's drugstore. These manufactured cigarettes were prized by everyone, including marauding rogue policemen who stopped their black squad cars at random, without provocation, and frisked all the young men standing under the lamppost. They confiscated anything of value, including personal items, but were like pigs after truffles when it came to cigarettes.

Those of us hanging around the perimeter were designated "lookouts," and whenever we saw a "Flying Squad Car" with the Latin motto espousing "Security, Justice, Duty" emblazoned on the front doors approaching at the tell-tale crawling speed, we would holler "Car!" All things of value were then quickly tossed into the dark or handed to us young ones because we were never searched. When that happened, the responsibility made us feel more mature...part of a team facing a common danger together. When all was secure, Basil took over with his banjo, or we formed a diversionary game of "kick-the-can."

"Car!" I shouted. It thrilled me to be the first to spot the squad car. It gave me a feeling of power, like shouting a command. With one word I could activate everybody, including Frankie, to scramble to their prescribed posts and roles. It was *us* against *them*.

The black Model A Ford with the pistol grip spotlight mounted through the right side of the windshield pulled to the curb before it reached the light of the lamppost. Two cops got out, motioned the guys into a line facing the lamppost, made them assume the position, selected their booty, and left, without uttering a word through the lips that sagged on the side that held their dangling cigarettes.

"Sons-a-bitches," said Frankie, as he watched the car disappear down Clark. Vinnie came out of the shadows and with the look of a kid trying to impress his favorite teacher with a bunch of wildflowers, handed Frankie a pile of various-sized thin books, illustrated pamphlets, and photographs. "Here," he said, glancing up at Frankie, then down to his shoetops.

Frankie took the pile of stuff absentmindedly with his eyes and mind still following the vanishing car of the uniformed robbers. When he focused on what Vinnie had handed him, he rifled through the pile of pornography, and said, "Holy shit! H-o-l-y shit!" He looked over his right shoulder, then his left, and added, "Where did you get this?"

"Same place I got this," said Vinnie, as he handed Frankie a black-jack, a nightstick, and a badge.

"From the police car?"

Vinnie was rocking side to side with his hands deep in his pockets, staring at his shoes. "You always said, 'fair is fair.' While they was robbin' you, I was robbin' them. Did I do good?"

Frankie dropped the boodle, grabbed Vinnie by the armpits and raised him over his head with elation. He set him back down on his feet, and tousled his hair.

"Vinnie," said Frankie, "you got brass balls, you know that? That was a dumb, dangerous thing to do...but ya done good, real good!"

Cheers and applause rippled through the crowd of boys as the news spread. Frankie, who'd had enough of the police harassing, now had the retaliation counter-measure he'd been trying to formulate for a long time.

A couple of nights later, the a cappella quartet that had made it to the finals of the Major Bowes Amateur Hour radio program stopped dead in the middle of a maudlin lyric when someone shouted, "Car!"

We watched the cop get out of the squad car and amble sluggishly toward the light to start his shameless looting. Frankie was ready and waiting for him.

Before the humiliating shake-down could begin, Frankie had lit up two cigarettes and offered one to the unsuspecting cop. While they stood there puffing, Frankie casually challenged the cop to a spontaneous game of chance. How about if they smoked their cigarettes and the one left with the longest surviving ash still attached to his cigarette won? The cop smiled and looked interested. This sounded better than the same old dumb arm wrestling he always won.

A few minutes into the contest Frankie made the *ad hoc* rules even more interesting. If the ash on Frankie's cigarette was intact after the cop's ash had fallen from his, Frankie kept his cigarettes and the cop would relinquish pornographic books and paraphernalia that he had confiscated elsewhere. If it turned out the other way around, Frankie would surrender packs of cigarettes. With a cocked eyebrow, the cop accepted the challenge, hook, line, and sinker. And lost. Same thing the next time they came, and most nights after that.

Frankie didn't win every time, of course. He was too smart for that. He let the cops win occasionally but there was no doubt that he was in control of the outcome. With accentuated bravado, he even announced to us beforehand when they were going to win and what he would surrender.

"They're starting to dry up," said Frankie. "I'm gonna juice 'em up by letting 'em win a big one. A whole carton. That'll give 'em the fever."

"How the hell do you know who's gonna win each time? For sure, I mean?" asked Mamaluk.

"When the time comes," said Frankie, with the tolerant smile of a sage, "I'll let you know...don't worry."

After a while both cops got out of the car and got involved. They tried various strategies like puffing slowly, not puffing at all, or puffing such long sustained drags that they would ultimately gasp out clouds of smoke in coughing jags. They sometimes bent at the waist with the cigarette hanging straight down, the suffocating smoke rising into their faces. They even tried sitting on the curb with their heads tilted back to put the cigarette in a more vertical position. In the meantime, Frankie would calmly and confidently puff away with over one inch of ash still attached to his cigarette long after both policemen watched with frustration as their own futile attempts fell to the ground.

Before long, we all had stacks of pornographic comic books called "big little books" which graphically showed "Tillie the Toiler," "Popeye," and the "Katzenjammer Kids" in vivid, sexually explicit situations.

The impressive accumulation created a serious logistics problem. Namely, where to hide such a large supply of top-priority taboos like the mortal-sin raincoats and the federal-pen pornography in a house where discovery, I was convinced, would mean banishment from the whole LaBianca family forever, in total disgrace. A horrifying contemplation.

I anxiously moved my forbidden cache from one chancy nook and cranny to another, looking for a good hiding place. No, not good. It had to be perfect.

And then one night, like a bolt outta the dark blue, it came to me. One of my chores was to keep the huge dark-blue cast-iron furnace in our basement stoked and heated all winter long. As a result, I had exclusive access to the coal bin, so just inside the entry door, in the corner, I placed a wooden orange crate on its side and covered it with irregular lumps of the anthracite coal. Thereafter, the orange crate became my secret, secure, treasure chest and any contraband that had "fallen off the truck" and was not disposable was stored there.

The police replenished their endless supply of pornography by confiscating material from illicit pornographic "smokers" that had been organized in their district. They then organized their own smokers and eventually the material was sold back to the original owners at discount prices.

It wasn't long before my cache in the coal bin was bulging with prophylactics and sex literature of every description. I learned about things that I had no idea were going on in the adult world. Absolutely no idea.

"Do ladies really do that stuff?" I asked, incredulously.

"Sure they do. Some anyway. I'll betcha some even like it," said Vinnie.

"Get out'ta here! Does Rosie next door do this stuff?"

"Sure she does. Prob'ly."

I tried to imagine Rosie and some other women in some of the bizarre situations I had seen illustrated. I thought of my sister and immediately dismissed any link as impossible. All the ladies in my family were too refined to know about this kinda crud. And how about my teachers? They were too refined to even use a toilet, for God's sake. Use the bathtub and mirror in there? Maybe. Toilet? Never.

The police never did figure out what was going on but they did not like the odds and got bored. The contest stopped abruptly and the exchange became straight barter. That's when we learned how the scam worked. Frankie would insert a sewing needle into the end of his cigarette and with a little experimenting learned how to arrange the needle so it would easily support at least one inch of tobacco ash. After each victorious session with the police he would put out the cigarette with a twist against the lamppost, thereby pressing the needle deep into the remainder of the cigarette and out of sight.

Each night, in the quiet security of my bedroom, I would lie in the dark with my head on the pillow, with my back to my sleeping older brother Ric on the other pillow, and contemplate the torrent of puzzling, often contradictory, fragments of information my sensors had picked up during the day and funnelled into my memory bank which was already swirling and overflowing with unresolved matters.

Although Ric wasn't much older than me, I couldn't confide in him because he hung out with a different crowd, and was more interested in building model airplanes at night than he was in the guys on the corner. To discuss these kinds of intimate things with Ric, a "born-again" church devotee, would be as risky as it would be with my parents, who didn't even allow the dirty "s" word in our house. Talking to Vinnie about these matters almost always muddied the waters even more.

"A girl starts having the curse and gets headaches as soon as she does 'it,'" shared Vinnie, "so, when you see a lady with cucumber ends stuck on her temples, you know she's having 'The Curse'."

So what the heck was that supposed to mean? Was "The Curse" the same as the "*mal-occhio*" or "evil eye" curse I'd heard older Italian ladies talk about in hushed tones as they repeatedly crossed themselves? I knew the "evil eye" caused swollen ankles and feet, severe cramps and really bad constipation and other stuff in old people, but I also knew that Mamma's "healing hands," incantations, and floating candles could neutralize any curse on anybody, anytime. So, if Vinnie told me which ladies had "the curse," should I let Mamma know? Or not? Maybe I should just tell our priest.

And what about God? Maybe at my next confession, I should tell him about my stuff in the orange crate. But wait a minute. I didn't steal any of that stuff. No-sir-ee. This was between *Frankie* and God. Right?

But just supposin' I did confess. Exactly what would I say? I inched further away from Ric to the edge of the mattress and silently rehearsed the confession in my mind.

"Bless me Father for I have sinned. My last worthy confession was one week ago."

"And what are your sins, my son?" the benevolent priest would ask, with a reassuring tone in his voice.

Suddenly, it wasn't the new young priest whose name I did not know, but the head of the church, the mean, no-nonsense, Father Gatto! As usual, I hoped he couldn't see me as well as I could see him through the woven cane screen that separated us.

"Well, Father," I would begin, "I have these books that show Tillie the Toiler and Popeye, naked."

"Naked? Naked? And what are Tillie the Toiler and Popeye doing in your dirty, filthy books?"

"Well, they are...you know —"

"And where did you get these dirty, filthy, books, Jamie LaBianca?"

"From Frankie the Foot."

"Frankie the Foot! That's it! That does it! You're both going to jail! Striped suits, the whole thing! No, better yet, you're both going straight to hell! Guaranteed!"

"But Father," I haggled, "my Papa let the church use his dump truck, remember?"

"Oh. OK, then. Ah'right. Frankie the Foot, *he* goes *straight* to Hell. You? Jamie LaBianca? Well, let's see...you...you go to Purgatory. At'tsa the best I can do. Say ten Our Fathers, ten Hail Marys."

I rolled over on my back and dismissed that scenario as too dreadful to contemplate any further. Forget it. No orange-crate confession. No way. This was definitely Frankie's problem. On the other hand it would be nice to go into the confessional just once with a blockbuster instead of my one-minute confessions with the same old tired three sins. "I disobeyed my parents...." Like my friends, I noticed that the older guys were in there, confessing, 15-20 minutes. Sometimes more. Just think about it. Yeah. *That's* how reputations get made, and that's what I call a divine revelation.

The following Saturday I entered St. Francis' church with a plan and fell into line kneeling in the pew closest to the confessional. The bare kneeling planks instantly hurt my knees.

When my turn came I entered the darkness of the confessional and knelt with pain, facing the screen. The wooden panel behind the screen was slid open and I was relieved to see the new young priest and not Father Gatto. The novice priest had opened the curtain on his side of the confessional to let more air into his cramped quarters. With the added light I could clearly see his bony head tilted back against the wall of the cubicle and his eyes were closed. He was breathing through parted lips as if he was deep in meditation or half asleep, I couldn't tell which.

"Bless me Father for I have sinned," I began nervously, "my last..." Suddenly, I couldn't remember if it was *worthy* or *worthless*. Worthless or worthy? Maybe wordy? I decided to go with worthless.

"...my last worthless confession was one week ago."

I watched his enormous adam's apple bob up and down on his stretched neck as he mechanically recited something unintelligible in what I assumed was Latin. He did this without moving his lips. Like a ventriloquist.

I started my pathetic dissertation of venial sins with "I disobeyed my parents." I waited for his response which was slow in coming. Eventually he said, "Don't do that anymore."

"I took the name of The Lord in vain."

His eyes opened slightly and there were no pupils showing. They were rolled back in his head.

"Don't do that anymore."

"I thought bad thoughts."

40

"Don't do that anymore."

At this point I was usually hard pressed to come up with anything that could make my colorless confession worthwhile. But this time I had come prepared.

"Father," I said, "I...I...I put on one o' Frankie's raincoats an' got in the bathtub."

"Don't do that anymore. Say ten Our Fathers...."

Wait a minute. That's it? I'm going out'ta here in the same minute an' a half? No way.

"Father —"

"Yes, my son?"

"I forgot something." I carefully unfolded the mimeographed list of sins I had acquired at catechism and selected the one I planned to use as a possible back-up. This would cover any transgression that may have been committed on the corner or in the coal bin.

I went down the list of mortal sins and came to the one I had underlined. I had absolutely no idea what the sin meant but since it was in the ten commandments it surely would be good enough to cover Tillie the Toiler and Popeye.

Because the light on my side of the screen was so dim, I read with difficulty...and pride.

"I coveted my neighbor's wife."

There was a long pause, like he was catching glimpses of the exact spot in hell I would occupy. His head, which was still lolling against the back wall of the confessional, rolled slowly back and forth with his eyes closed, and came to rest, facing me. He slowly pushed the sliding panel closed without saying a word, like this sin was too contemptible for forgiveness. Then, just before the panel was completely closed, he hesitated.

"Don't do that anymore," he said, closing the panel.

Chapter III

"*C'era una volta —*"

"Mamma," I interrupted, "the stove's on fire."

Mamma slowly looked over her shoulder to the smoke seeping through the leaky oven door, calmly took out the first three trays of smoking cookies that had baked to a golden black, and scattered them over the snow outside the kitchen door for Blackie, the birds and other scavengers. Before the flung burned cookies from the fourth tray hit the snow, Mamma hurled herself after them and started to scoop them back onto the tray as fast as she could, but it was too late.

She saw Mrs. Lazzarone peering from behind her sheer curtain and quickly scurried, breathless, to the safety of our vestibule, where Vinnie and I joined her.

"What happened, Mamma...what happened?"

"I don't want her to see me give Blackie the cookies. You know how she talks...." She switched to Mrs. Lazzarone's grating voice, "...had to give her cookies to the dog. Nobody else would eat them." We all giggled. Mamma could find a silver lining even when there was none.

Mrs. Lazzarone, Mamma's next-door nemesis, owned a party-line telephone and her mission in life was to do as much damage as she could with her vicious gossip. She had mastered the expertise necessary to make her outlandish fabrications sound plausible and the consequences ranged from nuisance to destructive. She enjoyed spreading misery indiscriminately, but because she had a window overlooking our backyard, Mamma often became a prime target.

It was Christmas Eve, in the early 30's, during our holiday vacation. Vinnie and I were sitting in Mamma's kitchen, the warmest room in the house, sampling a variety of cookies that she was baking, and listening to the sublime tales of wonder and magic she read to us to wile away the baking-cycle time.

Before the cookie burn-out, she had been selecting stories from her favorite book, "Tales of Wizards, Witches, and Other Short Stories." Mamma could enthrall us with her convincing imitation of the screech of the ogres and the cackle of the witches in primeval forests and foggy marshes. Her stories were even more mesmerizing than anything we ever heard down at the hangout corner.

Mamma carefully arranged four new trays of cookies in the oven and closed the oven door. She adjusted the kerchief that covered her hair, wiped her hands on her apron, and reached for her glasses. She sat at the little clearing she had left at the table for the book which resembled a large family Bible and slowly turned the pages. Vinnie and I stopped chewing as we caught glimpses of the elaborate pen and ink drawings as Mamma selected the next story.

When she made her choice she pressed the open book with her hands and looked first at me, then at Vinnie, and then back at me over the top of her glasses. It served the same purpose as lowering the house lights in a theatre.

Satisfied that she had our full attention, she once again pronounced the riveting words, *"C'era una volta..."* in her Italian dialect from the Adriatic side of Italy.

"Once upon a time..." she enunciated crisply, "there was a

young, handsome, sleeping prince...."

She described how the spellbound prince was cursed to sleep lying on his back with his hands folded on his chest. His faithful dog Chetrone patiently stood guard at his bedside. Everyone knew that on Christmas Eve, at exactly the stroke of midnight, all animals could talk.

"Mrs. LaBianca," said Vinnie, to create the interruption he knew would ultimately lead to another offering of warm cookies, "that's jus' like St. Francis an' the animals, huh?"

"You righta, Vinchenze," she said, as she crossed herself and passed the cookies.

Everyone in the neighborhood knew that St. Francis of Assisi, who tamed the She-wolf of Gubbio, could talk to all animals. But in addition, a "chosen few" who were pure of heart and free of sin could also talk to all animals, fish, or fowl, at exactly the stroke of midnight on Christmas Eve. Fish, it was said, were difficult to understand because they were underwater. All of this could be confirmed somewhere in the Bible.

Terrific! If the Bible says so, that's it! Tonight, at midnight, I would talk to Blackie. I had just gone to confession to be free of sin and chances were pretty good that I was pure of heart. For fear of jeopardizing my chances of talking to Blackie, I decided not to discuss my plans with Vinnie. Vinnie had a big mouth. I couldn't risk it.

Blackie, a gentle stray who'd made his home under our stoop about the same time I was born, was very friendly and was loved by all, including Mamma, who fed him table scraps and checked his water bowl regularly. Whenever he sensed a threat to our home or any member of our family, Blackie, always on duty and alert at his station under our steps, instantly transformed into a battle-ready junk yard dog.

Mamma finished the story by describing how the prince went forth to right the wrongs and broadcast happiness throughout the kingdom like he was sowing seeds of joy in a high wind. She closed the book for a long intermission and checked the cookies in the oven as she hummed her favorite Italian Christmas carol.

Vinnie and I bundled up, drained the hot cocoa in our cups that Mamma had replenished several times, went to the bathroom and discussed our pastime options. We considered walking down to the Garden Theatre to study the trailer photographs of the coming attractions hanging out front in the shallow display cases. After a short deliberation, we decided it might be too risky to wander that far from home without the security of a larger group because we might run into the deranged neighborhood bully, Cookie Occarro.

Frankie the Foot had warned, "Be careful to never get caught alone by that bastard, Coo-Coo Occarro. He's a really dangerous fruitcake. Bad enough to kill. The police won't say it, but, like me, they think he could'a thrown that kid from the top of the Walton firescape and killed 'im."

Frankie's fear was well founded. Cookie intimidated even the dreaded Paris Street gang that occasionally made forays into our area. He sent them running in disorderly retreat when he chased them in a rage with his four foot length of lead pipe. He was well known to the truant officer and the police. When Mrs. Pulaski complained to the school authorities that her son, Paul, had been beat-up in the boys room by him, Cookie retaliated by climbing up on the pitched roof of her house and throwing her cat down the chimney. Other housewives had experienced bricks through their windows.

We chose to go down to Costello's grocery store where

Christmas trees were for sale. It was nice to hang around the transported pine forest to smell and touch the pine needles. We hoped the sales of the trees were going badly because Mr. Costello's son Georgie, a good friend of mine, had tipped us off last year that if sales were poor, Mr. Costello would let us have a tree to take home free of charge, the day after Christmas.

Left of the store entrance, multi-colored Christmas tree lights were strung around the border of the plate glass window and cotton balls had been pasted on the inside of the glass in a meticulously regular pattern to replicate snowflakes. On the floor of the window display area, a toy train eagerly raced around and around a strange creche.

The curious assemblage encircled by the track was an odd assortment of figures and animals that had been collected over the years with little consideration given to the appropriateness. Two of the wise men and an unidentifiable gaudy figure escorted a small stamped-metal figure of Little Orphan Annie to the holy crib. It was obvious that neither Mr. Costello nor any of his sons had an apptitude for window dressing.

Vinnie went to a tree at the back of the store lot and snapped about 12 inches off of the end of a pine branch and hid it under his coat.

"What'cha do that for?" I asked.

"Every time I come down I break off a little branch an' take it home. I gotta box full."

"For what?"

"I'm gonna use airplane glue to build a tree for Ma. Your Ma. For Christmas."

"What! For what?" I was annoyed that he was trying to steal my thunder.

"I jus' wanna. Aw'right? I jus' wanna." Vinnie's mother,

whom he worshiped, was dead for two years now.

Later that evening, Vinnie came to my house to join the festivities and presented his assembled miniature tree to Mamma. She gushed, embraced him, and set the tree on the kitchen table as a centerpiece. The slight jarring caused one of the drooping sprigs to fall off, exposing several straight pins. Papa easily slipped the sprig back into place.

My relatives, who were crowded around the table sipping anisette and coffee and laughing uproariously at old world exploits, stopped to applaud Vinnie's gift. Although no one could afford to exchange trivial store-bought gifts, Vinnie accepted one of the symbolic oranges we had all received from my parents earlier that evening.

"*Che bello ragazzo,*" said Uncle Nick, the traditional master of ceremonies at all family gatherings. He stood up, did his annual parody of an Italian Christmas Carol, and everyone responded with the expected hoots and applause. He held up his hands to indicate he was shifting moods to deliver his philosophical Christmas-Thanksgiving sermonette. We knew from experience that to add gravity, the oration would be delivered in "real" Italian, not the more common dialect.

"*Amicizie sono fabbricate dal fuoco.*" For dramatic effect, he repeated the proverb again. "*Friendships...are forged in fire.* You don't know...if you have a friend...until the friendship has been tested by fire." Uncle Nick emoted like he was on a balcony overlooking St. Peter's Square in the Vatican. "Get the two pieces *red-hot*...one on top of the other...and beat them with a hammer on an anvil. *That's*...how you learn if two people, or two metals...are really compatible. The harder the pounding —"

At this point, two of the infants chasing each other from room to room, knocked over a framed print of a patron saint, which, in turn, sent Mamma's cookies all over the kitchen like shrapnel. The babies immediately released the piercing screech most toddlers feel is appropriate in these circumstances. They sustained the shrill scream with remarkable breath control, until their respective mothers swept them up and bounced them in loving arms to another part of the house.

"Where was I?" asked Uncle Nick, when the room had returned to a semblance of order.

"The harder the pounding..." said the ladies in the room, in unison. They'd heard the recitation so many times, they had it memorized.

"What?" asked a perplexed Uncle Nick. "Oh...yes... yes...Ah, the harder the pounding...the more perfect the fusing —"

"No! No! *The more perfect the bond...*" corrected the ladies.

"Oh...." Uncle Nick looked confused, threw up his hands,and in the midst of the good-natured whooping, added, "Eh...have it your way. I don't care."

The audience cheered, clapped their hands and repeated in cadence, "Bond, bond, bond, bond...."

"Listen...listen," said Uncle Nick, "You might not think I know how to...talk...but...this sweet child of mine, is gonna tell you the same thing, the right way...with her great song. Go ahead, sweet angel, you can tell 'em better than I can. Go ahead."

Cousin Angie, who was not much older than me, stood on a chair and sang an Italian folksong by rote. It made no difference that she had no idea what the words meant. At this moment she was the embodiment of a reincarnated diva. Her mother, Aunt Mary, beamed and silently mouthed the words as my inspired cousin mangled one stanza after the next. The enraptured audience, their eyes moist with emotion, nodded their heads.

"*Che bello ragazzo!*" said Mamma.

When Angie was done, she curtsied like an old trouper and the room exploded with approval. Aunt Mary, with tears rolling down her cheeks, swept Angie up in a hug and smothered her with kisses. Angie's jealous sister sulked in the doorway of the darkened bathroom like a stand-in in the wings.

As the applause subsided, Blackie did something very unusual. He started to bay, out back, like he was warming-up for our impending midnight talk-fest. Everyone stopped to listen as the baying continued. In the Old Country, animals in general, and dogs in particular, in addition to talking on Christmas Eve, played an important role in the miraculous events that supposedly occurred in and around the mountain villages that my family came from. With the relatives' attention now directed to Blackie, they lavished him with praise for his loyalty, intelligence, and heroism. Papa brought up the legendary Costello story.

Blackie had been credited with saving the lives of the Grocer Costello's family. They all, reportedly, would have burned in their beds if Blackie hadn't awakened them with his persistent barking one cold winter night while he was on one of his dawn patrols. Thanks to our alert dog the fire was confined to the chicken coops that were stacked behind the store. With all the embellishments and refining that occurred with each retelling, it wasn't long before the story took on the patina of a "miracle." Our family basked in the reflected glory the heroic dog bestowed on us all but I secretly wondered what he was really doing back there sniffing around those chicken coops at that time in the morning.

The kitchen clock now said nineteen minutes before my secret meeting with Blackie. I hoped he was psychic so

I could find out what kind of grade I'd gotten on my geography test. I was also going to ask him if Emma Vettor, who sat in front of me in Miss Casey's class, liked me.

Vinnie, who was stunned with sleep, stumbled into my bedroom to find his coat, which was somewhere in the heap of coats, hats, and scarves piled on my bed. I told my mother I would escort him home.

I slipped the bedroom alarm clock into one of the large pockets in my sheepskin lined cloth coat. In the other pocket I stuffed a stubby candle and the crudely painted unfired clay candlestick holder I had recently made in school and given to my mother as a Christmas present. Scratched into the uneven clay bottom were the words: "Mery Xmas Ma." The irregularly scratched letters looked like hieroglyphics and there was no spacing between words so, unless you studied it carefully, it actually read: MERYXMASMA.

When we got to Vinnie's house, he said, "Hey...look. The lights are on at Eleanor's bedroom. There's always a space under the shade. Let's go watch her undress."

"Not tonight," I said, as I leapt from the top step onto the walk that led to my house. Time was running short so I scurried to the entrance to Blackie's shelter under our door stoop, brushed away some of the snow, checked the clock and saw that I had only six minutes left. I pressed the candle into the candleholder for support but after several unsuccessful attempts at lighting a wooden match in the piercing cold wind, I realized that the candle would not be lit until I was well into Blackie's foreboding black cave.

I pulled the collar of my coat together and with great difficulty started to crawl on my hands and knees into the cramped space under the stoop that Blackie had turned into his own filthy little shelter from the elements.

I inched forward until I was pressed against Blackie's dusty body and could feel that he had made a nest bedding for himself out of what seemed to be dirty, dusty burlap potato sacks. I struck a match and touched the candlewick. The reek of sulphur, mixed with all the other foul odors, made it difficult to breathe the precious little air that was available.

I watched the alarm clock and waited in silence for the stroke of midnight. When the big hand hit twelve I turned towards Blackie's face which was only inches away from mine and whispered, "Merry Christmas, Blackie." I was so close to his face that my eyes were out of focus so I don't know if his expression changed but he made no audible response.

"Merry Christmas, Blackie." The puffs of vapor from my breath struck him squarely between the eyes so he blinked and turned away. Staring at his mouth for some sign of his first attempt to talk, I repeated the greeting several times and waited. And waited. It became apparent that I was doing something wrong. I cupped his jaw in my gloved hand. "Merry Christmas," I said, more forcefully. "You hear me?" I tried to activate the proper response by shaping the words on his lips with my hands but he just lay there, sphinx-like and bewildered. Only his eyes moved to give me an occasional side glance of scorn.

"How about a cookie? Can you say, 'I want the cookie'?" I took out the treat I'd brought along as a possible reward. His tail wagged, sending up a cloud of dust, and he let out a soft whimpering sound.

"That's it, Blackie! Just say it...*cookie.*"

He lurched forward to take the pastry from me. The action initiated a wrestling match that snuffed out the candle. As I frantically twisted toward the narrow exit tunnel and the fresh night air, I was startled to hear voices just outside the entrance. I retreated into the excavation and dragged my huge embarrassment in with me.

It turned out to be my older sister Annie, being escorted home from a Christmas party by one of her girlfriends. They had observed the movement at the entrance but since it was too dark for identification, they assumed it was Blackie.

"Here Blackie. C'mon Blackie. Here, dog." she called, with her head close to the opening. Blackie and I remained mute and motionless with his jaw resting on my chest.

"Merry Christmas, Blackie," she cooed. When they were both leaning close to the entrance, I squawked with a distorted voice that sounded like a wounded Donald Duck, "Merry Christmas, ho, ho, ho!"

The penetrating scream that followed set off lights here and there and emptied the surrounding houses like a fire drill.

"He talked!" my wide-eyed sister burbled. "Honest t' God, I heard him talk! I swear to God!" Her proclamation was verified by her equally shocked friend who wandered about sputtering things like, "I swear on my mother's grave I heard that dog say, 'Merry Christmas, how are ya?' "

Our other neighbor, Mrs. Fantonetti, clasped her hands together, rolled her eyes to heaven and shrieked, "*Miracolo! Miracolo! Miracolo!*"

With this unexpected turn of events, I withdrew deeper. One of my mother's authoritative friends had just identified a new miracle and fate had ordained that I would spend the night with Blackie. I balled myself into the fetal position to suffer the impending long, uncomfortable vigil.

Blackie was easily coaxed out of our sanctuary with Christmas goodies and received a very tumultuous reception.

Although he had never been allowed inside before today, he now found himself being joyously escorted into Mamma's kitchen. As soon as I could, I slipped into the raucous crowd.

Much to the everyone's disappointment, no amount of coaxing, pats or praise could get the guest of honor to speak again that night. Some diehards were pretty sure they'd heard a slurred word or two.

It only took a couple of days for a distorted version of what actually took place to permeate the neighborhood. The embellished story that now circulated was that Blackie had gone to St. Francis' Church at midnight on Christmas Eve, Father Gatto had blessed him and the two of them had a lengthy conversation in Latin.

"See that kid?" strangers would say, pointing to me. "He's part of the LaBianca family that owns the talking dog. Come'er, kid. Lemme rub your head. Maybe it'll bring me good luck."

People stepped out of their homes and walked across the street to admire this exalted, reverent dog, this ally of the House of the Lord. Some women crossed themselves before they touched his head and almost everyone gave him treats. He started to put on weight.

There was virtually no one who doubted the truth of the story. After all, if you couldn't believe Father Gatto...or Mrs. Lazzarone...or Uncle Nick...who could you believe?

Chapter IV

The opinion was unanimous. Concerned school authorities, horrified parents, and the missing-finger janitor that everyone feared, had slammed down the edict in no uncertain terms. We were *not* to go near "that place." Ever. But since we were still having our Christmas vacation and the school would be empty, Lino, Bill, Vinnie and I decided that after lunch would be just about the perfect time to meet at "that place," on the school's outside fire escape.

One of the options we had considered to wile away the afternoon was to put pennies on the streetcar track to squish the copper into irregular shapes but that could be more dangerous than "that place." Derailment. We knew from the movies that a railroad spike on a track could derail a train. What if the speeding streetcar hit the penny and went skidding down the cobblestone street on its side in a shower of sparks and tearing metal and someone we knew and liked was on board? We could do it in front of the bully Cookie Occarro's house and if someone got hurt the police would blame him, haul him off to jail, and we'd be rid of that rotten scumbag, once and for all. Also, we'd become the neighborhood heros.

But there was another thing. On the radio, Eliott Ness had warned that defacing or mutilating currency was a federal offense which could mean years in a federal penitentiary. Paul

Muni and Edward G. Robinson had demonstrated in their movies that escape was a regular, almost expected, occurrence. But, did we want to go through all that?

Naw. Not worth it. So we agreed to meet at the forbidden place at the Walton Elementary School, a short block away from my house, to scamper around on the tangle of girders, cross-members and other black metal bracing that supported the three-story fire escape attached to the exterior corner of the brick building from which a student had once mysteriously fallen to his death. Nobody could prove it, but everybody suspected Cookie had something to do with it.

The structure was perfect for a breathtaking, risky game of tag. Kids had soon learned that what was more exciting than dodging the person who was "it" around the maze of concrete and steel bases, was to climb into the tangle of metal itself at the second-floor level. The more foolhardy upped the ante and teetered precariously, like a tight-rope walker, until they managed to reach the middle of the I-beam at the third-floor level. They then lowered themselves, carefully, and sat straddling the I-beam with their legs dangling, until an equally daring tagger repeated the process to force a daring high-wire showdown.

A narrow path, lined with shoveled snowbanks, had been conveniently cleared from the schoolyard entrance to the side door of the school with an offshoot leading to the fire escape. As soon as Vinnie and I reached the third-floor landing to drop snowballs on Bill and Lino when they showed up, I began to question the wisdom of this choice of games. It was tough enough to move around with any security on this thing in warm weather, but bundled in my thick sheepskin coat and cloth gloves made body movement difficult and gripping with fingers that already ached from the bitter cold, almost impossible.

Vinnie climbed onto the narrow stair rail, hugged the heavy upright support and reached out tentatively with his foot to see if the shine on the topside of the I-beam was water or black ice. As he moved his foot back and forth, a loud voice of indeterminate origin reverberated in the echo-chamber created by the juxtaposition of the dark brick walls.

"Get your asses down here you assholes!" From our perspective we couldn't identify through the asymmetrical openings created by the criss-crossing metal who belonged to the top of the head and shoulders we had located at the base of the steel staircase. As we reluctantly made our way down I said, "God Almighty, Vin, I think it's the janitor."

We rounded the corner onto the second-floor landing and Vinnie stopped dead in his tracks. "Jesus Christ! It's worse than that. Don't crap in your pants, but it's Cookie Occarro." I instinctively turned to race back up to the top but Vinnie grabbed me by the arm and added, "No. No. He'll trap us up there and throw us both off. Keep going down an' see if one of us can get past him for help. Lemme handle this. Jus' keep your mouth shut. An' don't look scared."

Cookie might'a been somewhere around our age. Hard to tell. He was held back in second or third grade, something like that. Maybe he was so much bigger than us because he was probably a little older.

He stopped us on the first step with spread hands that pressed into our chests. Although he was standing on the icy ground a full step lower than us, we were looking straight into his pink eyes. His soiled wool stocking cap, pulled over his dirty scraggly hair, came down over his forehead and ears in long, greasy, blond strands. A half-inch-wide festering scab ran over the bridge of his broken nose and continued down over his right cheek. He wore a grimace that exposed his smoke-stained Jack-O-Lantern teeth and his lips were so chapped the cracks were also scabbed. His nose was running and with his tongue he kept swiping the shiny drip that collected over his upper lip. But that was not his most outstanding feature.

The most frightening aspect was the realization that despite the cold, which I could feel through my sheepskin-lined coat, he was wearing only a filthy undershirt and a scarf on his upper body and appeared to be immune to the cold or pain like some kinda cold-blooded reptile. His skin was a patchwork of red and blue splotches. His corduroy knickers, wool socks, and ankle-high button shoes were scruffy and he had the pungent smell of sliced raw onions.

Vinnie and I stood side by side looking at the vapor puffing out of Cookie's ragged mouth. "Now, you two turds been bad boys. You ain't s'posed to be on the fire'scape —"

"Listen, Cookie," started Vinnie, "we got permission from Miss Schlessinger—" Cookie grabbed Vinnie by the lapels of his coat, lifted him bodily, and slammed him into the snowbank that enclosed the shoveled clearing in which we were entrapped.

From where I stood, at the base of the iron steps, flight was not possible because Cookie stood between me and the only snow-walled path that led to the schoolyard exit. Fight, the other self-preservation instinct, I had dismissed off-hand. That left only one other thing I could do, so I did it. I escalated my fear to terror.

As Vinnie started to crawl away, Cookie picked him up and slammed him into the opposite snowbank. Vinnie tried to protect his face with his arms as he was picked up again like a rag doll and thrown to the ground repeatedly with Cookie making strange animal sounds in his throat.

Vinnie was lying on his back and when he raised his arm from his face I could see tears on his cheeks. I started to move toward Vinnie but Cookie pushed me to the steps and said in a flat voice, "Don' choo move from there. You hear me? I ain't done with this turd. Him first, you next." As I stood by helplessly hyper-ventilating, I blinked away the rivulets of sweat that made their way into my eye sockets. He walked back to Vinnie and planted a foot on Vinnie's chest.

"This is MY fire'scape. You gotta ax ME for permission. You hear me!" He kicked Vinnie repeatedly in the ribs and said, "You hear me?"

"I hear you, Cookie," said Vinnie, from under the arms that covered his face. Cookie kicked Vinnie repeatedly all over his body. "Who told 'ja you could talk?"

I could see that Cookie was working himself into a lather and by the time he got to me he'd probably kill us both and everyone would think we'd fallen off the fire escape. I looked toward the schoolyard entrance for some sign of Lino or Bill, but they were nowhere in sight.

"OK, turd," said Cookie, as he stood over Vinnie motioning with his finger. "Git up. It's time for me to kick shit outta ya."

Cookie had placed himself so that he effectively blocked the only way out. I stood up, hoping to throw myself on his mercy. "Cookie, I don't wanna fight with you."

He took his foot off of Vinnie's chest and turned to me. Vinnie took the opportunity to roll over onto his side. With two swift boots into his back, Cookie rolled Vinnie onto his back and snarled, "An' no more movin'. You move once't more and you're dead. YOU HEAR ME!"

He turned his full attention to me and said, "An' you,

turd, who axed you if you wanna fight? I dint say you was gonna fight. ME...! Ahm the one gonna...hey, maybe dat ain't such a bad idea. Yeah. You an' me gonna fight. I'll show ya how Schmelling beat the piss outta Sharkey. Bam! Left-hook. Boom! Right uppah cut. We got a new heavyweight champ a'da woild. A friggin' Kraut champ. B-bam! C'mon put em' up."

He got into the classic boxer's position, made a few jabs in the air and lashed out a clenched fist toward my head. He put his full weight behind the punch and when I ducked my head he missed me completely, spun around, slipped, and went sprawling down the exit path. Awkwardly, he got up with hate in his pink eyes and said, "Ah right you somabitch, this time I kill ya. Put 'em up."

I started making promises to God, to Father Gatto, to Ma, to Pa, and as I mentally raced through the family album, I shot past, then went back to Uncle Mike. Uncle Mike and Smiley...Smiley! That's worth a try.

Uncle Mike and his oldest son "Smiley" were attic bootleggers. Smiley was a boxing buff who settled disputes physically, often violently, and hung out at the 25th Street Gym to stay in shape and to huddle with his bootlegging buddies. He had a collection of illustrated "how-to" boxing books which he allowed me to look at but most of the boxing techniques described were beyond my comprehension. However, in this desperate situation it was worth a shot.

"Cookie, wait a minute," I said, "Before we go on, we gotta make this fair and square."

Cookie continued to jab into the air, bobbing and weaving. "What the hell you talkin' about, turd?"

"You notice how you missed me altogether just then? Well that's gonna go on all day because...because I'm a boxer and you ain't, and that's the God's truth."

"What the hell you talkin' about?" he said, as he continued to jab the air between us. The fact that he was talking and not punching gave me a glimmer of hope.

"You know my cousin Smiley?"

"Nah."

"Well," I lied, "my cousin Smiley is a boxing coach at the gym and he showed me a couple things that Max Schmelling does that made him champ and I think in all fairness I outta show you these things before we go on so you can fight like the champ of the world too." Cookie was curious and stopped jabbing the phantom fighter he'd pinned against the ropes.

"Here," I said, as I tried to maneuver him out of the way. "Lemme show you. Put your dukes up like this." My strategy failed. He put up his dukes but kept checking his relative position to the path behind him. "No. Higher. So you cover your face." He covered his face.

"Ready?" I checked to see if there was any sign of Bill, Lino, or our self-appointed neighborhood patroller, Tony Giardello. There was no one in sight.

I threw my full weight into a straight right jab hard into his stomach. The blow took us both by surprise and sent him stumbling backwards. He collapsed again into the path he was guarding, pressing the pain with his hands.

"No, no, no, Cookie," I said, "ya see what I mean? I gotta show ya a couple a things or you're gonna get killed."

Vinnie was still lying on his back but had raised himself up on his elbows watching the proceedings with fascination and disbelief.

The wind had been knocked out of Cookie and he was gasping as I helped him to his feet. But he had enough wind left to turn to Vinnie and say from his bent over position, "I...thought I...tol' you...not...to move." Vinnie fell on his back and stared at the sky.

"Now," I said, "where were we? Oh yeah. You left your stomach open altogether. That's bad. Drop your elbows down to here. Ready?" He nodded. I feinted with my left to his stomach again and when he lowered his arms I shot a hard right cross to his face. He staggered backward and started to bleed from his nostril and the scab on the bridge of his nose.

I kept improvising and he kept bleeding and falling but I was still frightened out of my wits. I repeatedly looked in the direction of the schoolyard entrance and hoping. There was no sign of help. I was running out of ideas and was afraid that before long he would lash out and that would be the end of me.

I helped him up and said, "OK, Cookie. I think this is enough for now. But ya gotta practice. That's the whole thing. Ya gotta practice."

I patted him on the back as he climbed over the snowbank and stomped his way through the snow toward the rear of the schoolyard jabbing at the air. He turned around with a grin and said, "Hey, turd. We gotta do dis some more sometime. An' tanks."

"Sure, Cookie, sure. Anytime," I said, with a rattling sigh of relief as he shadow-boxed his way toward the far side of the playground area.

I helped Vinnie up and we walked on very unsteady legs to the fire escape and sat down on the frozen metal steps. I was trembling and felt like throwing up so I instinctively put my head between my legs.

"Jamie," said Vinnie, "I used to think Frankie the Foot was the smartest guy around here. An' maybe he is. But even he couldn't a handled that one better. You saved both our asses with your head. You ah' right?"

"Yeah," I said, without looking up, "I'm ah' right. You OK?"

He nodded, "...an' not just your head. Your uncle...cousin... aunt...whoever the hell Smiley is, did a damn good job of showing you how to use your dukes. You really kicked the shit outta that asshole. And...Jesus Christ! He thanked you! If I hadn't heard it with my own ears, I wouldn't a believed it. Frankie the Foot could never do that. Nobody else could." There was a long pause and he added, "So St. Francis got some animals to talk. That's a miracle? Kickin' the shit outta Cookie Occarro an' gettin' him to thank you for it...now *that's* a miracle...an' I was there to see it! Next procession, they're gonna be carrying *you* around.... Hey, get a load a this...."

I looked up and saw Blackie rounding the corner at the entrance. Everyday when I started for home from school, there was punctual and loyal Blackie waiting to walk me home. Even on weekends and holidays. And here he was, right on time.

As soon as he recognized me he wagged his tail with a whipping action and bared his teeth in his attempt to smile. He strutted snappily toward me, made a whimpering sound, swung his head from side to side and started to snort. He squeezed between my legs as I sat there and buried his head as I gave him a big hug.

Vinnie straddled the other end of Blackie and scrubbed his ribs. "Where the hell were you, and God, when we needed ya," he said, as he reached down and wrapped his arms around Blackie's belly. He looked up in time to see Cookie Occarro still shadow boxing as he disappeared around the back corner of the school building.

"Blackie, I hear you can talk on Christmas Eve. Your Jamie,

here, just did ya one better. He just talked Coo-Coo Occarro outta killin' the both of us. *You* gotta wait 'till it's Christmas. Your master, here, can talk his way outta anything, every day o' the week, and twice on Sunday."

"Look who finally showed up," I said, as Bill and Lino rounded the entrance gate.

Vinnie looked over his shoulder then bent forward, closer to my face, and said, "Jamie...don't tell Bill and Lino that Cookie beat the crap outta me —" His eyes were pleading.

"Hey," said Lino, in a hushed voice. "Was that Cookie Occarro I jus' saw?"

"Yeah," I said. "That was him alright."

"You don't look so hot," said Bill. "Are you guys OK?"

"Yeah," I said, "we're OK."

"God Ah'mighty, what happened? Did he hurt you?"

"Naw. He didn't hurt us, but I think I wanna get outta here. Right now."

"Holy mackerel!" said Lino. "Look at all the blood!" He stooped to get a closer look at the blood splattered in the snow.

"Look over here!" said Bill. "Holy crow! It looks like somebody really got killed here."

"Lemme see your face," said Lino. He turned my perspiration dripping face from side to side, then pulled off my ribbed stocking cap and examined the back of my head. "He didn't stab you, did he?"

I took a deep breath and exhaled through pursed lips. "No, we're alright. C'mon. Let's get outta here."

Blackie swung his head from side to side and started to grin and snort again.

"Holy shit! I get it!" said Lino. "BLACKIE got the dirty bastard!" Lino and Bill started to whoop and holler as they danced on the blood spatters. I made eye contact with Vinnie and he raised his eyebrows.

As we walked towards the exit gate, Lino was giving Blackie a congratulatory rubdown, Bill put his arm around my shoulder and said, "Man-o-man...I tell you...with that kinda protection, nobody better try to monkey around with this kid unless they're lookin' for a whole lot'ta trouble."

"You can say that again," said Vinnie, as he caught my eye and winked.

Chapter V

Vinnie searched the newspapers Mamma had scattered on the recently scrubbed floor. "Ah. Here it is. Listen to this shit. Blah, blah, blah...here, here it is. 'President Franklin Delano Roosevelt has urged be...beleaguered citizens that *if what you are doing isn't working, above all else, try something else.*' So, when small-time people like us do what he says an' make a little booze in the attic to make ends meet, what does he do? He sics the Feds on the bootleggers...after he *tells* 'em to do it! The son-of-a-bitch. And is Al Capone goin' to jail? Nah. Nah. He's too big a fish to go to jail. He makes 100 million dollars a year. Maybe more. He owns Chicago, the cops, the judges, prob'ly even that two-faced F.D.R. who's after the small fry like your father and my father...*after he tells 'em to do it!* Can you imagine? What a sneaky son-of-a-bitch."

Although the rumors were that the 21st amendment would soon repeal Prohibition, illegal stills brewing "bathtub gin" continued to sprout like weeds around the depressed neighborhood. My foolhardy Uncle Mike was the first, then Vinnie's father, then a bunch of neighbors, and finally, after desperate soul-searching, when the survival of the family was at stake, my father succumbed.

This calamity-baiting decision really scared all of us because if you got nailed, you made little rocks out of big rocks for 20 years. No plea bargaining, no parole, no community service. That's it. Bingo. 20 years. See ya pal.

G-men, the federal agents, could usually tell which houses operated stills by the amount of gas or water being consumed on a monthly basis. They enlisted meter readers as bounty hunters to report any inordinate consumption, or anything else that looked suspicious. When irregularities were reported, a court order based on "probable cause" was quickly issued and this gave the agents the legal authority to raid the house. But the amateur bootleggers had their own bag of tricks. Since almost all gas and water meters were located in the basements, the makers of "white lightning" soon learned to bypass the meters by utilizing their own acquired plumbing skills. When the meters registered the desired reading, they disconnected the galvanized pipes that led into and out of the meters.

Each month, when the "gas-man" was expected, they reconnected the pipes and threw a handful of sand, scraped from the crawl space, over the meters, to make them look like they hadn't been disturbed.

When that ruse was discovered, the meters were read at more random times. The bootleggers countered by establishing a network of runners who sounded the alarm when utility vehicles were spotted anywhere in the neighborhood. The system worked efficiently until that unforgettable day, when we were caught off guard and disaster struck.

I was standing on a counter in the kitchen, stretching to fasten an uncoiled spiral of gooey "Tanglefoot" fly paper into the ceiling. Vinnie was waving a kitchen towel over his head to agitate the flies. Through the patched window screen, I could see my mother, with a kerchief tied around her head to protect her hair, beating a carpet that was draped over a clothes line which was raised to a manageable height with a clothes pole.

With each forceful swing the tennis-racquet-shaped beater she was using created a loud report and a cloud of dust.

My brother Ric came racing down the narrow driveway that separated our rented modest clapboard house from our neighbors, the Fantonetti's. The houses were mirror images with even the same rate of deterioration. The builder had flipped the house plan and divided the original lot into two narrower lots that shared the same driveway.

As Ric made the turn into the kitchen my mother instinctively hollered, "Don't slam the screen door!" The coil spring on the screen door twanged and the door slammed shut several times before it came to rest.

Ric burst into the kitchen and gasped, "Where's Ma?"

"Right there," I said, pointing through the screen to the backyard.

"Ma!" shouted Ric. "Ma! The gas-man is coming!"

With a look of horror, my mother froze in the middle of a swing. Vinnie stopped waving the towel.

"*E Madonna!*" she sputtered, as the significance of the situation struck her. She took a few steps, stopped, dropped the carpet beater, and raced into the house.

My father, who had been visited by our family physician just a short time earlier, was lying on his bed delirious with a high fever, and perspiring profusely. The doctor had diagnosed double-pneumonia.

My alarmed mother dashed into the bedroom. "Patsy! The gas-man is coming! I don't know what to do!"

Papa, who was in no condition to get out of his bed, let alone go down into the cellar and perform the arduous task of reconnecting the meters, rolled his head from side to side and muttered, "*Jesu Christo mio.*"

"Ma," said Ric, as he looked out the front door window, "the gas-man's coming down the driveway!"

"*E Madonna!*" said my mother, with a tremble in her voice, "Mary, Mother of God, help us!"

The uniformed stranger who could destroy my family stood outside between the opposing kitchen doors of the twin houses and yelled, "Gas-man!"

From where we stood, frozen, we saw someone in the Fantonetti household open the door to let the man in. We watched him disappear into their house and the cellar lights went on. In a minute or two the bounty hunter would be at our door and our world would end.

Mamma leaned over my helpless father who lay gasping for breath and said, "Patsy! I don't know what to do!" She was visibly shaking.

The only sound in the room was the heavy breathing and the buzzing of the flies trying to extricate themselves from the sheet of fly paper lying on the dresser top. My father's right hand rose and fell as he muttered something unintelligible.

"What?" asked my mother, as she put her ear to his mouth. "Oh God. I can't hear what he's saying."

"Lock the cellar door," said Vinnie. "Lock the cellar door and tell him you can't find the key."

The terrifying menace exited the Fantonetti basement, writing on his clipboard. From under the stoop, Blackie growled at the mailman-type uniform. The prospective bounty hunter completed his report, clipped his pencil into his breast pocket, took a few steps toward our door and shouted, "Gas-man!" The announcement could not have had a more chilling effect if he had screamed, "You're all under arrest!"

Mamma stepped to the door with her hands trembling

and let the towering man into the house. She composed herself and in a controlled, apologetic voice announced to the skeptical man twisting the cellar door knob that she had locked the cellar door to keep the kids out and had misplaced the key.

"Me. Ah'm the troublemaker," said Vinnie, defiantly, as he touched toes with the giant and craned his neck to look up to his face. "She told us a million times...don't...not...not to stick our fingers in the apple butter jars...so...but...we don't listen. We break the wax on the jars an' I stole the key...an' we were on the woodpile, playing, an'...when she tol' us...."

The man looked down, wrinkled his nose like he was smelling something bad and said, "Oh, really?" He twisted the knob back and forth. "You're right, sonny, you're a troublemaker. Now I gotta come back." He wrote on a form attached to his clipboard. "OK, lady," he said through the screen door as he left, "we'll be seeing you soon."

Mamma had learned through the grapevine that "soon" meant the following morning. That's how long it would take to process the red tape necessary for the Feds to raid the house. And that's all the time we had to dismantle the entire operation in the attic and eliminate all traces of incriminating evidence. The task was virtually impossible.

As soon as the red utility car was out of sight, Mamma bounded up the steps through the bedroom and into the attic to work out a plan of action. She stood at the attic entrance, turned on the three bare bulbs tacked to the ridgepole timber, and threw her hands up in despair. "Merciful God," she said, in her Italian dialect, "give me strength and wisdom." She scanned the tangle of vats, barrels, copper equipment, and sacks of sugar and grain, and slapped her thighs in a gesture of hopelessness and said flatly, "I don't know what to do."

"I do," said Vinnie, who had raced up the stairs directly behind her and my brother. His eyes were glistening and he eagerly tugged at invisible restraints. He wanted to get into the game as a first-stringer.

"Hold it, Vinnie," said Ric. "First thing we do is start pouring the mash down the drains." Ric was a precocious child of eleven with remarkable innate mechanical abilities and a "take charge" instinct. He had helped to install the plumbing, the drains, and the electrical wiring on this entire operation, and like Vinnie, in his own attic, had even assisted in the soldering of the still. The closer adversity rose to the catastrophic level, the more brilliant the gleam on Ric's suit of armor. He had the capacity to remain remarkably calm in frightening situations that would buckle most adults, let alone kids his own age.

"Jimmy," he went on, "I'll start to siphon the mash down this drain from this big barrel over here. Vinnie, you've seen how this works at your house. Hold this hose over here and see that it doesn't spill. I'm gonna start breakin' down the still. Ma, get Annie up here to help. It's gonna take all day and maybe all night but I think we can do it."

Luckily, there was nothing brewing in the gas-heated distilling apparatus. We worked at a feverish pace and by midnight we were near exhaustion. With Vinnie's help, the distillery gear had been broken down into pieces that would fit into my father's Model T Ford Tudor Sedan.

Once again, Ric took charge. Although the only driving he had ever done was back and forth in our driveway, it now became his awesome responsibility to load the Model T with the paraphernalia and dispose of it. Especially fearsome was the prospect of driving after dark with only the dim light of the inadequate head lamps to light our way.

The first load was made up of empty, shiny, five-gallon tins which were heaped to the ceiling of the car with various pieces of the still and different lengths of copper pipe stuffed into cavities between the metal tins. A pile of twenty-five-pound cloth bags of Jack Frost sugar was stacked on the floor on the passenger side of the front seat.

We triple checked our preparations, but to better our chances of surviving this perilous journey into the unknown, we stopped in to see my father for last-minute instructions. The bedroom was hot and stuffy. In the dim light of the one incandescent lamp, we could see my father lying in a pool of sweat and struggling for breath. My mother sat on one side of him cradling my sleeping infant brother George with one arm while she tried, unsuccessfully, to wring out the compresses she was preparing to apply to my father's forehead. She gave up in frustration and delegated my father's comfort to my sister Annie, and Vinnie.

Ric and I stood on the other side of the bed and looked at each other for reassurance. Without opening his eyes, Papa croaked in a very feeble voice, *"Rico...figlio mio."*

"Yes, Papa," said Ric, as he patted Papa's damp hand.

"You think...you think...you can do this thing?" asked Papa, with great effort.

"I'm sure I can do this, Papa." Ric continued to pat Papa's hand. "Don't worry." He caught Mamma's eyes and repeated, "Don't worry, it's gonna be alright." The room was silent except for the rattling in Papa's chest.

"Before you start," Papa cautioned, "put some oil in...and check the gas...." After a long delay he added, "...and don't dump everything in one place...spread it around." He rolled his head toward Ric, opened his eyes, and stared at him

71

for a few seconds with his mouth gaping. When he was able to bring his eyes into focus he said, "Be very careful... and God be with you my wonderful son." As we left the room we could see that Mamma was weeping. The baby never stirred.

Ric took Vinnie aside and said, "Vinnie, you've been a big help. We couldn't a done it without you. You stay here an' get the loads ready and keep the ladies calm as you can. Me and Jimmy can take care of the car. I don't know how long this is gonna take. Can you stay overnight?"

"Yeah. Don't worry about me. Just take care of your half."

I followed Ric to the car and held the flashlight as he filled the quart container from the five-gallon drum. He poured the oil into the crankcase and went through the rest of the preparation checklist with confidence. He'd been maintaining the car and even helped replace the cork gaskets on the 22 horsepower, four-cylinder engine.

He removed the front seat on the passenger side, unscrewed the gas cap and stuck a wooden ruler into the tank until it hit the bottom. He pulled the ruler up and checked the level of gas with the flashlight.

"We've got enough. Let's go." Although he had never attempted it before, Ric would have to squiggle back and forth enough to face the car in the direction of the street.

The Model T had no gear-shift lever. Its two forward speeds, reverse and brake, were controlled by three aligned pedals located at the base of the steering column. There was no floor gas pedal. To vary the engine speed the driver pulled or pushed the gas lever located on the right side of the steering column just under the large wooden steering wheel. The spark was just opposite the gas lever. Ric pressed the spark lever all the way up, pulled the gas lever down a bit, then helped me climb up behind the steering wheel.

"Now do exactly what I tell ya to do," he said. "Don't move this spark over here, this thing, until I tell you to or you'll break my arm while I'm cranking, OK? When I tell you to, you move both of them down this far. Right to here. But not 'till I tell you to. OK?"

I nodded. Ric inserted the crank at the base of the radiator and cried out, "Ready?"

"Ready!" I yelled back.

He gave the crank a snappy quarter turn and the car growled, sputtered, and died. "OK," shouted Ric, "here we go again." He gave the crank another hard turn and the car once again shook itself to a stop. Ric opened the car door and advanced the spark just a little.

"Hey, this is a piece o'cake. Are you OK?" he asked, to calm any anxiety I might be harboring.

"Yeah," I said, "I'm OK. Whatta we gonna do if we can't start the car?"

"Ready?" he called from the front of the car, ignoring the question. "Ric...what are we gonna do if the car won't start?" Again he ignored the question.

"Are...you...ready?" he yelled with a hint of annoyance.

"Ready!" I bellowed back.

This time the engine ignited and the car shimmied and shook but stayed alive. "Pull the spark!" The engine settled down to a rhythmical pockety-pockety-pock sound.

"Good job, move over." He got in, turned on the faint headlights and adjusted himself on the seat until he could reach all three pedals. He pressed the left low gear pedal and slowly pulled the hand throttle down to move the car forward. His coordinated movements put us squarely behind our house where he brought the car to a rocking stop.

Vinnie banged on my door until I opened it. "Here," he said, as he handed me a kerosene lantern, "take this, in case the flashlight goes out. I wish I was goin' with ya. Jamie, next trip, if you get tired or somethin', I'll give ya a break. Ya hear?"

"Where's Blackie?" asked Ric. "I don't wanna hit him."

"It's OK," said Vinnie, "I got him right here. I got 'im by the collar. Let 'er rip!"

"OK," said Ric, "Here we go." He released the left pedal to put the car in high gear. With a neck-snapping bound and a forewarning mournful howl from the transmission the flivver bolted forward and the harrowing mission was launched into the awaiting darkness.

We raced down the driveway between the houses with lots of bangs and clanks from the bouncing five-gallon metal tins piled up high behind us. When we reached the part of the concrete strips that sloped down toward the street, the tall narrow machine perched on a high chassis and loaded with damning federal evidence, quickly gained momentum.

We reached the curb moving so fast we were catapulted toward the other side of the street. Ric wrenched the wheel to the right and the car teetered until I was sure we would topple over. The maneuver put us on a collision course with the curb on our side of the street.

"Oh...my...God!" I tore a fingernail and bruised a finger when I grabbed the doorhandle.

Ric twisted the wheel to the left and we were headed for the opposite curb. Another violent turn to the right and we were once again racing back to the curb we'd started from. Luckily, the serpentine pattern we had cut careening from curb to curb had moved us down the street a little so that instead of crashing headlong into the curb, we wobbled down the side street on the other side of Tony's gas station, which was next door to our house.

We hit the entrance to Tony's gas station driveway with such force that two of the large clattering tins came crashing down over our heads. Ric leapt on all three pedals simultaneously and the transmission let out a gut-wrenching sound but we were still traveling forward directly toward the gas pumps even though the rear wheels were spinning backwards spewing gravel. The car skidded to a shuddering stop with the ear-splitting sound of five gallon tins banging hard against each other and the backs of our heads. We stalled just as the right front tire slid into the concrete island on which the gas pumps loomed in front of us. This model car had no bumpers.

"We're all right! We're all right!" shouted Ric. "Calm down. We're all right. We're OK." We rearranged the cans, but the tangle of copper, lead, and tin pieces still looked precarious.

"I dun'no, Ric," I said, "I'm not sure we can do this by ourselves. Maybe we should get Uncle Mike or —"

"Jamie. Listen. I can drop you off to help Vinnie and —" I shook my head and waved him onward.

"OK, then. Listen to me. There's no *time* to get Uncle Mike or anybody else. *We...can...do...this*. We can do this. Trust me. We're gonna be all right. Help me put one of those sugar bags over here where I can sit on it so I can reach the pedals better." The extra height and the cap on his head gave Ric a more adult-looking silhouette for any police cars we might encounter on the deserted streets.

One turn of the crank and the warm engine started right up. Ric adjusted himself on the sack of sugar, pressed down on the reverse pedal, and the car moved backward in a smooth tight arc. We moved easily down the driveway and onto Clark Avenue on our way to our first stop a few miles down the road, the West 14th Street dump.

My brother's driving was a little erratic at first because he tended to overcorrect the wandering car. At one intersection he stopped part way into the crossroad because the brake bands were worn. But even that little problem was solved by applying the brake pedal and the reverse pedal at the same time. With minimal fuss Ric resolved the problems as they came up. I was very proud of him.

The operation was coming together very nicely. Mamma and Annie were so excited they could barely function, but Vinnie had risen to the task admirably. He had disassembled the large wooden barrels used for the fermenting mash and had stacked the individual curved staves neatly so that Mamma and Annie could easily carry them down the attic stairs to the car. The second trip, to the Scranton Road dump, went smoothly.

By the third trip, Ric had everything under control. We had not passed a single moving object all night and the entrance to the Franklin Avenue dump was well marked by a street light.

This is where our luck ran out. We drove through the entrance into the darkness to the brim of the dump. As we were unloading the car and heaving things over the edge, Ric suddenly pulled off his cap and threw it over the taillight. "Kill the lights! Kill the lights!"

I smacked the toggle switch and stood frozen in the darkness without comprehending what Ric was obviously alarmed about. I walked over to where he was standing and asked quietly, "What'sa matter?"

"That," said Ric, as he pointed me toward the entrance.

My heart leaped into my throat as I saw a car parked under the street light. The light mounted on the roof told us it was a police car.

I was terrified. We could get dragged from here in striped suits and go right to prison for 20 years and Mamma would never know what happened to us. I stepped closer to Ric and grasped his hand.

"What'll we do?" I whispered.

"Sh-h-h," said Ric, staring intently in the direction of the danger. "Be quiet and don't move."

The door on our side of the police car opened and a large policeman got out and stretched. He slammed the car door and stretched again. We could see a second figure sitting at the wheel of the car.

The man who had gotten out started to walk slowly, deliberately, in our direction. Ric and I were now crouching in front of our car near the brink of the dump. We didn't dare move any further back so I bent lower to make myself as inconspicuous as possible. Ric remained standing as he clutched the "dog-bone" thermometer that was mounted on the radiator cap. I kept a tight grip on his damp, rigid hand which was not trembling, like mine.

When the silhouette of the man had taken about 30 cautious steps toward us he stopped and turned in profile. He looked back at the police car, clumsily unbuttoned his fly and started to urinate.

Because he was back-lit we could see the stream of urine very clearly and I was surprised at how well the sound travelled. The process seemed to take an unusually long time, like a big horse splashing on a cobblestone street.

When the officer completed the discharge we could see

77

both hands working the area of his groin as he tucked things in and buttoned his fly. He took a few steps toward his car and stopped in his tracks as if he was listening. We held our breaths and Ric squeezed my hand.

Then, as if to add insult to injury, the lawman cocked a leg and released a loud flatulent report that resounded throughout the dump. With all of the bodily functions completed, he got back into his car and they drove off. As soon as they were out of sight we finished our mission at the dump and drove cautiously toward the street.

As we headed for home I slumped back on my side of the seat, exhausted, and studied Ric's profile as each passing street lamp flashed light across his face. I swelled with pride and felt the same nurturing and protection I'd known whenever Papa was in control.

"You know what Ric?" I said, "You are a really, really, smart guy." I caught his grin in the next flash of light and he said, "Jimmy, that's a nice thing to hear. Makes me think of what Pa says, 'There's only one thing worse than a stupid person an' that's a stupid person in charge.'"

Finally, we were safely back home. The house was quiet and Mamma was sprawled in the over-stuffed chair in the living room, unconscious with sleep. Ric and I staggered up the steps to our bedroom, where Vinnie had arranged, on the floor, two urine-stained mattresses from the baby's crib. He was lying, sound asleep, in such a grotesque posture, that Ric leaned close to him to make sure he was all right. We threw ourselves on the bed we shared without taking our clothes off and slept the sleep of the dead.

Later that morning, in that twilight period between being asleep and awake, we became aware of the sound of voices, an occasional shout, and engines right outside our house. We leapt up and looked out the high clerestory windows that lined our bedroom wall. With eyes that were almost puffed shut, Vinnie clumsily made his way next to me.

"What the hell is goin' on?" he moaned.

What we saw was chilling. There were six or seven big black cars with large circular emblems painted on their doors parked helter-skelter in the drive and on the area in front of the two houses that once was lawn, but now was hard-packed brown dirt. Several of the cars had spotlights mounted on a post on the running board on the driver's side.

There were lots of sinister-looking men in fedora hats, dark suits, white shirts and ties milling about in clusters. Several were strung out along the driveway and had drawn guns and long-handled axes. The man standing by the Fantonetti's porch carried a "Tommy Gun" at his side. In the movies only mobsters and G-men carried them. I was thrilled to see how much it resembled the full-scale model I had carved out of wood and stained with black shoe polish for our cops-and-robbers games.

Ric and I led the way down the dark stairway. Vinnie followed with a firm grip on the handrail. He was so puffy he didn't look like Vinnie.

"You know who squealed, don'tcha?" muttered Vinnie.

"Whata-ya talkin' about?" whispered Ric.

"That goddam Mrs. Lazzarone," said Vinnie, "that's who the hell I'm talkin' about. We're all goin' to jail because of that big-mouth witch an' her friggin' dog."

Ric hesitated at the foot of the steps and turned his head. "Whata-ya talkin' about?"

Vinnie reminded Ric that when Mamma, speaking for

all the surrounding houses, tactfully, with carefully chosen words, had asked Mrs. Lazzarone if she could do something about the nighttime barking at her house, Mrs. Lazzarone had snapped back, "When *you* get rid of the nighttime whiskey smell, *I'll* get rid of the nighttime barking!"

"You may be right, Vinnie, you may be right."

The pinhole perforations riddling the drawn old shades allowed enough of the morning light to penetrate the relatively dark living room so that we could make out Mamma and my sister Annie timidly peeking through gaps they'd made in the shades to see if they could make sense of what was going on. My baby brother George was entertaining himself by vigorously pulling his toes to his mouth as he lay in his baby carriage. Papa had not moved from his bed. Blackie had been brought into the safety of the kitchen where he lay obediently quiet except for the occasional growl which he directed, ears twitching, toward the unfamiliar sounds outside. No one, as yet, had come to the door.

Mamma, wearing her blue chenille bathrobe and slippers, went upstairs and nervously checked the attic yet one more time. She got on her hands and knees and ran a butter knife down the cracks between the floor boards of the attic floor to make sure no mash residue was left behind as evidence. At one point she even burned an old sock and fanned the smoke to mask any lingering smell of whiskey.

There was more shouting outside and several automobile engines roared to life. We raced upstairs to get a better look. By the time we found a vantage point, most of the cars had backed out of the drive and positioned themselves so that all traffic on Clark was effectively blocked. It looked like they were arranging the agents strategically and we braced ourselves for the assault.

"Our Father, who art in heaven —" chanted Mamma and Annie, with their eyes squeezed shut.

A long dark green car with shiny black fenders remained on our drive with its engine idling and its restless driver and his partner sitting in the front seat. A rear door had been left open. A tall handsome man, wearing a pencil mustache and a gray homburg hat, was standing in front of the car talking to a completely subjugated and confused Mr. Fantonetti.

A cluster of agents, wielding hand guns, formed a semicircle as if to shield the two men. Our neighbor, who was half the size of the elegant G-man, kept nodding his head as he stood there in his undershirt, brown baggy pants, untied shoes, and no socks. He spoke almost no English so his daughter Carmella was acting as interpreter.

"Hail Mary, full of grace, the Lord is with thee —"

The G-man in charge seemed to be strangely conciliatory. He smiled, patted Mr. Fantonetti on the shoulder, shook his hand like they were settling a deal they'd worked out, and withdrew into the rear seat. After a clashing of gears the car groaned backward out of the driveway, arced into the street, and roared off with the other cars in pursuit.

Mamma and my sister had stopped praying aloud but continued crossing themselves. Mamma stood facing a reproduction of *La Madonna Della Pozzo*, her guardian saint; Annie sat on the couch, sobbing softly. Outside, it was very quiet. Mr. Fantonetti and Carmella walked into their house and the screen door slammed with a bang behind them.

The irresistible, monstrous force of the Treasury Department of the United States Government had unleashed its fury, swooped down like an avenging baldheaded American eagle in a power dive on our little innocuous compound at 3307 and 3309 Clark Avenue...*and raided the wrong house!*

This sensational event would normally have provided fuel for the widow Lazzarone's spite mill for years, but there was one little problem. Mr. Fantonetti, the focus of the crowd of onlookers that had accumulated, was her brother-in-law.

"God forbid. Maybe they gonna come again, maybe not," said Mamma, her voice so shaky we could barely make out what she was saying. She peeked through the slit in the shade with tears running down her cheeks.

"I want all my babies around me," sobbed Mamma, as we formed a circle around the fluttering candle she'd placed in the center of the living room floor. *"Thank you, Mother of Mercy —"* she prayed, as we knelt and clutched hands. We finished our thanksgiving prayer with the sign of the cross, and as we stood, Mamma opened her eyes and said, "Rico, Jeemie, Vinchenze, go quick an' find-a Frankie DaFutte. God forbid, they comma back when they talk onna gas man, I wanna Frankie here. He know what to do. Go quick, figlio mio."

Chapter VI

My father, puffing contentedly on the old pipe which seemed to have taken root in his mouth, was treating the family to the traditional Sunday afternoon drive through the park area of the Brookside Zoo. A couple of years had elapsed since Ric had driven this same Model T Ford the night before "The Big Raid." We were in the line of cars going up the steep exit incline when the vintage car sputtered and stalled. This was obviously a gas problem. The Model T had become an embarrassment not only because of its antiquity, but because its' rudimentary mechanical design, although very ingenious for its time, left a lot to be desired.

Papa turned the car around and got back in line, reversed, to raise the gas tank higher than the gravity-fed carburetor. As the newer cars crawled forward up the hill, with traffic light pauses at the top of the hill, we inched up backwards with my father twisted half-way round in his seat. For fear that some of the tittering pedestrians might be friends of ours, we slouched down out of sight in the back seat.

The following day, as Vinnie and I sat with our legs dangling over the projecting deck of the portable ice house that had been moved onto the Texaco gas station apron next to our house, Vinnie said, "You know what would be better than seeing a Model T going up the hill backwards on the Brookside Hill? With nobody in the back seat?"

"No, Vinnie, tell me. This I gotta know," I said, as I turned my head away to conceal my mortification.

"If your mother and father ducked out'ta sight, too, it would look like the flivver was takin' *itself* out for a Sunday drive!" He pushed me so hard I almost fell to the ground. "Now *that* story would make the headlines, not whatever this donkey is hollerin', towing his wagon like a well trained "Paper Rex" jackass. What the hell is he yelling, anyway?"

"Extra! Extra! Read all about it! Extra! Extra! Primo Carnera Drops Sharkey!" The young boy hawking the special edition of the Cleveland News like a horse-drawn "Paper! Rags!" man, held up the newspaper with the banner headline that read: "Carnera Wins." These sporadic interruptions of the neighborhood norm, like the wail of the ambulance or police siren, most often intimated news of disaster, but this kind of headline produced elation that spread through the neighborhood like a surprise shower on a hot dusty summer afternoon.

"Hoo-r-r-ray for the paesan'! That's our boy!" said Vinnie. "Ah-m-m in fine condition. Ah wanna take 'im agin'." He was mimicking Sharkey's radio interview as he had left the ring right after the fight. Vinnie jabbed at the air and added, "Now, let's see him take on Cookie Occarro." He shifted to his ringside interview voice again: "Ah jes' wanna thank ole 'Satchel Feet' Carnera for beatin' my brains into pasta mush.... Yeah. Until I hear those words, Jamie, YOU are still the world's champ, far as I'm concerned."

A car pulled up to the gas pumps and Vinnie and I slid off the ice-house deck and walked over to the pumps. Tony Cristafarro, the gas station and ice-house entrepreneur, paid us each ten cents to take charge of both places while he tended to his store-front business down the street where he sold odds and ends, new and used. He also sold "one of a kind" handpainted lampshades created by "Daisy," a simple woman from the hills of Tennessee who fascinated me with her ability to paint primitive animals, landscapes, and birds on the paper lampshades, "to order, while you wait."

Tony taught us many "tricks-o'-the-trade." When a car pulled up to the pumps, we could usually guess what the sale would amount to by the size, condition, and make of the car. Tony had a simple, but explicit sales strategy: "Always try to sell them one more gallon of gas or the more expensive oil." Then he coached us on how to do that.

"Bet'cha it's two gallons of nine-cents gas and one quart of ten-cent oil," I said, as we approached the pumps.

"Nope," said Vinnie, "that beat-up Essex is gettin' three gallons of 12 and one quart of 15-cent oil."

As we stepped up onto the cement island supporting the two gas pumps that Ric and I had almost rammed into the night of the big raid, we took our positions on either side of the lamppost so we could look down into the car. Tony wanted us higher than the customer for psychological reasons. "You stand on the ground, you look too short. They'll jerk you around. Look down at 'em, an' look right straight into their eyes. An' never look at your shoes."

"Can I help you, sir?"

"I'll take two gallons of the nine and one quart of oil," he ordered, exactly as I had predicted.

"Oil is five, ten, and 15 cents a quart, sir. Which one would you like?" I asked, knowing full well he was going to select the ten-cent. They almost always did. Tony had emphatically explained that five cents sounded inferior, 15 cents sounded extravagant, and would be ordered almost exclusively by the large flashy cars of the prohibition mobsters or the municipal vehicles such as the police, who always paid with bills, not coins.

"I'll take the ten-cent oil," came the expected response.

Normally at this point I would shift into Mr. Cristafarro's strategy to wring out an extended sale but this poor guy looked like he could barely afford the two gallons he'd ordered. As he carefully lined up the required coins on the seat next to him, I said, "That's fine, sir, may we wipe your windshield?"

"Can I point out, sir," said Vinnie, with rehearsed confidentiality, as he stepped between me and the old man, "that you are very close to getting a free Texaco prize. I don't wanna tell you what to do, but —"

"Vinnie —" I interrupted.

"...but..." he continued, as he pushed me aside, "... for three gallons of gas and one quart of 15-cent oil, you get one o' these genuine Ed Wynn Texaco Fire Chief hats." He tapped the red cheesecloth give-away fireman's hat on his head.

"Naw. I don't need no better oil."

"Vinnie —" I persisted, as I tapped him on the shoulder.

"OK," he said to the old man, as he brushed my hand away, "I'll tell you what. The owner's not here right now. Buy just one more gallon of gas and the hat and the 15-cent oil is yours at no extra charge."

"You got a deal!" said the grinning old man, pointing to Vinnie. "You have a deal, an' no backin' down!"

I cranked the handle on the side of the Tokheim Visible Gas Pump until three gallons of gas rose gurgling up the calibrated glass cylinder perched on the red metal base. The cautious customer watched carefully to make sure the gasoline reached the proper level so he wouldn't be cheated and nodded his approval. I nudged the handle one more time around for another burst of bubbles that raised the gas level a smidgen. The old man raised his eyebrows and winked at me. I placed the nozzle into the neck of the gas tank and tripped the release valve. I liked the smell of the gas fumes and inhaled deeply as the gas poured into the tank.

With the adept moves of an old pro, I wiped his windshield with a damp cloth and scrunched-up newspaper. Vinnie came out from the back room with the open quart container of bulk oil brimming and tipped the flexible metal spout into the crankcase without spilling a drop. The car owner checked the dipstick and nodded his approval. He carefully placed the red fireman's hat on the seat next to him and said, "Thanks kids. I appreciate this." As he drove off, he waved and Vinnie saluted to another satisfied customer.

The thing was, all of Mr. Cristafarro's oil came out of the same 50-gallon drum in the back room and the twelve-cents-a-gallon and nine-cents-a-gallon gas came from the same storage tank in the ground.

Vinnie took nine cents out of the puddle of small change the old man had paid him, dropped the coins into his pants pocket and dropped the rest into the cigar box. Whenever Mr. Cristafarro was gone, he always locked the cash register.

"Vinnie," I said, as he walked away from me toward the ice house, "what'ta ya doin'?" He continued to the ice house without answering. I sat on the deck next to him, looked squarely into his face and said, "You can't do that."

"Can't do what?"

"First of all," I said, with an edge to my voice, "the hat's free. It's a give-away. Second, you cheated a guy who couldn't afford it. Third, I saw you steal from Tony and put the money you stole into your pocket. I think you should put that money in the cigar box. I think —"

"You think, you think. Well, you don't think enough. Here's what I think. That guy at the West Side Market, the guy with the shell game. Is he cheatin' the suckers plunkin' down their money week after week trying to beat him? They're the ones cheatin' themselves trying to beat the odds. Everybody's lookin' for somethin' for nuthin'."

"Vinnie, you plain stole nine cents from Tony."

"You know that kid haulin' the Carnera newspapers? He pulls his red wagon full o' papers from Twenty-fifth street to Trent an' makes a buck, maybe a buck an' a half in an hour, hour an' a half. We watch Tony's gas station and his ice house all day and he pays us ten cents. Ten goddam cents! Who the hell is cheatin' who, here? You tell me."

"Wait a minute, Vinnie, that old man —"

"That ole man thought we were cheatin' on the owner to do him a favor. Did you hear him say, 'Oh, you can't cheat the owner?' Bullshit! Besides, he didn't get cheated. He got just what he paid for. No less, no more. No, come to think of it, you gave him more gas than he paid for. You're the one who cheated Tony to make the ole man feel good. An' another thing. You don't mind cheatin' the big flashy cars, do you? Don't gim'me your honesty bullshit, Jamie. The whole friggin' world is one big shell game. You just gotta learn to keep your eye on the pea, or you'll end up at the bottom of the totem pole with everybody else piled on top o' ya. Or worse yet, you could end up being the part buried in the ground."

A police car pulled up to the pumps and we both slid to the ground from the deck. When we saw that it was occupied by the two rogue cops that used to hassle the gang on the corner, Vinnie stopped me with his arm across my chest.

"No. You wait right here," he said, "Lemme handle this. I want these assholes by myself. You stay right here. Don't move. I know how to move the shells around, you don't."

Halfway to the pumps he turned to me and said, "When I'm done with these guys, I'm taking you, your brother Ric, Bill, and Lino to the Garden Saturday." As he stepped on the cement island, he turned once more toward me and shouted, "I'm even splurgin' on the popcorn!" He then turned to the two smoking cops and said, "Sorry, officers, the law says you have to distinguish all cigarettes at the pumps. Now, how can I help you. Gentlemen? Sirs?"

I don't know what went on with the cops, but Vinnie did treat us to the Garden on Saturday — movie, popcorn, and Ju-ju Babies. The works. And only Lino had to go throw up in the men's room.

Chapter VII

"Extra! Extra! Read all about it! Prohibition is over!" In December, the bundled up kid pulling the red wagon full of newspapers wasn't doing too well. As he moved down the street, smiling people poured out of their houses to hear the news, but only the sullen looking ones bought and scurried back indoors. If the Feds were smart, they'd follow that kid around and mark the houses that bought papers if they wanted to know where the bootleg stills were.

Unemployment was still widespread in the late thirties and prosperity was still "just around the corner," but things were beginning to look better economically. "That man in the White House," as Franklin Delano Roosevelt was referred to by the elite who didn't understand the ramifications of the New Deal, brought to my family the alphabet soup of programs that proved to be a source of relief from the relentless deprivation associated with the earlier part of the decade.

Between the odd jobs my father was able to muster, and the work he got from the WPA, we were now getting nutritious meals on a more regular basis. The orange glow of the steel mills, a reliable economic barometer, also appeared more often at night on the eastern horizon.

We were relieved when the Model T was traded up to a five-year-old Plymouth. It was the first car we owned that had a gear-shift lever and a fuel pump, which, happily, eliminated the necessity of driving up hills backwards.

But the streetcar was still the primary mode of transportation in day-to-day living. On one of our exciting streetcar trips to the West Side Market, my mother herded us past the crowd gathered around the intriguingly swift hands of the shell-game gambler who was switching the confounding pea under the walnut half-shells. She ducked us into a large post office to watch WPA artists working from a scaffold as they painted a spectacular mural.

I was so enthralled I lost my grip on Mamma's hand. One artist was lettering the legend "The Heritage My Community Offers" across the bottom of the mural.

It had never occurred to me that real people actually painted these incredible wall decorations. And, on top of that, judging by the WPA "Your tax dollars at work" sign propped up against the scaffolding, they were getting paid money to do this! Aside from Daisy painting her lampshades for a living, I had never, personally, considered painting pictures as a way to make a buck. Watching this mural in progress was a stunning revelation. Right up there with the exploits of Tillie-the-Toiler, condoms, and talking dogs.

"Jeemie. Hey...Jeemie! C'mon, we gotta go. C'mon," said Mamma. She walked back to where I stood, transfixed, took me by the hand, and tugged me away.

This was better than the mural behind the altar at St. Francis which was also so entrancing that I often blocked out Father Gatto's shouted fire and damnation sermons. The huge, realistic mural featured St. Francis of Assisi, with upraised arms, taming the She-wolf of Gubbio and blessing all the other animals that had gathered to witness the Holy event. Cherubs trailing ribbons with messages on them floated in the over head cumulus clouds. The painting was so realistic and detailed I wondered if some parts, like the folds in the robe, were actually three dimensional.

At the Scranton Avenue Public Library, about a 40-minute walk from our house, I'd sit and read Robert Louis Stevenson's adventure books under the large reproduction of a mural that covered a wall of the fiction room. I got the same comforting feeling I got in church. "N.C. Wyeth" appeared in the lower corner of the printed mural and also in the breathtaking illustrations in most of Stevenson's exciting novels. I never connected the name with the producer of the art work.

Books tripped off daydreams about career choices, which changed on a regular basis, and I was eager to move on to junior high school so I could get to my ultimate goal, West Tech, where I would learn a trade.

When we graduated from Walton, the thing I missed most was Blackie escorting me home. Over time, he had developed severe rheumatism and cataracts and now spent most of his time coddled in Mamma's aromatic kitchen, sampling recipes. With everyone else gone during the day, Mamma welcomed his company. But even in his prime, he never would have been allowed to risk the long distance through the hazardous streets to Thomas Jefferson Junior High.

Thomas Jefferson was more formal and structured than Walton. For the first time in our school careers, we had homerooms and lockers. We passed from class to class at regular intervals, and we went to assemblies. The most important thing we learned in the gym class was: "Never step on the gym floor with street shoes." Those who could afford it were privileged to use the school cafeteria where they were treated to a never-altered menu of macaroni and cheese, hot dogs, Spanish rice, and milk, which could be sprayed through straws.

"Give ya a penny for a bite a' yer hot dog."

"Two cents. Only up to here. An' don't bite my fingertips or you get the rest up your nose."

At "T.J." my interest in school was accelerated. My friends and I soon achieved scholastic recognition and a feeling of well-being, but there were days, clearly, when some of us should have stayed home. Instead, we came to school with our winter colds and runny noses and sat next to the upright cast-iron radiators we located in each classroom as we passed from room to room. We weren't trying to keep warm. These were the days before throw-a-way paper tissues, and the afflicted persons had learned to drape one of the two cloth handkerchiefs they had brought with them over the hot radiator where it would dry by the end of the class period and be ready for another round of sneezes. It was a procedure that would give any certified hygienist the shudders.

"Hey, Jamie, how d'ja get the cold?" asked one of the kids.

"My mother said I don't listen to her and I stepped outside for a minute without my coat," I said, through perpetually parted chapped lips that made me look like a droopy-eyed guppie.

"Serves ya right. You should listen to your mother."

Vinnie had failed a grade at Walton and although he was a year older than the rest of us, he was now a classmate. A lowly freshman "flat" just like us. The age difference, however, gave him a clear-cut advantage. Not in the classroom; he wasn't much interested in academics.

What he did instead was blossom so rapidly, physically, that it was like watching a kernel of corn burst into popcorn. It seemed like one day he had the same lollypop build we all had, and the next thing we knew, he showed up at one of our daily touch football games two heads higher and fully developed. Naturally, after that, everyone wanted him on their side. And, for the first time, we had girl spectators.

"Hey, Grosso, the girls are lookin' at'cha again."

"Hey!" yelled Vinnie in the direction of the girls, "who's the head cheerleader?" The girls all turned their backs and walked away with cupped hands to their mouths.

There was a lineal logic to math, social studies, and the sciences that made these subjects fun to conquer, and it was therefore easy for me to maintain a string of straight A grades. But it wasn't until I encountered Miss Schmidt, the art teacher, that the element of real excitement was added to the curriculum. Then and there, I knew I had met my mentor.

On our first day with her she finished taking roll call and faced us sitting against the edge of her desk with her arms folded. Her eyes swept the room.

"Oh, my," she said, "I feel so privileged. I have never had a class where everybody...where everybody...was so good-looking and looked so smart." We all blushed, studied our desktops, and fell in love.

I developed a wonderful relationship with Miss Schmidt. As often as I could, I would hang around the art room working on all kinds of fascinating projects that Miss Schmidt got me involved in. I learned how to mix poster paints, how to carve plaster, and how to make automobile and architectural models that continually improved under her tutelage.

Miss Schmidt created individual problem-solving projects for each of us that required the application of the abstractions we had learned in the other disciplines. She had us make toothpick truss bridges, and working models of hand-pump wells, complete with painted backdrop scenery. We also constructed various projects to help us understand the principles of simple machines such as the lever, the pulley, the screw, the inclined plane, and the wheel and axle.

"You have a natural aptitude for engineering," she said once, as she appraised my improvement. "You'll make a fine engineer." I smiled and imagined myself leaning out of the cab window of a roaring locomotive, squinting into the wind with one hand holding onto my striped train-engineer's hat while I kept the other hand on the throttle.

It was all coming together nicely. I had learned street skills from Frankie the Foot and the guys down at the corner; security and loyalty from the neighborhood; honor, honesty and integrity from my parents; the slippery ethics of the business world from Mr. Cristafarro; and my teachers had reinforced my confidence in my abilities. I was a product of my gene pool and experiences — a composite. A survivor with his eye on the *Capo dei capi*...the capping head on the totem pole.

At the Thomas Jefferson Junior High graduation, Miss Schmidt met my parents, took me aside and said, "We will miss you. You have a fine mind, a loving family, and you are motivated." She hugged me to her body and kissed the top of my head. She looked into my eyes, smiled, and added, "All the parts for success are in place. We'll all be watching to see what you do with them."

Chapter VIII

It was early on that warm September morning as my brother Ric and I walked the short distance to the corner of Clark and Fulton to catch the streetcar that would take Ric to his first day of his last year at West Technical High School. He was energized and self-assured.

I, on the other hand, felt excited but somewhat apprehensive as I walked at a lively pace to keep up with him. I was grateful that Ric was there to help guide me through the preliminary steps of my first venture into the intimidating far-off galaxy of young adulthood. At breakfast, Ric had been supportive and calming.

"Aye, Rico, Jamie," said a grinning Mr. Costello, as he interrupted the sidewalk sweeping in front of his corner grocery store. "Jerry give you a nice'a haircut." Good observation. Annie's fiance, a part-time barber, had clipped Ric, Vinnie, and me in Mamma's kitchen, just yesterday.

Most of the other boys dispersed around the corner had first-day-of-school haircuts rendered by frugal mothers with low aptitude ratings for barbering. Those boys looked sheared, with white "bites" showing, like they'd cut their own hair without the aid of a mirror.

A few steps more and we were in the midst of a large assemblage of neighborhood faces. Ric burst into a broad smile as he walked over to a group of his friends and they punched each other ritualistically on the upper arm.

Vinnie Grosso had one foot stretched up to the top of the dark green fireplug and was rocking back and forth like a sprinter warming up for a 100-yard dash. With the combination of the right genetic make-up, regular workouts at the gym, and a narcissistic fascination with his physique, Vinnie had developed into an impressive physical specimen.

"That your kid brother trying to pound the fireplug into the ground with his foot?" asked Ric's friend, Freddie.

"Naw," answered Ric, with pride. "This one right here is my kid brother, Jamie,"

"Then this other guy must be the sissy on the beach who got sand kicked in his face and took the Charles Atlas Body Building Course so he could go back, beat the crap outta the bully, and impress the girls." They snorted and punched each other on the upper arm. Several of the guys imitated and grossly exaggerated the Charles Atlas weight-lifter posturing they'd seen in the advertisements on the back cover of every comic book. They all howled. Except Vinnie.

Although his muscle building had, in fact, been developed to impress the opposite sex, the only females gathered in the group so far this morning were four frightened girls huddled against the wall of Costello's Grocery. Three of the four were wearing no make-up, wore flower-patterned dresses with white collars and cuffs, and held clenched lips that were slits. The fourth girl, the overweight member of the clutch, wore a generous application of Tangee lipstick. She was the only one whose eyes darted in the direction of Vinnie who was undeterred by the abusive rebuke and continued to run through his repertoire of peacock preening.

"Tell ya somethin' else," said Freddie, "whenever these guys start pumpin' iron, the first thing that swells is their head." That brought on another round of guffaws.

"C'mon you guys, go easy," said Ric. "Vinnie's an OK guy."

"Funny thing," said one of Ric's other friends, "all three of you guys look like brothers. Even Charles Atlas, over there, not only looks like you guys, he's even got the same haircut."

"Maybe so," said Ric, who was trying to keep me buoyant, "but this brother is the best looking of the bunch, don'cha think?" He put his arm around my bony shoulder and tugged me toward him several times.

"No doubt about it," said Freddie, who saw Ric's purpose.

"Here she comes!" someone hollered. We all turned in the direction of the approaching streetcar as the crowd shuffled into a tighter and tighter group in preparation for the boarding. The two-tone tan and cream colored streetcar pulled up noisily to the stop with metal squealing and brakes hissing. This was the first time I was about to board a streetcar without my mother at my side.

Like the others around me, I paid the conductor 50-cents for my bright green weekly pass and we filed between him and the small cast-iron coal stove which in the winter served as the only source of heat. The car started with a lurch and quickly reached cruising speed.

"Ful-ton Road and Low-rain Avenue!" shouted the conductor to the back of the car, which was by now packed with the students we had picked up along the way. He turned to the jammed front of the car and repeated, "Fulton Road and Lorain!" This was where we would transfer.

On the other side of the intersection, perpendicular to the direction in which we had been traveling, were three stationary streetcars in tandem and almost touching. A mob of students, part of the 6,000 that attended West Tech, were stuffing themselves into the waiting cars.

The car we had transferred to got underway with crammed students gripping the white baked-enamel overhead bars that ran the length of the aisle. Ric and I were lucky to get seats together and Vinnie wrestled his way into a seat directly behind us. He had no sooner settled into the seat he had fought for when he leaped to his feet. He pressed against the students standing in the aisle behind him, cleared a tenuous space to his seat, turned to a pretty girl student standing next to him, and with a bowing-scraping gesture worthy of Sir Walter Raleigh, gestured to the vacated seat.

"At your service, madam," said Vinnie, like he was on stage.

"Oh! Gosh...you really? O-o-oh, thank you!" said the pretty art major, struggling with a stretched canvas painting she tried to manage, along with other cumbersome packages.

"My pleasure. Here, let me take some of that stuff...from... oops! Here we go. I can take that from you —"

"O-o-oh, aren't you sw-e-e-et! You are a gentleman —" gushed the seated girl looking up at Vinnie with long batting eyelashes.

"...and a scholar," added Vinnie. The girl's flirtatious laugh lasted longer than was required.

"...and a humorist!" she countered. "Oh, my. Oh...." She was obviously flustered.

For the rest of the ride to school, Vinnie stood over the seated girl with the "peasant blouse" and focused on her cleavage as he flexed his well-developed muscles and charm.

As the tandem streetcars, jammed exclusively with students, swayed past stops like unlimited express trains, I unconsciously reached down and touched the master combination lock fastened to my belt loop.

Ric had warned me that I'd better be prompt for homeroom, which was the same as Vinnie's, and better be ready to show a lock for our assigned lockers or we might get "Tuck's Track Team." Getting the "Triple T" meant you were going to report to school a lot earlier every morning, for God knows how long. Starting at the main entrance, you jogged around the city block with other problem kids and were subjected to the jeering and the catcalls of the cruel store owners and housewives, while the fearsome Principal C.C. Tuck watched from the roof of the school with binoculars.

When the streetcars disgorged their passengers at 91st Street it was bedlam. We stepped from the car into the boiling crowd and all of the familiar faces quickly disappeared, except for the female art student and Vinnie, who still had her packages, including the canvas painting, tucked under his arm.

As we moved with the crowd down the side street toward the school, Vinnie introduced Ric and me to Gretchen Goering, a junior art major who'd studied with Mr. Unger for a year. When she learned that I had been accepted into the art program, she became animated and focused her attention on me.

"Oh! You're going to just love it! Congratulations! Oh, you are so-o lucky to make it! So-o-o many kids try and so-o-o many don't make it...and those that do are like, The Chosen. You know? Like, I don't know ...like one of us. A special fraternity or sorority, or whatever. Hey, wait a minute. You mean you got Mrs. Unger, right? Not...Mister. You're only a flat...a 10th grader, right?"

"Yeah," I said, "I'm a flat, and I got Mister Unger."

"You better check...oh I get it. I get it. Tony, right? You're related to Tony LaBianca, right?"

"No. Who's Tony LaBianca?"

"Who's Tony LaBianca?" she said. "Are you kidding? Only the greatest football legend this school has ever known, that's who. Wait till you see the trophy cases. LaBianca, most passes. LaBianca, most touchdowns. LaBianca walks on water! Oh God! I wish my last name was LaBianca at this school!"

"Not me," said Ric.

"Why not?" I asked, surprised he wasn't sharing my sudden pride in our apparently famous surname.

"Because every teacher you get today is gonna ask that question and then expect you to come up to his level of achievement, or else."

"I'm going out for football," said Vinnie. "Watch that trophy showcase for a while. I think you are gonna like Grosso better than LaBianca."

Gretchen ignored the interjection and enthusiastically talked more about the art program and Mr. Unger. "Call me Gee-Gee. All my friends call me Gee-Gee. I can't believe you're starting right out with him," she said to me. "Usually everyone has to go through Basic Art with Mrs. Unger. Survive her and you go on to him. You're so-o-o lucky." Mr. Unger, she expanded, like she was his P.R. agent, had operated a commercial art agency, was a renown watercolorist, had paintings hanging at museums around the country and had written a bunch of art books. "He's like a God, and not just around here."

Ric lost interest in the conversation and picked up the pace as he walked ahead of us. "Nice to meet you Gretchen," he said, "I gotta go all the way to Automotive. You take them from here? OK?" He turned to me and added, "You're gonna be fine. Tell Ma I'll get home when I get home." From a short distance ahead of us, he pointed and yelled, "There it is!"

The brick-and-stone trimmed building was awesome.

It was three stories high and stretched all the way down 93rd Street to the school stadium. We made our way through the main entrance doors and encountered the strong smell of paint, shellac, and soap that most schools have on opening day. Just inside the doors was a larger-than-life bronze statue of Abraham Lincoln. Propped against his legs was a large poster that read: BEAT LINCOLN.

"Beat Lincoln?" asked Vinnie. "Whoa. Do we just slap him around a little? Maybe a couple kicks in the ribs? Or if we're from the sunny south do we let him know how we really felt about the E-mancipation Proc-lamation?" Then in a southern dialect he added, "Holy Mackerel, Amos. Shou' we really do a cakewalk on 'im an' use de baseball bats?"

"Now that's very funny!" chortled Gretchen. "No, and it's not a tenth-grade entrance thing to beat up Lincoln, either. The opening football game this year is against our archenemy, Lincoln High. But you're not too far off the mark. We'll go at it like it's the war between the states all over again. Wait 'till you see what these halls look like by game time."

We walked up the second set of marble steps and through the second set of vestibule doors where three converging locker-lined hallways met and vanished to three points on the horizon. On either side of the main stairs was a dark brown, freshly painted paneled door. The top of the door frames bore the lavatory signs that indicated that the one on the right was for MEN. Not BOYS' TOILET like at T.J. and Walton. It said it right there in black and white, above the heads of the shuffling crowd. MEN. The realization that I was about to join their ranks made me feel calm, manly. Proud.

Gretchen led us to the third floor and Vinnie followed her into room 312, the art room, her homeroom. I remained in the corridor gaping at an astonishing exhibit of students' art work with a concentration unbroken by the crush of jostling homeroom bound students.

When the throngs thinned to a few stragglers, Gretchen and Vinnie stepped out of the art room and Gretchen pointed down the hall in the general direction of Cincinnati with her long-handled paintbrush.

"The building's shaped like a big letter 'E.' Go down this way to the first corridor, make a right, all the way to the last room. That's your homeroom. And you'd better hurry. The bell's about to ring. And one more very important thing. Don't ever get caught in the hall without a pass, ever, or you'll get 'Tuck's Track Team'." As she was about to disappear behind the closing door, she reappeared and added, "And don't ever go DOWN the UP stairs!"

"Hey!" said Vinnie, as the door closed behind her, "when am I gonna see —"

"C'mon Vin, let's get going, quick. God A'mighty, we sure don't wanna be late the first day." I grabbed Vinnie's arm and dragged him away from the art room.

We had been warned about running in the halls so we scurried with long strides that resembled the action of a cross-country skier. A loud bell rang and it was as if someone in total darkness had turned on a bright light in a cockroach-infested kitchen at midnight. Bodies scurried into cavities all the way up and down the corridor.

With the sound of the bell still reverberating in my ears we were standing by ourselves in the corridor — except for the big young man blocking our path, with his hands on his hips. The lettered crimson and grey sweater with the three varsity athletic stripes on one upper arm and the hall-guard arm band on the other identified him as a distinguished student, not a faculty member. He smiled a greeting, extended his hand to Vinnie, who'd attended football tryouts all summer.

"Hey, Grosso! I never got to tell you after practice last week. H-o-l-y jumpin' Jesus! That...was...some...broken-field running." He swagged his head from side to side with admiration. "Nobody ever got past me like that before. Ever! You made me look like a shit in front of Coach Blakely, but, man-o-man, I'm glad you're on our side." Then he warned us not to be in the halls again after the bell.

"Well, I know better," said Vinnie, with his arm around me, "but my little friend, here, had first-day heave-ho's in the crapper and I couldn't leave him 'till I knew he was OK." They shook hands like old friends.

"I got a good night's sleep last night, Grosso," said the guard, as he walked back toward his post. "You're gonna hav'ta work to get past me today. See ya at practice."

After the first-day homeroom formalities we were released to locate our assigned lockers. Vinnie and I happened to be side by side just outside of our homeroom door. Once, twice, three times and slowly, carefully, a fourth time, I dialed the combination on my lock, which was still attached to my belt loop. It wouldn't open. I thought of Tuck's Track Team and felt a wave of panic ripple its way from my hairline to my toenails.

"Yes. I'm sure it's 5-2-24," I told Vinnie.

"Stick your stuff in my locker 'till you get another lock," he said, as he rearranged the stuff in his locker.

"Thanks, Vinnie. I...ah...jeez —" My tension was beginning to show. Vinnie put his arm around me reassuringly, and shook me gently.

"Hey, ole buddy. Don't sweat it. Just keep an eagle eye on

Gretchen for me. Wait 'till you see the babes an' boobs in that art room! Holy shit. I think I'm gonna drop Foundry an' switch to Art. I wish I could draw more than a straight line with a ruler. Wait 'till you see the boobs! *Madone!*" One hand cupped his crotch while the other thumped his forehead. He rolled his eyes back into his head and said, *"Jesu Christo Mio!"*

I stepped through the door marked 312 and was surprised at the number of projects already in various stages of development on this first day of school.

I gravitated toward Gretchen who was bent over a palette mixing paint. When she straightened up, I couldn't help locking onto the cleavage exposed by her scoop neck blouse. Our eyes made contact for an instant. She smiled and I blushed.

"Hey. Hi, Jamie!" She beamed as she tucked strands of her long blond hair behind her ear with her thumb. "You're probably wondering what the heck is goin' on here. Some of us advanced students have been coming to school all summer and working on these projects on our own."

"I can't believe how good some of this stuff is," I said.

"Oh, God, Jamie. Wait 'till you see. When some of these guys really get goin'...God...you're...you ain't seen nuthin' yet!"

Vinnie was right. About half the class was made up of attractive females. Except for a few of the new tenth-grade girls who were standing around the periphery of the room, all of the shapely girls had well developed boobs. Three solid years of girls with remarkable boobs! The adult world was looking better all the time.

When the revered art teacher Paul V. Unger finally made his appearance, it was as if we were witnessing The Second Coming. This former football player and coach was a large muscular "older" man with a developing paunch, thick arms, and a thick neck. His salt-and-pepper hair was parted on one side and some of it fell casually over his forehead. On his upper lip was a neatly trimmed narrow gray mustache that was the same width as his mouth. He was wearing a short-sleeved white shirt and a plain tan-colored necktie.

His steel-blue eyes quickly scanned the room before he completed the step over the threshold and everyone immediately fell silent. Nobody moved. The kids at the etching press froze in their tracks even though they were halfway into a run.

Mr. Unger stomped his way to his desk and seemed to be oblivious of anyone else being in the room. Minutes went by before he put on his black horn-rimmed granny-glasses and skimmed over the first day of school papers he had brought with him from the office. The Regulator Clock that hung on the wall above the sink made a tick-tock sound with each swing of the pendulum. Nobody stirred. Somebody coughed. Mr. Unger looked up over the top of his glasses in the direction of the sound. Then he went back to reading in the silent room.

He put the papers down, sat back in his swivel chair, scanned the room once more over the top of his glasses, cracked his knuckles audibly and in a low rumbling voice said, "OK, you jerks. Don't shirk. Work!" There was immediate activity, like someone had hit a switch, but the room remained quiet and everyone spoke in hushed tones.

"I would like to see the following people. Hanks, Jedder, LaBianca, Munk, Perry, Seldon, and Sucsy."

We lined up in front of his desk and without looking up he said, "Which one of you is LaBianca?"

I raised my hand.

"Are you related to Tony LaBianca?"

"No," I said.

"Too bad. You would have come from good stock. Best quarterback this school has ever seen."

He busied himself for a few minutes writing all of our names on a card and went on. "Now listen carefully, because I'm going to say this just once. I want each of you to go to that rack, take out a drawing board, tack four sheets of bond paper to the board, take two pencils and one eraser from those boxes on that counter. Then all of you will go see Mr. A.L. Hagedorn in the horticulture department and tell him all of you will spend the morning doing a drawing of the Gloxinia. There are seven of you. I hope that's your lucky number. Your results will determine whether or not you remain in this department." The rumor was that before the week was over, half this class would be kicked out to another department. If it came to that, my next choice was Aeronautics.

"LaBianca," he said as he handed the pass to me, "I want you to show this pass to Mr. Hagedorn and get this group back up into this room by 11:40. Is that clear?"

"Yes sir," I said, appreciating the responsibility.

He focused on the Master combination lock that was still locked around my belt loop and asked in a low voice, through the corner of his mouth, "You ain't afraid someone's gonna steal your pants, are you?"

"No sir," I said sheepishly.

He looked over the top of his glasses past his raised eyebrows and added, "If you've got any of Tony LaBianca's genes running through your veins, you ought'a play it safe and put that lock on your fly." He gave me a quick wink and I grinned with relief.

I led the expedition through the labyrinth of corridors and doors that led to the first greenhouse. A female student in a black rubber apron introduced us to Mr. Hagedorn, who asked us to take one of the stools stacked in a corner. We followed him in single file past tray after tray of cactus, ferns, roses, lilies, phlox, and African violets.

The smells, the filtered light coming through the white-washed glass, the warm humid air slowly moving from greenhouse to greenhouse through the humming built-in fans, all contributed to a very seductive atmosphere.

An immediate protective bond developed between the seven fledgling art students, and everyone shared valuable suggestions regarding the composition, style, and rendering of the others. The pooled effort accounted for the best work any of us had ever done.

Mr. Unger appeared pleased as he called each of us up to his desk to evaluate and comment on our work. I handed him my drawings and felt a trickle of sweat run down my ribs.

"Hey. Not bad, kid. Not bad at all." He said, "You sure you're not related to Tony LaBianca?"

I smiled and said, "I'm pretty sure."

The rest of the day went just as well. After lunch, I went from one academic subject to the other, and it looked as if all of my teachers were going to be male. However, when I went to the last period class, I met Miss Aitken, my very attractive, vivacious English teacher. Ric's surname prediction was almost right, but not quite. She turned out to be the only teacher that did not ask me if I was related to Tony LaBianca.

At the end of the day, I found my way back to the art room which was filled with students silently working on their projects. Mr. Unger, with his back to me, was critiquing Gretchen's poster. She glanced past his shoulder, caught my eye momentarily and looked back down at her poster. Then, without looking away again, she moved her hand beyond Mr. Unger's range of vision and wiggled her fingers at me.

Five of the seven boys I had gone to the greenhouse with earlier that morning were there and two of them, Jedder and Suscy, lived near my neighborhood, so we would be traveling home on the same streetcar.

Homeward bound, we burbled excitedly about experiences we'd had that day and carried on, endlessly, until Bobby and Zoltan got off at their respective stops.

As I sat alone on the last leg of the journey, my hand inadvertently fell on the Master lock, which was still attached to my belt loop. I tried to imagine the sound it would make in the washing machine when my mother washed my pants.

That night, as we prepared for bed, I told Ric how much I loved my new school, my new friends, and especially the art department. As I described other exciting events of the day, I took off my pants, with the lock still attached to the belt-loop, and draped them over the chair-back.

Once, twice, three times, I turned the combination numbers on the lock in the proper sequence, and the lock popped open each time.

"Well," said Ric, as he rolled away from me on the bed and turned out the light, "now Ma won't hafta cut the pants apart. Good-night."

"You really think she'd hafta do that?" I asked.

"Either that, or we put 'em in the washer with you still in 'em." We both laughed.

"Ric," I said, in the comfort of the dark, "Thanks for getting me started. I was acting brave, but I was scared." Ric snapped on the table lamp and turned toward me.

"You were acting? Huh. You fooled me. In case you didn't

notice it, little brother, you went through the hard part all by yourself. You weren't acting. I brought you to the menu. You made the selections. All by yourself. Sure you were scared; who isn't once in a while. Point is, you proved to yourself, and to all of us, that you made the right choices. And, knowing you like I do, now that you are on your own, there's nothin' can hold you back. Good-night." He turned out the light and added, "Just don't get too big for your britches ...or put the lock back around the belt loop." We laughed again.

"Good-night, big brother."

"Good-night, Jamie."

As I lay in the quiet darkness, my dark thoughts started to surface. I had shown Mr. Unger the best drawing I'd ever done and all he said was, "Not bad, kid, not bad." Is that good or bad? When Gee-Gee waved at me after school and Mr. Unger couldn't see her hand, she wiggled her fingers, then gave me a thumbs-down signal.

God Almighty! What was that for? Was I gonna end up next to Vinnie in the foundry?

I rolled closer to the mattress edge with my back to Ric and whispered softly, "Our Father, who art in heaven —"

Chapter IX

"You never noticed," said Gee-Gee, "but three of the flats have disappeared, and so did that big guy that always used to work quietly in the corner by himself. Poof! Gone bye-bye...and you're not one of 'em. *'Not bad, kid, not bad,'* is as good as it gets. And the thumbs down? That was not for you. Mr. Unger was criticizing my composition and was telling me to start over. I may be wrong, but I think the Lucky Seven are locked in. If he sinks one, he's gonna have to sink 'em all. Don't worry, Jamie. Take it from me. If you were going, you'd be gone."

The crackling energy field and spiritual levitation I had experienced that first day in the art room did not abate with time; it got more intense. So did my sexual urges. Although I wasn't going around holding my crotch and sucking my thumb or thumping my forehead like Vinnie, I did notice that I no longer sighed with exasperation when he brought up his obsession with female body parts.

When I lamented to Vinnie that I feared this place wouldn't be the same when the senior girls with their protruding breasts eventually graduated, he assured me, "not to worry." They'd be replaced with a steady flow of attractive, budding, tenth-grade girls.

"It's like a Coca-Cola bottling plant," he said. "Clean sterile bottles line up at one end, move along the conveyer belt 'till they become filled-up, curvy seniors." He traced the curvy shape of the coke bottle in the air with his cupped hands. "Then, when they're sweet and delicious at the other end, they get capped, like at graduation, and off they go to who the hell knows where. But the empties keep on coming." He threw out his arms like Al Jolson and sang the last line from "Old Man River": "They...just...keeps...roll-l-l-ling...ah...long! Hot damn!" He snapped his fingers and booted a phantom football between invisible goal posts.

My quantum leaping sexual drive *had* to be sublimated and channeled into my art work. As far as my parents were concerned, old world doctrine dictated that the day I could cut perfect "figure eights" skating on the ice in hell, is the day I'd be allowed to date in high school. Among my friends, Vinnie was the only exception to this edict. He had convinced his widower father that hell had frozen over and his on-again-off-again relationship with Gretchen continued to stumble on from semester to semester.

The contained energy generated by my repressed longing for the opposite sex, plus my fascination with the art world, drove me directly into the art room each morning even before Tuck's Track Team had assembled at the main entrance.

When there were deadlines for contests involved, it was not unusual to have as many as 15 to 20 students working at a feverish pace until eight o'clock at night, long after Mr. Unger had gone home. Sometimes we stayed until eleven o'clock, which was the curfew dictated by the last scheduled streetcar.

In a relatively short time a close bond developed between the new students and Mr. Unger.

"Will the Lucky Seven set up their boards around the model stand...puh-leeze," said Mr. Unger. The seven boys who had gone to the greenhouse on that first day so long ago, quickly

112

gathered the necessary materials and formed a semi-circle of slanted desks around the model stand on which a full scale plaster head and neck of a horse was spotlighted.

Mr. Unger leaned against the model stand and said, "Jedder. Do you know why I call you jerks 'The Lucky Seven'?"

"No sir," said Peter.

"Well, here's why," said Mr. Unger. "You're lucky you got this far, and you're lucky if you make it to the next semester." We feigned shock.

"Now, get your small minds off of the swishing skirts in the room and listen to what I'm about to tell you. You may have a brand new experience. You might actually learn something and *that* would be a brand new experience for me too." When he was finished, we had reams of valuable information we could not have acquired in any book.

The momentum and the excitement generated in the art room carried over into my afternoon academic subjects. By the end of my first year, I had made straight A's in all my subjects and the achievement was recorded in a photograph on the first page of the school newspaper, *The Tatler*. The headline read: "Principal Congratulates Leaders."

On page three was a photograph taken in front of the trophy case. It showed a smiling football player and a beaming pretty girl with a gorgeous figure holding a large urn-shaped trophy between them. The headline over the photo read: "Vinnie, Vidi, Vici." The caption read: "Captain Vinnie Grosso, who led the area all-stars to victory in the coveted Kumquat Bowl Game in St. Petersburg, Florida, shares the glory with Gretchen 'Gee-Gee' Goering, Cleveland Bowl Game Queen."

When I took the paper home, my mother carefully cut my photograph out and pasted it into our family photo album. I had brought honor to the family.

In the second year, Mr. Unger methodically taught us how to paint with watercolor, oil, egg tempera, casein, and he even gave a demonstration of fresco, a technique used by Michelangelo on the Sistine Chapel ceiling.

I was particularly impressed with the endless possibilities of the air-brush. When my air-brush time came up on the roster, I selected from my preliminary sketches the dream car I had designed. I carefully laid out the linear perspective and when I completed the black Ford with the red leather interior and the white top, I amazed myself with the results. I was pleased by the compliments I received.

Mr. Unger said, "Not bad, kid. Not bad." I kept adding highlights to the shiny surfaces until the car looked like blown-glass with a bad case of the sparkles. The compliments stopped.

As our considerable skills increased, Mr. Unger's assignments went from poster, painting, and drawing contests, to experiencing reproduction-art techniques required for the school newspaper and literary magazine. This progression ultimately led us to professional outside jobs for Mr. Unger's well connected friends in the advertising world.

In one major undertaking, an eight-foot by 60-foot mural commissioned by the Cleveland Board of Education for their main building in downtown Cleveland, involved the entire art department. The huge oil-on-stretched-canvas panels depicted students participating in the large number of departmental activities and core-curriculum disciplines offered by the greater Cleveland educational system.

Vinnie was to be immortalized in one of the phys-ed series of panels. He arrived in the evening, in full uniform, and we experimented with his pose. First with his helmet tucked under his arm, then dangling at his side, then..."this way a little...up a little...too much," until the shapes and shadows were just right for the composition.

It turned out to be a very awkward evening because Gee-Gee was leader of the group assigned to the "jock" panel but she and Vinnie were avoiding each other. I filled-in with sketches and directed her group while she sulked and kept her back to him. The on-again-off-again relationship was obviously "off-again" and although I had succeeded in staying out of their affair up to now, this was a problem that was affecting all of us. She was already way behind schedule and as project manager, I was afraid she was going to cause a log-jam. But, before I crushed her with a replacement, I felt the only fair thing to do would be to talk to her as soon as Vinnie went home and the opportunity presented itself.

I was not prepared for what she told me. Walking and talking in fits and starts, Gee-Gee and I trailed the group strung out along the dark side-street as we made our way back to school from the Donut Villa where we'd gulped down our usual pressure-project supper of hamburgers, french fries and coke.

As the other muralists made their way back up to the art room, Gee-Gee and I sat down outside on the marble entrance steps with gusts from the gentle evening breeze stirring the dried leaves collecting on the walk before us.

"Gee-Gee, this...let me see if I have this right. Vinnie...tells you if you...don't..." I struggled for the euphemism, "...he's going out with...what's her name? Chief Cheerleader, the slut. Then you give in...you go to bed with him...."

She snuffled something unintelligible as she blew her nose into her handkerchief, folded it, and dabbed her eyes.

"What?"

"I said," she replied in a hoarse half-whisper, "we didn't go all the way. I could never go all the way before we got married." She took a deep breath and exhaled a wailing sigh.

"OK. So, whatever. Once you did...whatever..." I lowered my voice and leaned toward her until our heads were almost touching. "Once you did...he wants you to...do it with the other guys on the team?"

She nodded her head repeatedly and started to sob uncontrollably. I put my arm around her. "Gee-Gee. Vinnie and me go back a long time. He's done some pretty dumb things, really rotten things. But this...this is...this is...why don'tcha just tell this dumb shit to bug off?"

She struggled to compose herself, took another deep breath and squeaked, "Because...I...love...him."

OK. So maybe some of us were growing up, and some were just growing older. But Vinnie was not just growing older, he was definitely growing meaner. One afternoon, in the empty locker room, I broached the subject of Gee-Gee and he exploded.

"Hey! You just keep your fuckin' two cents outta this!" he snarled. "Understand? You're almost my size now, but I can still kick the shit outta ya! An' if you don't think so, just stick your nose in my business again."

He collapsed on a bench and buried his face in his hands.

"Shit! Shit! Shit! Shit!" he repeated, like he was sneezing. "I'm sorry, Jamie I shouldn't be taking this out on you. You have nuthin' to do with this. But the point is, I don't know who started this shit about Gee-Gee and the team. But I want you to know...it's not true. None of it." He looked up at me and said, "It's my fault. My dumb sense of humor...I just wanted her to streak through the locker room after a game. That's all. Streak through and get lost."

"You mean...streak through...naked?" I asked.

He nodded his head.

"Oh, Jesus, Vinnie. What the hell goes through that head of yours besides air?"

"I know, I know." said Vinnie. "It was a dumb-ass idea. I once got her to take her clothes off from the waist up and blurted it out. It seemed like a funny idea. I guess it wasn't."

Problems and values in the adult world were getting more and more complicated and harder to understand. At this stage of my maturation process I was having trouble sorting out so many of the conflicting signals battering my psyche. Maybe I was going through the normal growing pains, maybe not. But just when I felt like my finger in the dike was successfully holding back the flood of intense emotional highs and lows, another unexpected leak would occur. Like in the area of poise and sophistication. I definitely needed to work on my poise and sophistication.

This point was driven home when the mural was finished, the group publicity photos, with me in them, were pasted in Mamma's photo album, and Mr. Unger honored the Lucky Seven with a rare invitation to join his adult education class at night, once a week, to draw professional nude models.

None of us had ever seen a real live woman in the nude. I had images of one of the Lucky Seven losing control and rushing up on the model-stand ravaging the pretty young thing with the flowers in her hair while the adult men tried to pry the two writhing bodies apart and the horrified women sitting behind the easel-desks maintained ear-piercing screams until the police arrived. Mr. Unger, in the meantime, would have formed a bucket brigade to pour cold water on the prone, inextricably locked, bodies.

We entered the room single-file, sheepishly, with the model already posing under the spotlights and fifteen or sixteen men and women studiously drawing with their heads bobbing as they looked from their drawings to the model and back.

We self-consciously spent most of the evening fussing with our schoolbags, sharpening and re-sharpening with a razor blade anything that even resembled a pencil. Mr. Unger walked over to where we all sat in a group while the adults went out for their stretch in the hall. "Sooner or later," he said quietly, "you're going to have to look at the model. Try to do that before the night is over."

The following day I caved-in to Vinnie's pressure and showed him the drawings I'd done.

"Whuh...what the hell is this?" he said, in disgust. "This is what you did all night? This is what I'm gonna hang in my locker? A bunch of drawings of the model's head and feet? I can't believe this shit. These drawings are about as useless as a rubber-coated suppository."

The bond between Mr. Unger and the Lucky Seven strengthened in direct proportion to the weakening of the rules of protocol. As a result, our mischief got bolder and we escalated from pranks like hollowing-out and eating the fruit Mr. Unger had set up for still-lifes and stuffing the empty shells with clay, to the latest test of Mr. Unger's tolerance level.

"This mural is better than the one those guys painted down at the Post Office," said Zoltan. The gathered group agreed. "...and in half the time," added Peter.

"This mural is better than the Post Office and the Wyeth mural at the library," said Monkey Munk, accompanied by a round of applause.

"Wait...wait..." I said, to ratchet the standard-bar one more notch. "This mural is better than Wyeth, the Post Office, and...*and*...the altar at St. Francis!" We gave ourselves three hip-hip-hooray cheers.

We celebrated the completion of the last two panels of the mural by attaching them, one evening, to the fourteen foot high art room ceiling and placing a sign over the entrance door that read "Sistine Chapel." From enough strings attached to the ceiling to create the illusion of a rain shower, we also hung a large number of lightweight art equipment, along with thigh-slapper signs like "Michaelangelo's out to lunch. Back at 1:30" and "Not bad, kid, not bad."

The following morning, after the laughs subsided, Mr. Unger countered the audacity by making us re-assemble the scaffolding we had illicitly borrowed from, and returned to, the custodial staff. For the next two days we were forced to put the finishing touches on the mural as we lay on our backs, three feet from the ceiling, sweating in the hot, rising, smelly pocket of stagnant air, as Mr. Unger entertained group tours of guffawing faculty members, administrators, and custodial staff throughout the morning.

When the last traces of the humiliation were gone, he called us to his desk and over the rim of his glasses he asked, "Who drives?" We all raised our hands. "Who can get their hands on a car next Saturday evening?" Two hands went up.

"Good." Mr. Unger held up his finger to indicate he was saying this just once. "Perry, meet me here in the art room, Saturday, at five o'clock. Leave the car in the parking lot. Don't bring it up here. Mrs. Unger and I would like to have you over for dinner, and if you can stand the thought, you can ask these other goofy guys to join you. I have to know by tomorrow how many are coming. Is that clear?"

We could hear the metronome of the Regulator clock as we contemplated what he had just said. "Is that clear?" he repeated as his eyes shifted from one gaping mouth to another. We nodded. We'd never heard of Mr. Unger extending such an invitation to anyone before.

On Saturday, we met in the faculty parking lot in our suits and ties and four of the seven got into Perry's borrowed car. "Monkey," Hanks, and I watched Mr. Unger insert a key into the most beautiful shiny black convertible Ford I had ever seen. The white canvas top and the wide sidewalls were immaculate. This car was more stunning than the dream-car I had designed. The lines and details were similar and the identical colors included the red leather upholstery.

"This is a beautiful car, Mr. Unger," said Monkey Munk, from the back seat. "It looks brand new."

"Well," said Mr. Unger, "it's not. It's 48 hours old. No one has ever sat in the back seat before. But I have back seat rules. No handholding, no monkeying around, Munk. And you, Michaelangelo," he said as he glanced at me sitting beside him, "are the only person outside of Mrs. Unger to sit on that seat." None of the blue-collar students in the car had ever ridden in a new car before.

"Actually," Mr. Unger went on, "your design, LaBianca, even though it had too many highlights, was influential in my showroom decision. So, what do you think of that?"

Without thinking I blurted, "I think *your* car has too many highlights too." I looked over and saw he was smiling so I pushed my luck and added in a voice that mimicked his, "Actually, it's *'not bad, kid, not bad.'*" For the first time ever, I heard Mr. Unger laugh out loud. We all joined him. The Lucky Seven bond was stronger than ever.

That night I lay in bed and reviewed the extraordinary events of the evening. "I'm pleased to meet you," Mrs. Unger had said, "even though you're not related to Tony LaBianca." I thought about how gracious they both had been and how easily Mr. Unger smiled and laughed outside of the school environment. How awkward it had been trying to decide which piece of silverware to use. The delicious meal. The hugs we got from Mrs. Unger as we left. But most of all, I thought about the car — that incredible car. I was determined to own one just like it someday.

"Not bad, kid, not bad," I said to myself, with a grin.

Chapter X

Vinnie had succeeded in surpassing all of Tony LaBianca's achievements and he was now more than just a local athletic legend. His fame had spread state-wide and beyond. His remarkable athletic prowess had made national news and each successive interviewer felt compelled to delve deeper and deeper into the celebrity's personal life and habits.

How many hours a day did he work out? What did he eat, and how much? Had he been approached by professional football scouts? Did he have a special someone in his life? Vinnie gave bored responses to the anticipated stock questions.

"How many hours a night do you sleep?" asked an interviewer as they sat in the soundproofed booth at the WGAR radio station in downtown Cleveland.

"I try to maintain an eight hour regimen," answered Vinnie as his mind wandered.

"Alone?"

"What?"

The interviewer's instincts told him to press on.

"You had a steady girlfriend. Did she help you maintain your sleeping habits?"

"What? What do you mean?"

"I'm sorry," said the interviewer, "I know that question could be misinterpreted. I didn't mean to be so personal, of course. Whether or not you slept or are sleeping with anyone, is none of my business. My apologies for being so insensitive."

"Oh, it's OK," said Vinnie, trying to be conciliatory. Then to assuage the interviewer's apparent embarrassment, he made an attempt at humor and added, "Matter of fact, the whole team gets into one big bed every night."

"With the coach?" asked the interviewer, with a chuckle.

"Coach, team, cheerleaders...everybody!" giggled Vinnie. For good measure he threw in, "...my girlfriend...everybody!"

Vinnie had escorted Gee-Gee to her graduation prom a year earlier after another on-again-off-again interlude. Something happened that night that blew the relationship to smithereens. There had been lots of speculative gossip about what happened, but after the memorable radio interview, lynch-mob mentality swept through the community. Vinnie's old outrageous proposition to share Gee-Gee's sexual favors with the other members of the team suddenly reared its ugly head again and began to race like a fire-storm through the school and the old neighborhood in a variety of stunning variations.

Mrs. Lazzarone, our malicious muckraker neighbor, was ecstatic. This scandal was the godsend she'd been waiting for to revive her flagging centric role as miller of her still active rumor gristmill. The neighborhood ladies, with Mrs. Lazzarone clamoring in the lead, soon whipped themselves into an Apache-on-the-warpath frenzy and Vinnie's prestige rating plummeted. For the men, there was still a lot of nudging and winking connected to the bizarre stories that were making the rounds.

"Hey, I don't give a damn what you say," said one of the men hanging out at Morris's Tailor Shop. "What a guy does with his girl, or with how many, or whatever the hell, is his business. But when he brags about it on the radio, heh...heh...heh...*that's* a different story. Take it from me, that's not a man...that's a piece o' shit."

In school, Vinnie became a pariah. Most of the students who once showered him with adulation now gave him a wide berth and avoided eye contact for fear of provoking the savagery he had come to inflict on his opponents on the field. When he did his little gloating dance around fallen opponents to humiliate them, the gesture enraged everyone on both sides of the stadium even more than his unnecessary ferocity.

He beat up a team mate he suspected of resurrecting the Gee-Gee story, so badly, it almost became a police matter. But after many meetings between parents, administrators, and coaches, Vinnie suffered the degrading humiliation of Tuck's Track Team for the rest of the year.

In the final issue of the school newspaper, *The Tatler*, there were several photos of football players in action. Curiously, "Invincible Vinnie" Grosso was not included. He seldom was anymore, even though he continued to cram the trophy showcase with mementoes of his record breaking, bone-crushing, physical feats of wonder.

Out of town print-media and the Cleveland newspapers still glorified Vinnie with photographs and extensive articles, but the school newspaper buried his lengthening list of accomplishments amongst other athletic verbiage. His photographic image appeared only in wide angle shots, lost on the field amongst 21 other players.

Whenever I swam against the stream and came to Vinnie's defense, my presentation of facts was almost always met with raw emotion.

"What does that have to do with the fact that Vinnie Grosso is the best football player this school has ever seen, or will ever see?" I usually snapped back when the clashes began.

"Listen, LaBianca. He's got the best defense this school has ever seen, protecting him and makin' him look good. They open holes for him so big that even a cheerleading squad could walk through —"

"Oh, please! Don't give me that bullshit again. If it's all so easy, why the hell isn't anybody else doing it?"

"Because he's captain, that's why. He hogs the ball, calls the plays, and hogs the field. Ever see that pig hand the ball to anybody else? Ever see him leave a game so somebody else might have a chance to play once in a while?"

High schools played one-platoon football and there was no such thing as offensive and defensive squads. Players were required to go both ways, with minimal padding and helmets that had no face guards. Most players were relieved by second-string players before the game was over, but Vinnie, always battered and bruised, was determined to end his career without ever leaving a game. The more he was ostracized by the student body, the more savage he became, both on and off the field. It was a dichotomy that fed on itself.

"Vinnie," I asked, in one of our soul-searching interludes in the locker room, "why the hell do you have to maul those guys on the other team? You know you're comin' out looking like an out-of-control bully-shit."

"I know, and I can't help it, Jamie. I just can't help it. Ya know what happens? ...I can't believe I'm tellin' ya this....When I'm on that field, every one of those guys look...to me...now don't laugh...like he's that fuckin' Cookie Occarro." There was a meditative pause. "I don't know if I'll ever get over the... the...humiliation. I had nightmares for years. Nobody...*nobody!* is ever gonna push me around again. Ever!" He pounded the locker with his fist.

"Vinnie, I feel for you, but you're just eating yourself up."

"I know I'm making some dumb choices," he said, "I know what's goin' on. But I can't help it. Look at the two of us. You win a full scholarship to...what...The Cleveland School of Art? You're valedictorian of our class, you're taking the prettiest girl in the class to the prom. And me? I'm kickin' ass on a football field and headed for a fuckin' foundry, somewhere, where I'll cast trophies for the next Tony LaBianca. Great fuckin' outlook. Right? How's that for a fuckin' future?"

"Hey, don't leave out that I masterminded the break-in of the here-to-fore impregnable art room storeroom. Generations have tried, but the Lucky Seven did it. Planned for years, risked our asses on a tiny third floor ledge...woulda' made any cat burglar proud. Now...just what the hell does all this shit mean? Really? I mean, really?"

"It means you'll be the toast of art alumnae for years to come," said Vinnie, "You won the championship game."

"It means it's all so much bullshit, Vin," I said, "Things are seldom what they appear to be. Look at you. Everybody...thanks to you...thinks you're a gorilla. You're not. Lucky me, taking Delia Thomas to the prom. Did you know she's engaged to a guy who volunteered for the military and is training in Canada with the Royal Air Force to fight in the battle over Britain?"

"I didn't know that," said Vinnie.

"That makes two of us," I said. "For years I'm falling in love with girls across the room. Then Unger moves the prettiest girl in the class, with her perfect profile and perfect perfume, to work on the cork-board wall right next to me. Now, is that an omen, or what? I sweat the proposal, she accepts, and then I learn I'm goin' to my prom, with hard earned permission from my parents, and it's a non-date. I might as well be takin' my own sister, for Chris' sake, on my very first date ever. How's that for a kick in the ass?"

"That, ole buddy," said Vinnie, "*is*...a...royal...kick...in...the...balls. But...but...you're going with somebody. Ain't nobody, but *nobody*, wants to go with me."

Vinnie and I seemed to be on a PR see-saw. As his public profile and approval rating dropped, mine seemed to rise in direct proportion. In the home stretch of our senior year, Vinnie's life was bottom feeding in a cesspool. Conversely, my academic scores, my general well being, and my art career were soaring like an eagle riding the steady spiral ascension of the thermal current I had caught on my first day in school.

My choice of topics for my valedictory speech, "Food and Defense," was inspired by President Roosevelt's "A Day That Will Live In Infamy" speech that mobilized the country for war. The reaction of anger, confusion and resolution galvanized everyone as never before in a "rally 'round the flag" spirit with determination to fight for the survival of the nation and its loyal allies.

The graduation ceremony, which took place at the public auditorium in downtown Cleveland to accommodate the large crowd, had been well rehearsed and orchestrated. During the preliminaries, when Vinnie went up to get his well earned medals, certificates, and trophies, he was greeted with a mixture of applause, cheers and boo's. He stopped on stage and glared in the direction of the boo's. The audience fell silent.

When my turn came to speak, I remembered to walk up the steps to the podium with my shoulders thrown back and my head erect. I was never comfortable as a public speaker and although I had carefully memorized and honed my speech, facing this huge audience for the first time was overwhelming.

I gripped the top edge of the lectern and leaned forward into the microphone. My heart was thumping because I would give this speech without the safety net of a script. Our speech coaches felt the script would detract from the image of spontaneity.

I lowered my eyes from the blinding spotlights and focused momentarily on my family who were sitting down front to the right of the large body of graduates occupying the orchestra seats. My mother, sister and cousins all had the expression they wore in church when Father Gatto delivered his fire and brimstone sermon. My brothers, Ric and George, sat bolt-upright. My father held his unlit pipe to his mouth.

Several rows behind my family I saw an animated group flanking a large woman who looked like a wrinkled member of one of the moth-eaten itinerant Shakespearean troupes that were periodically inflicted on us at school assemblies. This one was badly costumed to play the role of the dowager queen.

As I watched, the person behind her asked her to remove her huge beribboned hat. My heart sank. This was no dowager queen, this was our dreaded Mrs. Lazzarone. One slip on my part and she'd be dashing up the aisle to the nearest phone with the scoop. I forced myself into focus.

"Napoleon," I enunciated clearly, "said that an army marches on its stomach. It is obvious, that *food* will be as important in winning the war and writing the peace as all of the tanks and airplanes now rolling off our industrial production lines. Therefore the United States —" I hesitated, because in rehearsal I kept pronouncing the next word, "goverment."

The coach had repeatedly shouted from the back of the auditorium, "I want to hear the 'N' back here. The word is <u>GOVERN</u>*ment*, not goverment!"

"— *government*," I said, with over-cooked enunciation.

"Government?" There was a long pause and my thoughts became cluttered. "Government? Oh, God, what government?" I asked myself. Suddenly, the motor racing in my head sputtered and went dead. I went blank. I could hear the wind of panic in the struts. This was going to be a dead-stick crash landing. My heart raced, and I felt an urge to escape. I looked up at the spotlights and it was like looking at a blinding sun. In the after-flare I saw Mrs. Lazzarone's ambulance chaser's face.

"— the same benevolent caretaker government of the greatest nation on the face of the earth —" I improvised, having no idea where I was going with this mortifying dilemma. I had never used the word benevolent before in my entire life. My knees started to buckle.

I looked at my tense family seated in front of me and Ric gave me a double "thumbs-up" sign. Thumbs up. The word UP jump-started my memory and I went on: "— has set UP the greatest farm program in the history of civilization. Its scope and magnitude —"

I went through the rest of the speech without another hitch. When it was over I bowed modestly to the applauding graduates in front of me. Grinning, I turned toward my family and raised my arms in a sign of victory. They rose in a body and gave me a standing ovation. Even my father tucked his pipe into his pocket and applauded. On the way back to my seat I passed my mother who was seated on the aisle. I took her hand and kissed it.

"You have brought honor to the family," she said, as she looked up at me with moist eyes.

The last diploma, the last handshake and suddenly, it was over. The gowned participants hugged and kissed and made promises they could not keep. This important phase of our development which had created such wonderful relationships, came to an abrupt, emotional end.

In her rush to leave the narrow wall-aisle, Mrs. Lazzarone tried to sweep up the wedding-cake-size hat she'd dropped by her feet and went sprawling to the floor with her entourage tangled on top of her. It was not a graceful exit.

I shook many congratulatory hands on my way out of the auditorium and as I lingered just outside the doors in a group of well-wishers, I barely recognized Miss Schmidt, my formally dressed junior high art teacher, standing alone on the fringe of the cluster. I had never seen her in anything but an art smock. I made my way through the bodies but this time I initiated the embrace and kissed her on the cheek.

"Oh my," she said, eyes glistening, head tilted, smiling, "I'm so proud of you. So tall and handsome."

"And you, Miss Schmidt, though I wouldn't think it possible, are getting even prettier, but shorter."

We chatted with our hands clasped. "If you'll remember, at the last graduation I told you that you had all the right parts in place for success," she said.

"I remember."

"Well, I can't wait to see how you're going to top this."

"Neither can I, Miss Schmidt, neither can I."

Chapter XI

Going to church dances, with the larger-than-life crucifix looming at the head of the hall, gave us an opportunity to touch girls but the overbearing prudish sisters of the Catholic Order of St. Francis and the glowering chaperon-parents circling the dancing couples made it seem as if we were dancing in clustered threesomes.

"When I'm dancin', I wanna rub up against a girl's crotch with only her dress and my pants between us an' I don't want no bleeding Jesus with thorns on his head trying to stare me out of it," said Vinnie.

"For cryin' out loud, Vinnie! Watch your mouth! I wish you wouldn't talk like that. We all know how you feel about the church. But it's still very upsetting. You just shouldn't talk like that. You're being very sacrilegious. And you should just... stop it. Just stop it."

"What sacrilegious?" said Vinnie. "For Christ's sake, I'm just telling you he doesn't want me rubbing up against a girl while we're in front of him."

"So?"

"So, no more blue balls. No more nuns tapping on me. Next time we hunt where the ducks are. Enough of this crap. Next time we're going to the Aragon."

"Vinnie," I said, "we don't know anything about the Aragon."

"I do," said Vinnie. "Just follow me and leave your rosary at home."

The Aragon Ballroom looked like a converted theatre.

I passed my loose change through the aperture in the box office window, made a fist and was stamped with a red-violet dye. The print read: SCRANTON PUBLIC LIBRARY. Lino, who preceded me in line, stared at his smeared print.

"What the hell is this for?" he asked.

"If you get lucky and you gotta go outside to get laid or something like that, you can come back in without paying again," explained Vinnie, sarcastically.

The image gave the dance a promising new dimension.

"But why the library?" asked Lino, again.

"Because if things get really boring in there, you can check out a picture book, you jackass," said Vinnie.

"All bullshittin' aside, why the library stamp?"

"Because that's a boozed-up, right-pew, wrong-church, Scranton Library librarian."

"Yeah," added Bill, " she thinks you're here to finally pay the fine for your over-due books."

"The only thing that's overdue here," said Vinnie, "is you losing your virginity."

"Cut the shit, let's go inside."

We stepped inside the cavernous ballroom and were overwhelmed by the sight and sound. As we stood frozen in a clutch just inside the doors, a glittering, rotating globe suspended in the zenith of a huge artificial galaxy projected a swarm of four-cornered stars that chased themselves endlessly in a fixed formation around the black planes of a structure that seemed as big and dark as the great outdoors from which we had just entered. Disorientation flirted with vertigo.

"Now *this* is a little bit of all-right," said Vinnie.

"When they're not using it as a dance hall, this must be

the hanger for the Goodyear blimp."

"Speaking of blimps, there's one...leaning against the wall."

"Now this is what I call a little bit of heaven," said Vinnie, "No nuns, no crucifix, no nuthin' but girls, girls, girls. Mamma...mia. Matter of fact, heaven can wait. *This* is what I call Paradise!"

The sixteen piece band shrieking "Sweet Georgia Brown" had their flailing, sweating drummer sitting as a focal point on the highest of the pyramiding stands, center stage. The tropical scene painted on his bass drum had stylized palm trees arching over the prominent red initials KT.

Four ceiling fans rotated in a futile attempt to lower the stifling heat generated by the gyrating bodies. Unless you were standing near the females who reeked of perfume, the room had the aroma of a locker room. The vestibule, which was separated from the dance floor by a five foot high wall, was thick with cigarette smoke and was littered with shreds from candy wrappers, crumpled cigarette butts, and paper cones.

A circular clearing had formed at one side of the crowded dance floor. In it, three violently jitterbugging couples looked like they were one step away from frothing at the mouth.

A soldier, whose overseas cap had fallen from his head, was dancing with a girl in bobby socks and saddle shoes. Next to the soldier, pulling a girl through his legs and pitching her high into the air, was a disheveled sailor who was close to being "out of uniform".

The third couple, civilians, danced like well-oiled gymnasts racing against a clock. He wore a puffed sleeved shirt and black pegged trousers designed for a faddish zoot suit. The wide suspenders were red. The shiny Valentino swung his Latin-looking female partner from a prone position to one in which her legs pointed straight up toward the ceiling. This maneuver caused her pleated skirt to fall down around her shoulders exposing her white panties. The crowd gasped.

The band repeated the first few notes of "Merrily we roll along" three times to signal they were taking a break, and the overheated crowd pressed like lemmings toward the lobby and the refreshments. All of the exit doors were thrown open in an attempt to cool the air.

Lino, Bill and I shuffled forward with the crowd through the vestibule, past the men and women who were lined up in front of the respective lavatory doors, on our way to the lobby. We passed Vinnie, our self-declared expert on women, who had a coarse-looking woman with a gardenia on either side of her thick black hair, pinned against the wall. A cigarette dangled from her wet-looking bright red puffy lips.

Earlier, on the way to the Aragon, Vinnie had huddled us at the rear of the streetcar, like a coach, and gave us last minute instructions he'd learned from his brother, Buddy-boy.

"The cigarette is a phallic symbol," he confided in us, "and women who smoke are sublimating an unconscious urge to have oral sex. The bigger the lips, the more she wants it. The bigger the boobs, the more they want them fondled." It was evident that the girl Vinnie was charming fulfilled his criteria.

Lino told us later that he had learned the "girl" Vinnie was with was a transvestite. He had to explain to Bill what a transvestite was. Bill wanted to know why the hell a man would want to dress like a girl.

"Well, see, Billy, baby, it's like this." said Lino. "Some guys got this not-so-unconscious need to *follow* in the dancing, not *lead*. If you're gonna follow, ya gotta dress like a woman. Those are the rules."

It was cooler in the lobby and the smokers went outside to lean against parked cars. At the concession stand I inched forward until I had only one girl in front of me. As she carried on her transaction with the concessionaire, I studied her thick auburn hair which was pulled back neatly and held in place with a barrette. Her fragile looking ears held pearl earrings and she had a long delicate neck that perfectly complemented her exposed upper back and spine. Her skin was flawless. I slowly breathed in her fragrance and mentally undressed her.

The voluptuous shape in front of me suddenly wheeled about with a great sweeping motion and the four paper cups of Italian-ice she was balancing exploded against my chest and up into my face and hair. I fell backward several steps, gasping. Everyone around us cried out as they ducked away and instinctively raised an arm to shield their faces.

"Oh my God! I'm so sorry!" she said, as she frantically brushed the shaved ice on my shoulders and effectively piled it against my neck. The ice shot down inside my shirt collar and quickly found its target in my shorts. I tilted my head to one side and tapped with the palm of my hand, alternating from one ear to the other, and snorted repeatedly to clear my ice packed nostrils.

"Oh, dear, dear, dear," she fretted. From a stooped position, I managed to hand the wide-eyed girl the handkerchief from my breast pocket and she brushed ice from her blouse.

"Hey! Snowman!" yelled someone from somewhere in the back of the line, "Can you keep the line moving up there so the rest of us can buy some ice to dump on each other?"

The ice-spattered young lady turned toward the sound of the rebuke, looked back at me with embarrassment, and tried unsuccessfully to stifle a nervous laugh.

"I know this is funny," I said, trying to smile, "but you made a mess here."

"I know, I know. I'm really, really sorry. And I hate myself. But he's right. For a minute you did look like a...a...melting snowman. Italian-ice man?" She cocked her head, squinted, and said, "No...just plain snowman."

"The coal eyes and the carrot nose, right?"

As the aproned counterman swept the slush toward the wall, the flustered girl got a pleading look on her face.

"Please accept my apology." she said, "You aren't really angry at me, are you?" Her hand fell on my arm.

"Nah...." I said, aware that she had made physical contact. "But if this becomes a habit, I wanna be there and you wanna be here." The concessionaire sprinkled what looked like sawdust out of a bucket into the puddles.

This remarkably beautiful girl extended her delicate hand. "I'm Jennifer Lange. My friends and family call me Jenny but you can call me Madam Klutz," she said, with a guilty giggle.

"I'm James LaBianca. My friends call me Jamie. Or from now on, maybe it'll be snowman. I hate it when they call me the Italian-ice man. That, to me, is the worst."

"Jenny and Jamie," she said, still holding onto my hand. "That sounds pretty good together. Better than Jenny and the big drip, or Jenny and the melting snowman, don'cha think?"

I blushed with excitement.

"Tell you what," I said, "can I replace the Italian ice?"

"*May I*," she corrected as she patted my arm.

"No, no. I insist. It was as much my fault as it was yours. This is...ahem...on me, so to speak."

"Aha. A double *entendre*. Now I also hate myself for correcting you. My mother was an English teacher and she's *always* correcting me on that one." In a deep-throat voice she mimicked her mother: "If you are asking permission, it's *may I*. If you're asking if you have the ability, it's *can I*."

"Well, I'm pretty sure *my* mother never taught English," I said, "but a friend of mine *is* English and he says *can I*. Does that count?"

"Touche!" she said gleefully, "You can, *m-a-y*, buy four lemon ice for me and my three girlfriends, whom I want you to meet. They use *can* and *may* interchangeably too. You'll like them."

She arranged three of the cups of ice in her fingers and started toward the open doors that led to the street.

"Don't follow too close," she chided.

I left the change on the counter, picked up the remaining two cups and followed her into the fresh air of the street and the bright lights of the marquee.

"This is Becky." She handed Becky a cup of lemon ice.

"This is Opal, and this is Elizabeth." She handed each a cup of what was already turning into lemon slush.

Two of the three were attractive high school age kids but the third girl was short, overweight and dumpy. When she was introduced she glanced up from the scruffy penny loafers she'd been staring at. Her pale blue eyes shifted rapidly, and she appeared to be very uncomfortable in this setting.

"This is Jamie LaBunko," beamed Jenny,

"LaBianca," I corrected.

"Oh, I'm sorry. Jamie LaBanonko."

I felt a tap on my elbow and turned to find Lino and Bill standing there holding bottles of orange soda-pop. We made room for the two new bodies and they arranged themselves into couples. This left Jenny, pudgy Elizabeth and me standing outside as Lino and Bill escorted their new dates to the very active concession stand inside the lobby.

"Well, ladies, how about another lemon-ice or a soda?" I asked, as I tried to figure out a way to isolate my "love at first sight" from her impassive friend.

"Jenny?"

"No, thank you."

"Elizabeth? Would you like another lemon-ice?"

"Yes."

"Uh-huh. Well, wait right here, I'll be right back." Wrong question. Wrong answer.

I was squeezing through the crowded lobby when the orchestra broke into a lively rendition of "Amour! Amour! Amour!" An irresistible force sucked a tide of crushing humanity toward the throbbing music. I felt myself lifted bodily, feet barely touching the floor, as the stampede carried me through the vestibule onto the fringe of the dance floor where the crush of bodies pulsed and gyrated madly to the cha-cha beat.

I elbowed my way out to the lobby and then to the street. Both were deserted. I walked the length of the vestibule which looked as if a ticker tape parade had just passed through, and eagerly looked over the girls standing along the wall, waiting to be asked. No Jenny. No friends.

The band broke into "I'm Forever Blowing Bubbles," the first of a medley of slow music and I saw this as my opportunity to get onto the floor to continue my search. I bolstered my courage, walked up to one of the girls slanted against the wall with her arms folded.

"May I...Can...May I please have this dance?" I asked, with a fake smile and unconvincing nonchalance.

The thin girl, who looked like a male longshoreman in drag, stared straight at me as the pink bubble gum balloon covering her lower face grew larger and larger until it burst with a popping sound. She continued to gape at me as she gathered the gum stuck to her face, and placed it back into her mouth. She sized me up from head to toe.

"Na...a...a...w," she answered. I heard another piece of my self-esteem splash into the toilet.

I glanced nervously around the room and was delighted to see Jenny's girlfriend, poor, sweet, dowdy Elizabeth, standing alone under one of the exit signs.

"Elizabeth!" I shouted, as I approached her. I extended my hand and this time she took it firmly in hers. "It's so good to see you. Where is everybody? Where's Jenny?"

She smiled confidently and answered in a sultry voice, "Oh, she's around." The sultry tone seemed incongruous.

"Do your friends call you Beth?"

"My friends back home do."

"Back home? I thought you lived near Jenny."

"Oh no. I just met Jenny and Opal tonight. Becky is my third cousin or something like that. I barely know her. We're visiting from Vandergrift, Pennsylvania."

The orchestra started to play "Sleepy Lagoon."

"May I have this dance, madam?" I asked, in an affected voice. I figured I'd do my good deed for the day and look for Jenny on the dance floor at the same time. I tried to imagine Beth's gratitude.

"No," she said, with a soft grin. "I don't dance."

"Sure you can," I assured her. "Everybody can dance the slow dances. Even me." I took her by the hands and gently pulled her toward the dance floor.

"Look," she said, with belligerence. "I said I don't dance."

"OK. OK," I said, startled, "I was just trying to be friendly.

So, dear Beth. Your choice. What do you want to do?"

"I want to give you a hand job."

"W-W-What?"

"I'll give you a hand job."

"What? C'mon. Lets just step out on the dance floor."

"No. No. Lets just step this way through this door. There's an alley right outside here. I'll give you a hand job like you've never had before and there's no charge."

"What?" I repeated as her remarkable proposition began to seep in. I had never heard such words uttered by a female before. It took my breath away.

"C'mon," I said, pretending I had misunderstood. "Let's just step out here and show Astaire how to dance."

"All right then, how about a blow job? Come on." She took my hand and tugged me toward the exit door.

To the tune of "Stormy Weather" she held my hand and sang under her breath: "Don't know why, there is lipstick on my fly...sloppy blow job. Did you notice I don't wear lipstick?"

I snapped my hand out of hers like I'd just been zapped by 120 volts of electricity. This was no Beth. God almighty, this was "Tillie the Toiler," in the flesh! Holy Shit! Frankie the Foot's warning came rushing back to me: THE CLAP... COOTIES...GONORRHEA... SYPHILIS....

I backed away from her holding my contaminated hand away from my body like it was saturated with leprosy and bumped into the swaying couples. When I turned around, I spotted Jenny in the crowd of dancers passing by, waved frantically with my sanitary hand, and caught her eye.

"Meet me in the lobby! Meet me in the lobby! OK?" I shouted, ecstatically. She nodded enthusiastically and waved her free hand from the guy's shoulder.

I rushed into the empty men's room but the small remnant of bar-soap I had noticed earlier was on the floor near a urinal. I yanked open the custodian's metal mop closet and scooped a handful of granular "Medi-Mop" floor soap from a large orange cardboard box. The wash basin overflowed with suds as I partially dried my hands on the only towel substitute available, toilet paper, and dashed towards the lobby drying the backs of my damp hands on my trousers.

It was getting late and the crowd had thinned considerably as I walked briskly toward the lobby. At one of the openings in the low vestibule wall, I encountered Vinnie, standing alone.

"Vinnie! Where the hell have you been? You're never gonna believe what just happened. How did you make out?"

"Not yet, but I'm getting laid before I leave this place tonight. I can feel it in my bones. Not my bones...my bone." He had both hands pressed deep into his pants pockets.

"Have you seen Bill and Lino?"

"Yeah. As a matter of fact, they're dancing right there," he said, as he pointed with his chin.

"Tell 'em to meet us in the lobby after the last dance."

The young man behind the concession counter was packing boxes and mopping up as he prepared to close for the night. Jenny came bursting through the arched opening between the dance floor and the lobby. She was beaming and looked as fresh and radiant as she did when I first saw her.

"My God! Where have you been?" I asked, with elation.

"Where have *I* been? Where have *you* been? I've been looking for you all night," she said. We clasped hands. "I saw your friends," she went on excitedly, "and we all thought you might have gone home. It's good to see you...Mr. La Bilanko?...no?...

OK then...how about...Mr. Snowman?"

"You don't know how good it is to see you, Jenny." I said, bursting with happiness.

"I hope it's as good as it is to see you, Jamie."

The orchestra broke into "Goodnight Sweetheart" to signal the last dance of the evening.

"Can I have this dance, Madam?" I asked, in a low voice. She slipped her hand behind my neck and gently pulled my head forward until our foreheads were touching.

"Are you asking permission, Mr. Big Foot?" she asked, softly.

"All right, all right. *May* I have the pleasure of this dance?" I led her onto the relatively sparse dance floor. The entire band was standing and the two vocalists sang with simulated intimacy: *"Good night Sweetheart / till we meet tomorrow / Good night Sweetheart / sleep will banish sorrow...."*

My arm went around her small waist and I drew her against me. I could feel her firm breasts against my chest as we danced cheek to cheek. There was a subtle fragrance of lilacs in her soft, lovely hair.

"I think I smell lilacs," I breathed.

"I think I smell Lifebuoy soap," she snickered.

We rocked back and forth, turning slowly. The music stopped, the houselights came on, and she squeezed my hand firmly before she let go. Two custodians vigorously pushed large push-brooms across the floor and the musicians began packing away their instruments.

We spotted Lino and Opal a short distance from where we stood and they were laughing uproariously at something. From the right, Bill and Becky walked toward us holding hands and wearing very pleased expressions. We made our way toward the lobby and picked up Vinnie whose darting eyes were frantically searching for unescorted females. I excused myself and took Vinnie aside.

"See this girl coming toward us?"

He looked around and focused on Beth. "Yeah? So?"

"She's the girl you've been looking for all night, Vinnie." He glanced at Beth, then turned toward me with a smirk.

"Oh, kiss my ass. Sometimes I just can't believe what I hear. Do I look like I wanna join the Salvation Army?"

"Vinnie, I'm telling you, if you want your ass kissed and a lot more, it's coming toward you right now."

"Jesus Christ," he sneered, "you are so full of crap. That one broke out of the nunnery. You can't tell that, for Chris' sake? What the hell's the matter with you, anyway?"

"Beth," I called out as she was passing us, "come here for a minute, will ya? This is Vinnie." Vinnie whirled with his hand extended and an instant smile on his face.

"Hey, Beth! How ya doin'?" He exuded his ever-ready charm. "How could I have missed you all evening?" We moved toward our gathered friends waiting in the empty lobby where they were having an energetic and boisterous exchange.

As Vinnie was introduced to the girls, he made a flattering remark to each of them. His projected warmth was quite convincing as he cupped and caressed each extended hand in both of his, like a politician working a crowd.

"My, my, my," he said, "What a pretty face. Love that blouse with that skirt. Opal, Opal. What an appropriate name."

As we made our way to the sidewalk Vinnie plucked a bottle of orange soda from one of the cases near the door and stepped outside. He positioned the bottle cap against the door frame and gave the bottle a tap to get the cap off.

"Aren't you gonna pay for that?" asked Beth.

"How can I, there's nobody around. I'll pay for it the next time I come." He tilted the open bottle to his lips and took a swig. "Anybody want some?"

As we passed the alleyway alongside the Aragon, Vinnie leaned back and hurled the empty bottle into the darkness. We could hear the bottle shatter as it hit the pavement.

"Next time," he said, "we go back to the church dances. I think I'd have more luck there with the nuns than I had at this jerk-off place. Who's stupid idea was it to come here, anyway?"

"I think it was yours, Vinnie."

He leaned close to my ear and said, "This whole fuckin' night's been about as useless as a second-hand suppository."

Chapter XII

"All right, here's the plan," said Vinnie, as we waited for the streetcar that would take us to where the girls lived within doors of each other. "I have a student pass and when the car comes, I'll get on first, go to the back of the car and hand one of you the pass through the back window. Then you get on and pass it to the next guy, and so forth."

"Vinnie," I said, "you're nuts, you know that? For a lousy dime you're going to risk a heavy fine and 30 days in the hoosegow. I don't think the shock treatments are helping you."

"I have my own pass," said Becky, the only undergraduate, and therefore the only one entitled to buy a student pass. She waved the pass around like it was a winning lottery ticket.

"It's yellow this week, right?" asked Vinnie. He took Becky's pass under the lamplight and compared it to his. "Perfect!" he said, as he spun on his heel and handed Becky her pass.

"Hey," said Becky, "gimme back my pass! This is one of those dumb counterfeit passes the art students are making."

Vinnie took back the phony pass he'd tried to switch and put it in a murky celluloid leaf in his billfold. He held it at arms length and said, "Look at that. Perfect! Yowza! Now that's a 90 yard perfect pass!"

"Vinnie," I said, "You really are gettin' cuckoo. Bad enough you wanna risk relay-passing the pass, but you wanna pass a *phony* pass through the window? You wouldn't get 30 days, you'd go straight to the chair. No trial. No jury. Zap!"

The streetcar hissed and screeched to a stop and the small crowd that had gathered at the stop made their way up the stamped metal treads between the bi-fold doors.

"Let's do it!" said Bill to Vinnie. "I'll see you at the back of the car. This ought'a be fun!"

"Now you're talking!" said Vinnie, with the same excited look he used to get when he came out of a football huddle.

I held my breath as Vinnie held up his billfold. The conductor waved him on with barely a glance and "Invincible Vin" hurried to the rear of the car where Bill was waiting. I couldn't believe they were going through with this stupid, risky stunt.

People continued to board as Vinnie pressed the brass clips on the rear window and attempted to raise it. It was shellacked shut. He tested other windows but they all seemed to be sealed. He tugged and grunted on the last handle and managed to get the window up about six inches.

"Here!" he croaked to the opening, "Here!"

The car doors were slammed shut and the conductor yanked the cord which ran through eyelets the length of the car just above the windows. A bell rang up front and the car lurched forward, gradually gaining momentum.

"Wait a minute!" hollered Becky. "Wait a minute! There's somebody out there that wants to get on! Stop the car!" Through the windows we could see Bill trotting alongside.

"Sorry, lady, I gotta schedule to keep." said the conductor. He looked at Becky impassively and glanced at a gold watch which he had pulled from the pocket of his stained vest. The car bolted into a swaying motion and quickly gained speed. We were all stunned except for Vinnie who fell into a seat laughing hysterically as he held his sides.

"Oh-my-God, look!" cried Opal, pointing out the rear windows. Off in the distance we caught glimpses of Bill as he passed in and out of the light cast by the streetlights. He was running as hard as he could in our wake, but was quickly losing ground. We leapt en masse toward the conductor.

"Stop the car! A friend of ours...Please! You have to stop!"

The conductor pushed back the black patent leather peak of his cap. In slow motion he pulled out the gold pocket-watch which dangled on a gold chain and let it sway back and forth. He leaned against the wall, tightened his lips and shook his head slowly from side to side.

We made our way to our seats and watched galloping Bill rapidly disappearing into the distance as we sailed into the night.

"Won't choo come home Bill Bailey —" chortled Vinnie.

"West Twenty-fifth and Lorain. Low-r-rain Aven-yue and West Twenty-fifth Str-r-eet!"

Someone in our group muttered, "I wonder what street ol' Billy's on by now?"

"He didn't pass us, did he?" asked Jenny, stifling a giggle.

As our eyes met, she let out a shriek and we all exploded into gales of laughter.

"Watch out Mistuh Jesse Owens!"

"For his next birthday we all gotta chip in an' buy ol' Billy some track shoes." We roared with uncontrollable laughter.

"From what I saw, I don't think he needs any!"

"Was he carrying any passengers?" More howls.

"No, but maybe for his next birthday we should get him not shoes...*seats*!" We were holding our sides.

"If you get him seats —" gasped Lino, through his streaming tears, "— yer gonna hafta...hafta...oh, jeez...get him a hat an' a gold...watch!" He barely got out the word "watch."

"No doubt about it. That guy is probably the best runner West Tech ever had," said Vinnie, "and nobody ever knew it. Where'd you girls go to school, anyway?"

"Lincoln."

"Lincoln!?" we chorused, in feigned disgust.

"And here," said Lino, "we've been treating you like normal people. Da-a-ah. You know you can apply for a Disabled Person's Pass? Don'tcha? OK. From now on I will talk real clear and slow. Here we go. Do-anybody-gotta-go-potty?"

We remained in the revelry mood until we heard the conductor call out our stop: "West Twenty-fifth and Dexter Aven-yue! Twenty-five and Deckster-r-r."

We walked from the stop to the side street on which they lived. As we left the shops and lights of the main thoroughfare we were enveloped in the quiet darkness of a typical working-class city neighborhood. The modest houses, on small lots, all had front porches and narrow side driveways that led to one-car garages. We talked in hushed tones but the sound of our footsteps alerted dogs that were tied or penned in backyards. Some barked, some growled, as we passed.

Jenny and I led the promenade followed by Becky who was having a time with Vinnie. Lino and Opal followed them and Elizabeth brought up the rear by herself.

As soon as we had reached the relative privacy of the dark street Vinnie pressed himself on Becky, who made it clear that she was not interested in his advances. Vinnie was not deterred. He kept trying to force his arm around her waist.

"Stop it! I mean it. You just *stop it!*" she kept snapping. She scurried into the street to get away and Vinnie followed her. I intercepted him there.

"Vinnie," I said, sternly, "knock it off for God's sake."

I pulled him further across the street and continued in a low voice, "Since you still got your balls in an uproar, why don't you go after Elizabeth? You'll find out soon enough that she'll be more than willing to take you on."

"Oh, bullshit," he sneered, "look who's become an expert all of a sudden." He had his hands deep in his pants pockets again, playing pocket pool.

"Vin, listen to me." I took his arm and spoke directly into his ear. "You two were meant for each other." He started to pull away from me but I hung onto his arm.

"All right, listen," I said with urgency, since he obviously intended to move on Becky again, "she tried to give me a hand job at the Aragon." I felt a stab, as if I'd betrayed a trust.

"You bullshitter. How the hell do you come up with this crap? They're all losers but that one's the worst for Chris' sake. She's gonna be the first female Pope."

When we reached Becky's home, her mother, who had been waiting on the porch swing in her housecoat, came down the brick steps to hug her daughter. They separated, and Becky introduced us to her mom.

"It's so late. I was getting concerned," said Becky's mother.

"I'm sorry you were worried, ma'm," said Vinnie, "but your daughter was in good hands." Concealed by the darkness he put his arm around Becky's waist and his hand slid down to her buttocks. "G-o-o-od hands."

Becky scurried to the other side of her mother, who had taken Elizabeth's hand, and the three of them walked up the steps. "I hope you all had a nice time," said her mother.

We waved our goodbyes, Lino and Opal walked across the street to her house, Jenny and I walked two doors down to her house and Vinnie walked back toward the streetcar stop.

Jenny's house looked much like all the other houses in the neighborhood except a floodlight hung from the side of the house and illuminated the driveway. A dim light from the living room window shed a faint glow on the porch swing. We stood facing each other in the darkness of the doorway alcove and I took her hands in mine.

"I had a great time," I said.

"So did I."

"Can I...whoops!...'scuse me!...*may* I have your telephone number so that I can call you sometime?" We snickered.

"You certainly *may* have my phone number. Wait here."

In her small beaded purse she found the housekey. Through the window I could see her writing on a pad by the phone. She came back, handed me the folded slip, and we stood silently in the dark.

"*May* I kiss you goodnight?" I asked, quietly.

"You certainly *may*," she whispered.

My arms went around her waist and I bent forward to kiss her. In the darkness my lips found her nose. Using that as a frame of reference, I lowered my sights and found her sensuous lips. Her arms went gently around my neck. We pulled our bodies closer together and I could feel those firm breasts against my chest. When our lower bodies touched, a rushing primal urge flooded my body and I was embarrassed to feel my swollen gland pressing between our bodies. I was sweating and the soap I had applied under my armpits as a deodorant began to lather. I reeled slightly, not knowing what to do next.

I hated this mortifying thing that was happening to me. I just wanted to reignite the euphoria we had experienced on the dance floor. Nothing more. What I had instead was a hormone-fed blowtorch. Since the humiliating eruption was imminent, I separated from Jenny, and took a step backward.

"I'll call you," I said, in a squeaky, unfamiliar voice. Hyperventilating, I turned and limped down the stairs.

Lino came back to my side of the street and we walked in silence toward the main street. Just before we entered the light he said, *"per la Madonna!"* then attempted, unsuccessfully, to jump up and click his heels.

We raced across the wide thoroughfare and reached the carstop, where Vinnie was brooding, just as the last scheduled streetcar of the evening came clattering up. Vinnie flashed his phony pass, we dropped our dimes into the coin box and settled into the seats in the rear. There were only three other passengers on board and they were scattered toward the front of the car. We were headed home.

"Well, gents," said Vinnie, as he noisily released gases from his alimentary canal, "This has been one shitty waste of time. I should'a stayed home and beat my dummy." He stretched out his legs and folded his hands behind his head. He started on a long, crude dissertation about sex, women, and life in general that was peppered with spurious psychological bits of jargon he had picked up from his older brother, Buddy Boy. We had heard this philosophical diatribe many times before.

"West Twenty-fifth and Clar-r-k Avenu-u-e. Twenty-five and Cl-lar-r-k Aven-u-e." We disembarked and walked across the intersection to the next car stop. As we waited, hoping we hadn't missed the last car, Vinnie picked up where he had left off.

"And what it all comes down to is there's only one thing in life that matters and that's *POON-N-TANG!*"

"That may be, Vinnie," I said, "but if poontang is so damn important to you, you sure as hell wouldn't recognize it if was wearing sandwich boards because those sandwich boards *did* walk up to you tonight and *did* say, 'Hi. My name is Beth. I would like very much to get laid.'"

"Ah-for-Chris'-sake. Don't give me that shit again. Let me tell you something. All four of those babes are losers but that one...your idol, your ideal sex-pot, couldn't find her bunghole to wipe herself." He shifted into an obsenity-riddled psuedo-intellectual mode he had learned from Buddy Boy.

"None of those bitches meets the criteria," he went on, "the bigger the lips, the stronger the urge...the boobs...shit, your pathetic idol Beth is not just another iceberg, she's so goddam frigid she's probably responsible for sinking the Titanic. That one's gonna *die* a virgin because her mother was a virgin. It's in the genes." He snorted at his own humor, jabbed the air with his finger and added, "And if she ever did have a kid... there...there'd be one more immaculate conception."

"Still better than what happened in your family," said Lino. "Your poor mother couldn't have normal children."

We were relieved to see our streetcar approaching.

"Vinnie," I said, as we waved down the streetcar, "you left out something very important."

"What's that?"

"Tell us just one more time, please, about how Chinese women's slits go the other way."

"Nah, Dad," said Lino, "tell us the story about the transvestite and the sex expert. That one makes me all goose-bumpy."

"Kiss my ass," said Vinnie, as he started to board.

The conductor was tall and very thin. He had a small withered mouth and large eyes that sank into dark holes above his prominent cheekbones. His black suit hung on him loosely and his hat was too large for his skeletal head.

As Vinnie flashed his phony pass a bony hand caught

152

him by the shoulder. "Hold it. Hold it right there. Take that pass outta the billfold," said the raspy voice.

"Why?"

"Now doan give me no sass. Lemme see that pass." He snatched the billfold from Vinnie and pulled the pass out of the celluloid leaf. He looked at Vinnie and looked at the pass, then back to Vinnie. "Get offa this car," he said, in a grating voice that was very menacing.

"Let me have my pass back or I'll report you."

"Hey, wait a minute," I said, in a conciliatory tone. "Here. I've got a dime, right here."

"I doan want your dime, I wan' *him* offa this car *right now!*" He reached under his vest and tucked the evidentiary pass into his shirt pocket. He tugged first on his vest, then on his baggy coat as if he was flattening out wrinkles and patted the hidden pass to emphasize that it was now irretrievable.

With an expression that looked like an alarmed Great Horned Owl protecting her young, he stepped from behind the coin box, took Vinnie by the arm and attempted to hustle him down the steps. Vinnie's reflex response was to smack the arm that was gripping him. The conductor, trembling with rage, grabbed the bell cord and jerked it repeatedly.

From the front of the car a huge dark shape came swiftly down the aisle toward us. The massive motorman towered over us with giant arms dangling at his sides, "What'sa matta Bennie?" he snarled.

"This turd got on my cah widda phony pass an' won't get off when I tell him to."

"Is 'at true sonny?"

"I'm willing to pay double."

"We doan wan' chur money. We wan'choo offa this cah

right now. You un'erstand English?"

"But this is the last car of the night. How am I supposed to get home? I'll pay you triple."

The motorman rammed a massive arm between Vinnie's legs and easily raised him from the floor. With his other hand he took him by the scruff of the neck and effortlessly walked him down the steps and placed him on the pavement.

"An' the nex' time you try to pull dat crap," he said, leaning out the open door, "I'll have you arrested, or worse." He came back up the steps and stomped to the front of the car with his knuckles dangling at mid-calf.

We could hear Vinnie pleading through the open door as the car started to move. The bony conductor went back to his post and assumed his scowling great horned owl expression. When it became evident that his pleas were ineffectual, Vinnie turned vindictive as he trotted alongside.

"You son-of-a-bitch! You dirty bastard!" he shrieked, shaking his fist, "I wouldn't ride your fuckin' streetcar if you begged me!" He picked something out of the gutter and threw it at the disappearing streetcar.

We watched him dropping further and further behind with a feeling of *deja vu.*

"Watch out Mistah Jesse Owens," said Lino, with a smug smile. "I wonder if he'll run into Bill?"

"If he does," I said, "he ain't boardin' ole Billy boy with his stupid phony pass. He'll pay a dime like everyone else."

"His phony-pass scheme," said Lino, laughing, "is about as useless as a second hand suppository."

Chapter XIII

Although only four days had elapsed since I had met Jenny Lange at the Aragon Ballroom and had experienced the rapture in her dark doorway, she was already etched on my brain as a gripping obsession that couldn't be more prominent if it was tattooed across my forehead in the form of an elaborate string of Cupid archers.

I longed to call her. To hear her voice. But there were many things to consider before I did. I instinctively felt that a proper amount of time should elapse so as not to appear too anxious. We had no telephone at our house and I had to decide where the call would be made from.

For emergency calls and the "show-off" calls required to create the illusion of an elevated social standing, we used our neighbor Mrs. Lazzarone's telephone. Her phone was in the kitchen where she and her family generally sat around the table like Walter Winchell clones, on alert and ready to go to press at her notorious gossip mill. My using her phone to call Jenny would be equivalent to a butter-basted chicken going to a fox's den for an informal dinner.

Since I wanted my first contact with my new found love to be impressive, I couldn't decide the critical opening gambit.

"Hello, Jenny Lange? This is The Snowman calling," I could say in a resonant voice that sounded like Ronald Coleman. But what if she didn't remember the reference? I might appear foolish so I dismissed that one. As soon as she picked up the phone I could sing the opening lines of "Good-night Sweetheart." After all, that was our first dance together and it could become "our song." I reserved that one as a possibility. I considered and rejected several more before I wrote out an elaborate script on a sheet of loose-leaf notebook paper. There soon were so many changes that I could not follow my own corrections so I reorganized and copied my presentation once more onto a fresh piece of paper.

For reasons that I cannot explain, I stood in front of the medicine cabinet mirror with my hair carefully combed and my best three-quarter view showing and started to practice an imitation of the French actor Charles Boyer: "Gude ee-fonning, madam-o-sal. Weel hew haff de honor —"

There was a knock on the bathroom door and my sister Annie asked, "Jamie? You OK?"

"Yeah. I'm OK."

"You alone?"

"Not exactly. I'm in here with Charles Boyer. We'll be out in a minute." I gave up on Charles Boyer and took my rehearsals to the cab of my father's truck for privacy. If I needed it, there was always the rear view mirror.

After endless revisions the final script was folded and refolded so many times that it started to tear at the creases. The notes in the margins had so many criss-cross reference arrows that it looked like a diagram for a very involved football play. After several torturous days of rewriting, I felt the result was acceptable. Maybe.

If I made the call from the drugstore phone booth the operator would interrupt every few minutes and Jenny probably would suspect we couldn't afford a phone and that was not the image I wanted to project. Miller's Drugstore would have afforded more privacy but I decided to call from Costello's Store on the adjacent corner at Clark and Fulton. The neighborhood institution had a torn, faded brown awning that shaded a large selection of fruits and vegetables displayed in wooden trays that were either tilted against the plate glass windows or lined up on saw-horses.

As I approached the store I read the faded, painted billboard on the brick wall that boasted: "Drink Coca Cola. Every Bottle Sterilized." Two women, their cloth shopping bags bulging, stepped from the store. I entered through the glass door and was immediately enveloped in the aromatic smells of the luscious fruits and vegetables.

Mr. Costello's old telephone had an upright stem, about the thickness of a broom-handle, that was attached to a heavy round base. At the top of the stem was a daffodil mouthpiece and a slingshot-shaped cradle supported the conical receiver. The phone, located on a counter between the produce and meat departments, had an empty glass next to it with an attached note that read: "All Call 10¢ This Mean You."

On the produce side of the counter, suspended from the ceiling, was a white enameled scale with a large calibration dial that almost came down to eye level.

The store was empty except for Mr. Costello who went back to building a pyramid with apples and whistling an aimless tune. He was wearing his herringbone tweed cap on his bald pate and the black and beige plaid woolen shirt that he wore year 'round because of his frequent trips into the frigid walk-in meat locker.

"Hello Mr. Costello," I said, "can I use your phone, please?"

"Aye! Jimmy! Shoo, you goan ahead, use da phone. Ma

you putta dime inna glass, OK?" He took a few steps, turned, and said, "Jerry, he sure give you boyza nice'a 'aircut all a' time."

"Thank you," I replied.

"Atts OK. I see you madre dissa morn. Yeah. You gonna have nice escarole soup tonighta. Yeah. Looka dat." He held up a large head of escarole. "How you like datta? I betcha you never gonna see betta dandetta, I guarantee," he chuckled.

As I made my way to the phone two women walked into the store and Mr. Costello turned his attention to them.

"Aye! Missa Nimberg! How you doon today?" he shouted, cheerily. "Clara! You wanna see some big orange? Take a look on diss one!" He scurried over to the orange pyramid and selected one from the top. "Aye! How's datta, huh?" he beamed. Size was an important factor when Mr. Costello made his selections down at the wholesale market early each morning.

"That's very nice, Frank," said Clara, who was accustomed to Mr. Costello's gushing, "but I don't think I need oranges today." She picked up a cantaloupe and put it to her nose.

I sat on the low stool by the phone, unfolded my script onto the counter and stroked it to get the creases out. I had rehearsed this moment many times in the last few days and my hands trembled slightly with nervousness and anticipation. I reread the opening lines.

As soon as Jenny picked up the phone I would say in a voice imitating the staccato delivery of the famous radio celebrity Walter Winchell, "Good evening Mr. and Mrs. America and all the ships at sea." I would follow this with very clever patter that I had honed and which got funnier with each reading. When the laughter tapered, I'd ask her for a date.

As I adjusted the mouthpiece, which was mounted on a swivel, Mr. Costello squeezed by me to get to the glass showcase which displayed various meat cuts, sausages, luncheon cold cuts, and large jars filled with pickled vegetables. His head bumped against one of the large cylindrical cheeses suspended from a galvanized pipe that was attached to the stamped metal ceiling. The huge roped cheese swayed back and forth like a pendulum.

I heard the tone as I put the receiver to my ear and carefully dialed Jenny's number. The phone rang repeatedly and I considered hanging up and dialing again. Mr. Costello pressed hard up against me once more. Someone at the other end picked up the phone and I took a deep breath to launch into my Walter Winchell imitation.

"Hello," said a male voice that sounded a lot like Charles Boyer. I was so surprised by the unexpected sound of a male voice that I sat there mute and paralyzed.

"Hello?" repeated the voice.

"Hey, you wanna see my big sauseech!" bellowed Mr Costello into the mouthpiece as he pressed against my right shoulder. He was holding up links of sausage for Mrs. Nimberger and Clara to admire.

"I beg your pardon?" said the voice on the phone.

"You ain' never gonna see a sauseech betta dan dis, I guarantee." shouted Mr. Costello to the ladies.

"Hello. Who is this?" asked the voice on the phone.

Putting the receiver back on the hook without saying a word, I folded my script and walked out of the store, totally rattled. I was standing on the uneven slabs of flagstone sidewalk, planning my next move, when my friend Georgie Costello, and his older brother Solly, pulled slowly into the wide driveway alongside the store.

The rusting brown panel truck groaned up the slight incline and sighed with relief when it came to a stop. The overheated engine made loud, funny, clicking sounds after the engine was turned off. Georgie slid down from the seat and slammed the truck door twice with force before it stayed closed.

"Hey, Jamie boy, how ya doing?"

"OK, Georgie, how you doing?"

"Million bucks," he replied. "Get what cha wanted?"

"I was just using the phone."

"Did you get my father's hollerin' or the opera?" he asked, as he grinned with his hands on his hips.

"The hollering," I said.

"Forget about it. You got the hollerin', you got no privacy. You want a private talk on the phone you gotta go across the street to Miller's drugstore."

A hand-scribbled sign hanging on the inside of the glass entrance door to Mr. Miller's drugstore read: "Sorry — We Are Temporarily Closed." I shielded my eyes against the glare on the glass with my cupped hands, leaned forward and touched the door with my forehead.

The floor was flooded with sudsy water and Mr. Miller's oldest daughter, Estelle, was maneuvering a soggy mop with difficulty around the base of the stools at the soda fountain. When I tried the door it opened and I stuck my head inside.

"Estelle," I said, "I just have to make a phone call."

She straightened up and brushed her hair out of her eyes with the back of her hand.

"You picked a bad time." She inhaled, puckered, then exhaled in a puff through her pursed lips like she was blowing out birthday candles. "Can't you come back?"

"It's important, Estelle," I said, in a flat tone that sounded serious. I was determined to use my vital script for Jenny as soon as possible before I lost my fading inspiration, which was teetering on the brink of evaporating.

"OK," she said, with reluctance, "but watch how you walk."

I made my way to the phone booth at the back of the store walking on the back edge of my heels, supporting myself from stool to stool until I could slide sideways into the narrow confines of the booth. Attached to the top of the wall phone was an instruction card.

I put the receiver to my ear, adjusted the mouthpiece, dropped a nickel in the slot, and dialed "0." I got the tone and waited. And waited. As I was about to hang up there was a loud click and a detached nasal voice said, "Your-number- puh-leeze." I grabbed at the folded sheet in my shirt pocket and tried to unfold it onto the tiny shelf just below the phone with my free hand. I subdued the resisting sheet and forced it flat.

"Your-number-puh-leeze."

"Just a minute," I said, as I struggled to find Jenny's number which was written somewhere on the script.

"Your-number-puh-leeze."

"It's Shadyside 4." Because of the folds in the lined paper I could not make out the other numbers.

"Your-complete-number-*PUH-LEEZE*."

With a slight tremor in my hands I managed to open the sheet completely and gave the operator the rest of the number.

"Deposit-five-cents. Do-*not*-use-pennies," she emphasized.

I laid the coins from my pocket out on the small metal shelf. There were two nickels and seven or eight pennies left. I dropped a nickel into the slot and it rattled its way down through the coin box.

Holding my script against the phone in front of me with my free hand, I reread the opening lines: "Good evening Mr. and Mrs. America and all the ships at sea." It was stifling in the confines of this small humid box and I started to perspire as the phone rang at the other end. One ring. Two rings. Three rings. "Good evening Mr. and Mrs. America," I read once more. Four rings. Five rings.

Somebody picked up the phone and there was a pause. "Leonette Lange speaking," said a mature woman's voice.

"C-can, I'm sorry, may I speak to Jennifer please?"

"Just one moment please," said the pleasant voice. I could hear that she had put her receiver down so I took the opportunity to let some air in to relieve the mounting discomfort.

I turned with difficulty and pushed the handle on the bi-fold door. Fresh air rushed into the booth as I watched my script slip from my hand and make two swoops before it settled face down into Estelle's soapy water on the floor. I let go of my earpiece and snatched the paper quickly from the floor, but it was too late. Water dripped from the soggy script and the running ink blurred the writing so it was no longer legible.

I stepped back into the booth and put the receiver to my ear with tension building. My mouth was dry and I was having a lot of difficulty swallowing.

"Hello," said the voice I immediately recognized as Jenny's. That one little sound and suddenly, everything was all right.

"Hello, Jenny!" I said, with elation.

"Snowman! Oh, I'm so glad you called. I wondered if you were going to. I had a whole bunch of things I was going to say if you called and now I can't think of one. Oh, it's so nice to hear from you," she said excitedly. "How are you?"

"I'm just fine Jenny, how are you?"

"Deposit-five-cents," said the operator. "Do-not-use-pennies."

I dropped my last nickel into the slot and waited for it to rattle its way through the phone.

162

"Listen, Jenny. I think the "Maltese Falcon" is showing at the Garden Saturday. How would you like to go?"

"I'd love to go!"

We chatted for a few minutes more and the operator cut in again: "Deposit-five-cents, do-not-use-pennies."

"What time?" asked Jenny.

"Deposit-five-cents, *puh-leeze*."

I looked at my pennies on the small shelf. "Just a minute operator, I need to get some change." I left the receiver dangling, put my left hand at the edge of the metal shelf and tapped five pennies into it. I splished and splashed on the flooded floor shouting, "Estelle! Estelle! I need a nickel quick!" Estelle was nowhere in sight. "Estelle? Estelle!"

I rushed back into the phone booth, picked up the receiver and said, "Operator, all I've got are five pennies."

"You-*MUST*-deposit-a-nickel. *DO-NOT-USE-PEN-NIES.*"

"*WHAT TIME?*" shouted Jenny, grasping the situation.

"*FIVE O'CLOCK!*" I shouted back.

"*FIVE O'CLOCK!*" she repeated.

There was a click and then silence.

I stepped once more into the flood with a grin on my face and wondered if HE felt this good when HE had walked on water.

Chapter XIV

By early afternoon I had my clothes all laid out. In a household where cleanliness was next to Godliness, dress selections were determined by what was recently washed, dry cleaned or looked new. Most apparel decisions were based on "What will the neighbors think?"

After attending the last wedding, my black, pointed, perforated wing-tip shoes had been shined, wrapped in the original tissue paper, placed in the shoe box and stored on the floor of the closet alongside the boxes of the other members of the family. The soles of the shoes were thick and inflexible and when I wore them I walked with a slap-stick comedian's exaggerated loping action. In addition, this equivalent to wooden Dutch shoes sounded like pine planks slapping the floor.

I dressed carefully, made the perfect seventh wave in my hair and pulled several strands over my forehead to duplicate the casual "strands on the forehead" trend initiated and perpetuated by Clark Gable.

When I stepped into the kitchen Mamma was busy with something in the oven. She straightened up, turned, looked at me and beamed.

"Figlio mio," she said, "you looka vera nice."

"Thank you, Mamma."

"You have a 'ankerchiff?"

"Yes, Mamma," I said. With my allergy history, I needed

no handkerchief reminders. "And I have clean shorts on." I stepped to the door, retraced my steps, and kissed her on the cheek. "I have to go, Ma. Bye."

"No comma home too late."

"OK. OK." I stepped through the door and she followed me as she wiped her hands on her apron.

"Be careful, Jeemie."

"OK, Mamma."

"Eh, Jeemie." She switched to the dialect. "Don't bring dishonor to your family."

"Mamma. I *promise* you. I won't bring dishonor to the family." I kissed her again on the cheek.

Once outside, I waved to our neighbor Mrs. Lazzarone whom I knew was on duty behind her sheer curtain.

I walked to the Clark and Fulton intersection, rising and falling with each heel-toe step and could already feel the backs of the shoes digging into my achilles tendons. I did manage to arrive at the stop at the same time the streetcar did.

The streetcar swayed rhythmically, dropping off passengers at stops along the way. I got off at Dexter Avenue, Jenny's stop, checked my reflection in a storefront window to make sure my Clark Gable hair was all in place, and straightened my necktie before I continued. Blisters started to form at the heel of each foot but I was too excited to care.

Jenny's neighborhood was strictly residential and every house had a neat patch of maintained grass between the sidewalk and the front porch. The brick street was lined with shade trees and there was an overall appearance of orderliness.

Although I had only seen it once, at night, I recognized Jenny's house immediately. It was larger than the others and tastefully decorated with a balanced combination of Tudor planks, grey stucco, and old bricks that had an aura of substance and grace. Unlike the strip driveways on the rest of the street, Jenny's house had an elaborate solid concrete drive leading to a two-car garage. This was intimidating opulence.

I took a deep breath and clumped up the curved walk to the brick steps of the porch. The first couple of steps I took across the wooden porch floor had the resonance of a bass drum so I walked carefully on my heels to the varnished front door. The white ceramic button on the right door frame activated the bell inside.

A very attractive woman with sparkling blue eyes and hair that was a little redder than Jenny's opened the door. She had Jenny's smile. The same bright, flawless, white teeth.

"Why, hello there," she said. "You must be James. Won't you please come in?" She extended a feminine hand with pale pink polish on her nails. "I'm Mrs. Lange. Jenny has told me all about you."

I tried to think of something clever to say but what came out was, "The feeling is mutual Ma'm."

"Jenny will be down in a minute. Won't you sit down?"

"Thank you, Mrs. Lange."

I never knew a housewife could be so attractive. The only other housewife I'd seen wearing fingernail polish was Myrna Loy, on screen. I tried to visualize my mother plucking chickens, or using the scrub-board with pink polish on her nails.

The parlor was beautifully decorated with heavy drapes, and plush furniture. The carpeting and accessories were color and texture coordinated. On the wall over the long classic couch was an oil painting of a pastoral scene. The cross-lighting from the horizontal brass lamp at the top of the painting accentuated the shadows of the uneven impasto surface. I had never seen an original painting in a private home before. This was better than a field trip to the Cleveland Museum of Art.

"Well," said Mrs. Lange as she sat with her ankles crossed and her hands folded in her lap, "isn't this lovely weather?"

"Yes Ma'm," I said. "It certainly is nice weather."

"Jenny tells me you have allergies. With the pollen count being what it is, are you in distress?" she asked, concerned.

"Oh no! It's not a problem at all. Really!" I regretted having said anything to Jenny. I never thought it would reach her parents. I didn't want Mrs. Lange, who was obviously evaluating me, to think her daughter was going out with someone who wasn't acceptable. I especially didn't want her to think her daughter was going out with a red-eyed, drippy nosed, wheezing, sneezing, asthmatic physical wreck.

"Just what are you allergic to?" she asked.

"Oh," I answered, "the usual. Grass, feathers, pollen." There was an an extended pause. "I'm also allergic to dust mites," I added, like I was pointing out an accomplishment.

"Oh," said Mrs. Lange, "what on earth are dust mites?"

I felt I was gaining a slight edge in this exchange. The words "They are tiny little micro-organisms," formed in my mind for my repartee. What I heard myself saying was, "They are tiny little micro-orgasms."

"I beg your pardon?" asked Mrs. Lange with raised brows.

What I had just said didn't quite sound right. Flustered, I tried again. "Oh, I'm sorry, they're tiny little micro-organasms."

"Oh my!" said Mrs Lange as she stood up. Just then Jenny came bouncing down the stairs.

"Hi!" she said, her white teeth gleaming.

I stood up, gaping. She was even more dazzling than I remembered. She was wearing a beautiful blue pleated skirt, and a white middy blouse with a sailor collar. In her left hand she dangled a small draw-string bag that matched her shoes.

"You two have met, I see," she said to her mother, "Isn't he nice?" She ignored my extended hand and took my arm.

"Yes," said Mrs. Lange, "he is a very nice young man."

Jenny squeezed my arm. "And isn't he handsome?"

"Jenny, you're going to embarrass this poor boy."

I turned lobster red. The compliment was unexpected. I looked down and shifted from one foot to the other.

"Well," said Jenny's mother, "you two have a good time. Do you have a handkerchief?"

"Yes, Mother."

I wondered if girls' mothers asked about their underwear.

As we stepped through the front door, Jenny's mother stuck her head out. "James —"

I turned to face her. I was sure she was going to say, "Don't bring dishonor to your family."

" — take good care of Jenny."

"I will, Mrs. Lange, I will."

As we turned to leave, the front door was swung partially open again and Mrs Lange's head appeared once more.

"And James," said Mrs. Lange with a twinkle, "you will get those naughty dust mites to behave themselves won't you?"

"Yes Ma'm," I replied, without grasping the innuendo.

Chapter XV

Jenny skipped deftly across the porch and down the brick steps like a ballerina defying gravity. I followed, clomping across the porch floor in my Dutch-boy wingtips. She took my arm as we walked toward West 25th Street. Suddenly, Jenny pulled her arm free and yanked off her shoes.

"Come on! Quick! Here comes the streetcar!" I took off my shoes and we shot forward with the unbridled glee of children just released for recess. We raced across 25th Street, waving to the approaching car.

We climbed the metal steps of the idling streetcar in our stocking feet and walked huffing and puffing down the aisle toward the rear. I was startled to see the same conductor that was on duty one week ago when we took the girls home from the Aragon. I dropped my coins into the top of the glass-walled coin box and the nickels and dimes clattered against metal deflectors to the bottom.

"Look!" said Jenny, gasping for air as she led me to a seat toward the rear. "Is...this all predestined...or what?" she said holding her side.

"What's...predestined?"

"Don't you see?" she said, as she caught her breath, "A streetcar filled with people...whew!...and the only seat open back here is the exact same seat...we sat in...when we first met!"

"And...that ain't...all," I added, between wheezes.

"What...do you mean?"

"It's...the exact same...conductor."

"My God! You're right! I can't believe this!" she turned her head slowly toward me and through squinted eyes added, "All right, Jamie LaBianca, did you manage to arrange all this for me? For little ole *moi?*" We laughed.

"Yes I did."

"Is our date over now or is there still more?" Her remark stoked the exhilaration as we drifted deeper into our private world of teenage infatuation, oblivious of our surroundings.

"West Twenty-five and Clark Aven-yue," came the call.

"Holy mackerel!" I said to Jenny, "this is our stop, already!"

I took a firm grip on her hand and in three long bounds we were on the sidewalk in front of an automobile salesroom. It was a Chrysler/ Plymouth/ DeSoto dealership but, oddly, the only car in the showroom was a beautiful black Ford Convertible Deluxe V8, similar to Mr. Unger's. The salesman behind the glass door motioned us in.

"I'm C.J. the sales rep. I caught the broad jump you two made from the streetcar to my doorway. I don't think either one of you touched the ground all the way over," he said, smiling. "Is there a 'couples only' broad-jump category in the Olympics?" I shook his extended hand.

"How come —" I said, as I gaped at the stunning, dislocated Ford. He anticipated my question and interrupted with a prepared response. "Well, we haven't been able to get our own product for some time now and from what we hear they won't be building any more for the duration. So, if we're going to stay in business, you do what you have to do. Go sit in it."

I held the door open for Jenny, then got in on the driver's side. I could have sat in this car with Jenny forever. We could grow old together right here. I looked at the narrow seats behind us and decided we could raise a family in this car without ever leaving it.

I looked outside and an unexpected rain shower was passing through. We had a few minutes to kill so I hit the daydream button and imagined myself turning slowly from Fulton Road into Clark with the top down and a tanned Jenny in her tennis whites, sitting next to me. Bob Eberley would be singing "Tangerine" on the car radio. I visualized myself casually waving to envious friends and neighbors. The Duke of Windsor waving limply to his subjects from a royal carriage.

"Come on, let's go," said Jenny, "the rain has stopped and the sun is back out." We dodged puddles on the wet pavement as we walked toward the theatre and I was grateful that the unexpected shower had cleansed the air completely of all traces of the blast furnace smell which was sometimes pungent at this short distance from the industrial "flats."

"Oh, look at this," said Jenny, as she yanked me to the window of a small jewelry shop, "a sapphire ring! My birthstone! Isn't it beautiful?"

"And expensive," I added.

"Almost as expensive as your car. Someday I'd like to celebrate my birthday with one of those on my finger."

"OK." I said, as I tugged her in the direction of the nearby theatre. "Some day I'll getcha your ring. Right now we're late for something more important. Hot buttered popcorn."

Jenny read the announcement on the marquee. "What is this *Flying Tigers*?"

"John Wayne is raising tigers that fly," I lied, to lure her into a war movie.

"John Wayne? Great!" she said, "John Wayne can just

come out on the screen and sit and stare at us for a nice long time and I'd stare back with goo-goo eyes. I don't even care if he's raising flying fish. Let's get in there!"

I passed my fifty cents through the semi-circular opening in the glass and the attendant pushed out two tickets.

"Hang onto your stubs," she said, "tonight is grocery night. You're a little bit late. It's been on for a while already."

"What's grocery night?" asked Jenny as we pushed through the glass doors into the lobby with its overwhelming aroma of buttered popcorn that jump-started my salivary glands.

"They have a raffle." I explained, "Half your ticket goes into this glass drum and if the number they call matches your stub number, you win all kinds of groceries and things."

As we walked from the concession stand, I handed the two bags of popcorn to Jenny and handed the tickets to the attendant. With the house lights turned up we located side-by-side seats in the packed theatre where scattered winners proudly displayed their grocery trophies. We squeezed past knees that supported pepperoni wrapped in butcher's paper and a box full of canned goods before we settled into our seats.

On stage, the theatre manager was rotating the crank attached to the multi-faceted drum in which the ticket stubs tumbled. An usher had just dropped our stubs into the container. A little girl in a white frilly dress reached through an opening, selected a winner, and handed it to the man in the business suit. He took the ticket, walked center-stage, and lowered the back-feeding microphone just a bit.

"And now..." the mike continued to squeal. He made another adjustment. "And now, ladies and gentlemen...last..." he said, between back-feed squeals, "last, but certainly not least...the liveliest prize of the evening." He pointed to the chicken coop, stage-left. "You can have one of these cuties over for dinner ...or you can walk them on a leash...like a pet."

"We have four fryers," he continued, "donated to us by the very generous Costello's Grocery Store." There was a hearty round of applause, hoots, and whistles. He raised a hand for silence and called out the winning number.

"Here!" shouted someone in front of us. A delighted provincial-looking woman waddled her way to the stage. The manager held one of the fryers upside-down as he attempted to tie a string around the resisting chicken's legs.

"No!" cried the lady with the babushka as she undid the string. "I gotta see 'im walk." She turned the chicken right-side up and placed it on the stage floor.

"Why?" asked the puzzled manager.

"How do I know he ain't sick?" said the woman, as she backed away to watch the chicken. She smacked her cupped hands together and the frightened chicken bolted forward for a few steps and froze.

"I don' know about this one," she said, shaking her head. She reached through the coop door and pulled out two more chickens and placed them alongside the first one. "Shoo! Shoo!"

"Hey, lady," said the concerned man-in-charge, who sensed an impending problem. "You can't do that!"

He stooped to retrieve one of the chickens just as the old woman stomped her foot, clapped her hands and shouted, "*HEE...AH...AH!*" The terrified chickens ran screeching and flapping in circles with the festivities director in hot pursuit.

"I take this one!" shouted the woman, as she attempted to scoop one up. The five frenzied bodies ricocheted off each other and the audience fell into the spirit of the fun with shouting, applause, whistles and screams of "Cock-a-doodle-do!"

One of the chickens made its way up to the balcony with feathers showering down like the start of a light snowfall, then found its way back on stage. Another chicken flapped its way to where Jenny and I were sitting and we ducked behind the seatbacks in front of us. Jenny's scream pierced the raucous bedlam that surrounded us.

"I take this one!" shouted the aggressive poultry judge, as she vanished into the wings. The last we heard from her was a bellow from behind the curtain, "I'm gonna getta you, you somma bitch!" The two other chickens also disappeared. So had the little girl.

"Ladies and Gentlemen," implored the sweaty manager with his arms raised like he was surrendering. "Ladies and gentlemen, *PLEASE!... PLEASE!...*" he repeated, until the din subsided. He adjusted the squealing microphone. "*I HAVE...*I have...I have to tell you this.... We still have one more chicken to go." The audience exploded into cheers.

"But...." The manager held up his hands for quiet. "But this time..." he hit the squealing mike with his palm. "you take the chicken as is!" The energized crowd broke into good-natured boos and catcalls.

The coatless manager walked to the drum, turned the crank several times, then pulled out a winner. He held the stub high in the air as he walked back to the defective microphone and made another adjustment.

"All right. Let's see what we've got here." He turned the stub slightly this way and that for better light.

"All right. The lucky number ...is...4...6...2...8...A."

There was a murmur in the crowd and people craned looking for the lucky winner but there was no response. The tieless man on stage rolled up his sleeves and called out the numbers again with exaggerated enunciation. He shaded his eyes and squinted into the balcony.

"Oh my God!" said Jenny, in a low voice. "I think it's me!"

"What?"

"I think it's me," she said, as she covered her eyes with embarrassment and shook her head from side to side.

"Let me see that. Holy mackerel! It is you! You won! Here!" I shouted. "Over here!"

"Please," whimpered a crimson Jenny hunched over with her face in her cupped hands. "I do *not* want a chicken!"

"What do you mean you don't want it? A prize is a prize."

By now Jenny was giggling convulsively and tapping her feet. "I can't believe this is happening," she said, in a whisper. "I want to hide. I'm so embarrassed. I do *not* want that poor... chicken. I'm about to crawl under my seat."

"If you don't claim it, I will," I said.

"I do *not* want it," replied Jenny, as she waved me away.

"Here!" I shouted as I made my way to the aisle. "Here!"

"All right! We have a winner! Come up here, son."

I galloped down the aisle, up the steps and onto the stage where I shook hands with the manager who had already tied the legs of the chicken together.

"Come over here." He led me to the humming microphone. "What's your name, son?"

"James."

"Do your friends call you Jamie?" he asked intimately.

"Yes."

"Do you mind if *I* call you Jamie?"

"No, not at all."

"OK, Jamie. Do you have a last name?"

"Yes."

Oddly, this response got a laugh from the audience.

"Sounds like you're one of these guys who doesn't volunteer too much. Give me a hint." The audience laughed again.

The MC put his arm around my shoulder. His instincts told him he had a receptive audience that he could milk.

"What's your last initial, Jamie?"

"L." The audience tittered.

"Is that 'L' as in Lindberg or Lincoln...or lousy?" He struck gold. The audience laughed and applauded. I located Jenny in the crowd. She had her hands over her ears and her mouth was gaping in astonishment.

"No," I said, "that's 'L' as in..." I looked directly at Jenny, "Lange. My name is Jamie Lange." I watched Jenny slither down in her seat and disappear from sight.

"Lange?" asked the manager. "You're a nice lookin' kid, but you don't look like a Lange. You look like one of us. You could be Italian."

"I used to be Italian." The crowd shrieked.

"Now you're English and your name is Lange?"

"That's my nickname. My full name is...Languini, which I prefer, because it sounds more English." The hysterical audience was beside itself.

"What are you gonna do with this chicken, Jamie Languini?" asked the manager after he'd shushed the throng by waving his arms.

"I'm going to start an egg farm."

The audience gave the predictable response.

"With this one chicken you're going to start an egg farm?"

"Yes." The house counterpointed each response with a roar.

"You do and your house will become a holy place, son!" he said with a big grin. The crowd exploded with delight.

"You don't know the half of it!" said the emcee, as he held the chicken up high. "This here is a rooster!" That was the shot that brought the house down.

"You've been a good sport, Jamie Lange. Here's your chicken. Good luck and God bless you. Lets hear it for Jamie Lange the egg man!" Part of the crowd was on their feet as they roared their approval.

"You gotta admit, folks," the manager went on, "you could go home right now and you've got your money's worth, right?" There was another explosion of applause. "But...the fun has just begun, so...without further adieu...let the show begin!"

By the time I got back to the row of seats in which Jenny cowered, the house lights were dimmed and an out-of-focus image appeared on the screen.

"Excuse me...excuse me...excuse me," I repeated, as I made my way past the row of knees to the empty seat next to Jenny who was supporting her head with her hand. I placed the chicken, which was making guttural sounds, on the floor at my feet and sat on the popcorn and candy bags. I leapt to my feet and half the contents of one of the popcorn bags spilled over the chicken which immediately stopped the guttural sound and began a hammering noise as it pecked at the large white puffed kernels scattered on the floor.

I could see Jenny's body twitching convulsively as she stifled her laughter with her hands. She wiped the tears from her eyes and said through the spasms, "And...and...they said... vaudeville...was dead!"

"Not on the chicken circuit," I replied, as I gathered what popcorn I could off the seat and put it back in the bag.

A silhouette of a couple, with a harvest moon overhead, finally came into focus on the screen. The booming voice-over introduction instructed: "Sing-along...follow the bouncing ball...and let's all sing like the birdie sings!"

The chicken at my feet was making guttural sounds again. I leaned toward Jenny, with a cupped hand over my mouth.

"Now they want us to sing like this birdie sings?"

That provoked yet another round of convulsive laughter which she tried unsuccessfully to stifle. She stood up with her handkerchief covering her mouth and her nose. "Excuse me." she said, with difficulty. "Can you move the... chicken...so I can get out please."

"Where are you going?"

"To the ladies room," she mumbled into my ear.

After the cacophonous sing-along was over Jenny returned and settled once more into her seat.

"Are you all right?" I asked quietly. She slipped her arm over mine on the armrest, took my hand, and as our fingers intertwined, she squeezed my hand several times.

"I'm fine," she said. "How's Chicken-Little?"

"Outside of the fact that he thinks the sky fell on his head, I think he's recovering very well, thank you."

The sing-a-long was followed by a Bugs Bunny Cartoon, Pathe News, Cavalcade of Sports and a Pete Smith Special. When the Pete Smith Special ended, the audience broke into applause and a number of people bolted up the aisles on their way to the rest rooms and the concession stand.

The house lights came on. More people filled the aisles while others, like us, stood up and stretched. After a few minutes the lights dimmed again. When the blurred words projected on the screen came into focus it said: "Flying Tigers. Starring John Wayne, also co-starring John Carroll and Anna Lee." Martial music played in the background.

Chicken Little, who had been relatively quiet for a while started making his guttural sound again. He let out a screech and flapped his wings noisily. I became aware of an overpowering chicken-coop smell.

When the words "The End" appeared on the screen the men in the audience were eager to enlist. The bored women were ready for home. The house lights came on and taut bodies slowly made their way to the lobby.

As I picked Chicken Little up by his legs and aroused him from a sound sleep, he squawked and flapped his wings. It hadn't occurred to me until this moment, but this upside-down chicken dangling by my side was now a dilemma.

Hansel and Gretel left a trail of bread-crumbs during their hand-holding saunter through never-never land, but the thought of a trail of bird droppings down the aisle of the streetcar, along the street Jenny lived on, right up to her door, did not conjure-up a fairy tale happy ending. Cyrano de Bergerac, at his best, couldn't come up with the words that would be necessary to overcome the awkwardness of trying to kiss Jenny at her doorway while we tried to ignore the pooping, clucking, chicken banging against my right leg.

Chapter XVI

As we stood blinking under the bright lights of the theatre marquee with a flapping chicken dangling at my side, I felt a hand on my shoulder.

"Hey-y-y, Jamie-Baby!" said a voice behind me. It was Solly Costello, with his perpetual smile and friendly disposition.

"Hey, Solly," I said, as we stepped out of the path of the crowd pouring through the swinging glass vestibule doors.

Solly, a few years older than we were, pulled his pretty date to one side and we followed. Chest-hair showed over the last button of his rumpled sport shirt and he hadn't shaved his face. He introduced his friend Carol and I reciprocated.

"This is Solly Costello. His father donated the chickens. This is Jennifer Lange."

"*Lange? Lange?* I wondered where in the heck that came from. Now I get it. Ya know, when you were on that stage and said your name was Jamie Lange, everybody who knows you thought you had lost your mind."

"Especially me!" said Jenny.

"I don't even know you and I thought you had lost your mind for going up and claiming this thing after what happened up there," chimed- in Carol good naturedly.

"I thought Mikey DaFutte was gonna lose *his* mind for a minute," added Solly, shaking his head.

"Who's Mikey DaFutte?" I asked.

"You don't know Mikey? The theatre manager? He wants to be a lawyer, an' he's gonna do it. Mikey's a good guy. I'm surprised...wait a minute. I *know* you know his brother Frank. Everybody knows Frankie."

"Frankie?"

"Yeah. Jamie, where you been? 'Scuse me ladies while I fill this guy in. Frank DaFutte. Remember? Also known on the street as Frankie the Foot and now known as 'The Honorable Francis A. DaFutte, Judge of the Court of Common Pleas.'"

"I can't believe this! Frankie the Foot is a judge? How long has this been going on?"

"Since he became a cop and studied law at night and graduated with honors. Now...he's being groomed for the State Supreme Court of Ohio."

I stood slack jawed, the thrashing chicken clenched in my fist. "Whuh...what? Frankie? Our Frankie the Foot is gonna be a Supreme Court Judge?"

"Yep! Damn good one, too. He's fair, feared, and respected. And smart. Actually, I don't see Frankie much anymore but Mikey and me are good friends an' he keeps me posted on his brother. We got a good thing going with Mikey. We give him groceries, he gives us free passes to the movie." He cracked his knuckles and added, "Everybody comes out OK. Hey...c'mon. Anybody hungry?" The girls shrugged. "OK. Let's get a bite."

"Yeah," I said, "I'm starved. Where do you wanna go?"

"Right down here, to the White Tower."

"What's the White Tower?" asked Jenny.

"They sell hamburgers and coffee. That's all, just coffee and hamburgers," I said. "Terrific place, if you eat like a bird."

"The hamburgers are about this big," said Carol, holding her thumb and first finger about one inch apart, "and it's mostly onions. I'm not saying Solly's cheap or anything like that, but these things sell for a nickel apiece. Can you imagine? Five cents each! Diamond Jim Brady here, is not about to spend a quarter for a hamburger." She put her arm around Solly's waist and gave him an affectionate squeeze.

"Quarter? If Tony Giardello's on duty, won't cost a cent."

"What do you mean?" asked Jenny.

"We have a deal," replied Solly. "He gives me...as a matter of fact, he gives *us* hamburgers," he pointed to each of us individually, "and I give him passes to the movies."

"Don't you use the passes you get?" asked Jenny.

"Sure. I go to the movies a lot, but I can't possibly use all the passes Mikey, gives me. So...I unload quite a few on Tony."

"It's Tony, then," said Jenny, "who lives at the movies...."

"No. Tony goes to the movies a lot, but he doesn't live there," said Solly. He had an after-thought and added, "His official voting residence is Clark and Fulton." That got the laughs he was after.

"And what does he do with *his* extra passes?" asked Jenny, with a look that implied she was keeping a mental count.

"He trades 'em here and there." said Solly.

"Like what's here and there?" I asked, joining the banter.

"He buys his meat from us and sometimes pays with passes."

"This is incredible!" said Jenny. "All of you business men deal with each other and no money is exchanged!"

"Money? *Money?* Who needs greenbacks? This is the sovereign state of Little Italy...*provincia di Clark and Fulton*. We use our own Italian treasury system. You wanna know something? We came *this close* to declaring war on the Lyceum Theatre! Heh...heh. Don't fool with us, baby. Who needs the Federal Government? We got our passes! Hey, *Fa-get-a-bout-it*," said Solly, with a little dance step and a shimmy of the shoulder.

"OK. Lets go get a bite," I said. "But...ah...I have a little problem hangin' from my right arm. What'll we do with—"

"No problem," said Solly, "I got the truck parked right down here. We put the chicken in the truck, I take him home an' you or your mother pick 'im up tomorrow...or when it's good for you. No big deal." He took the chicken from me, undid the excessive string tied around its legs and made a leash which he slipped over its head.

"Heel! Heel!" said Solly. The chicken pecked at the litter in the gutter. "Roll over!" commanded Solly. What he rolled over were the laughs. "Dead dog! Play dead dog or you'll be playing dead chicken!"

"You know," said Jenny, "I can't believe this. Here's a chicken...a chicken, mind you...that leaves home, goes for a ride, then goes to the movies. Then it goes for a walk on a leash, and *then*...it's driven home by a chauffeur." The anomaly was obvious once she pointed it out.

Jenny had never seen a live chicken before tonight. She watched with fascination as the leashed bird pecked, strutted in circles, and did an impromptu flamenco dance step.

"You know," she said, "if you look at him objectively, he's rather good looking." Everyone groaned in unison. "No, really! Look at him from a design point of view. Aesthetically speaking, he...is...really...well...designed."

Solly swept the chicken up under his arm and opened the rear door of the truck. He turned to Jenny and said, "You wanna kiss him on the lips before I tuck him in for the night?"

"Oh, stop it!" said Jenny, blushing as she slapped Solly's arm.

Carol turned to me. "You know, considering this girl's odd taste, I wouldn't be too flattered if I were you." Everyone guffawed and pointed a "gotcha" finger at me, then at Jenny.

Solly tucked his hands into his armpits and flapped his protruding elbows. "Who's better lookin', me or the chicken?"

"I think it's a draw," giggled Jenny.

We covered the short distance to the White Tower with Solly in the lead. He mimicked the chicken with an exaggerated swagger, flapping and clucking, with the rest of us hootin' and hollerin' in his wake.

The small one story building was made of white, shiny, glazed brick with black mortar. The top of the spotlighted front wall was designed to resemble the parapet of a castle wall and on one corner of the roof was a short tower. Crumpled white paper littered the sidewalk.

"Good!" said Solly, as he peered through the plate glass window. "Tony's on duty. We're in, like Flynn." About a half dozen people sat at one end of the long black and white checkered counter and we went to the far end and sat on swivel oak-seat stools. There were no booths.

Tony Giardello, like Solly, wore a shadow of a beard on his sweaty face, but unlike Solly he was built like the proverbial tank. He wore a white garrison-type cap perched on top of his curly black hair and an immaculate white apron with "White Tower" embroidered across the chest piece. He repeatedly wiped his hands on the white towel draped over his left shoulder as he served the customers at the other end.

I didn't know Tony all that well, but as a kid I was aware that he was often on the fringe of our activities, guarding our welfare. He was considerate and gentle with kids, women, and dogs. Especially dogs. Dogs could do no wrong. He loved all dogs and went out of his way to pet and reassure strays. But his behavior toward men was unpredictable.

His violent exploits in the neighborhood were legendary. It would be safe to describe him as "unstable." One day a new driver delivered a side of beef to the butcher shop where Tony used to work and asked Tony to sign a receipt in the owners absence. Tony was highly insulted.

"A receipt! You want me to sign a receipt you son-of-a-bitch? Whatsa matter, you don't trust me?" He lashed out with a right hook to the driver's mouth, splitting his lip and sending him staggering backward into a display case. "You want a receipt? Here's your fuckin' receipt!" This time he swung so hard with his left fist that when he missed the flabbergasted driver he threw himself into the sawdust on the floor. The terrified delivery-man stumbled out to his truck and was well on his way with gears clashing by the time Tony came rushing out of the shop shaking a meat-cleaver.

When he had satisfied the needs of the other customers Tony walked to where we sat. His broad grin exposed spaces between his cigarette stained teeth and two of his incisors were capped in gold.

"*Aye, goombah!*" he said, extending a large hairy hand toward Solly. "How the hell ya doin' you ole son-of-a-b...." He stopped short, with both hands thrown up in a gesture of capitulation and said, "Oh! 'scuse me, ladies! Sometimes I forget myself, but me an' Solly, we go way back, way back, like I dunno when. You know what I mean?"

Solly introduced the girls and started to introduce me when Tony interrupted, "Hey, I know this guy! Sure. Annie an' Rico's brother. Right? Sure I know Jamie." He turned to me and went on, "You still hangin' around with Vinnie, Lino, an' what's-izz-name?"

"Oh yeah. We're still pals but Lino and Bill are going to

Oak Ridge, Tennessee any day now. They're both studying to be electrical engineers." I paused, then added, "By the way, Tony, what ever happened to that little guy who used to play the one string banjo down at the corner?"

"Basil? DeBenedictis? Oh yeah. He comes in here. Owns a pawn shop up on Lorain. A whole wall full of hangin' guitars, banjos, mandolins. He can play any string instrument like a maestro. Gives lessons. Plays the Trentina Club every Saturday night. Really draws a crowd. You never been there?"

"Naw. Never been there on Saturday night."

"How about Blackie? You still got that dog Blackie?"

"Naw. He finally died."

"Ah. That's too bad," he said, with genuine regret.

He turned to Jenny. "You from around here?"

"No, I'm sorry. I'm not."

"Then you don't know about Blackie."

"No, I'm sorry I don't."

"You ask Solly here, about Blackie." Tony wiped his hands on his towel and continued. "One night, late, I mean like two, three in the morning, there's a fire at Solly's house which is on top of the store. Blackie gets to barkin' an' barkin' and he keeps it up and he runs around and he keeps it up until ol' man Costello comes down to see what the hell is going on and he finds the fire. Right, Solly? Am I lying? An' man, Ah'm telling you, if it wasn't for that dog, this guy probably wouldn't be here right now! Am I lying? Am I right, Solly?"

"You betcha," said Solly.

"An' another thing. You ain't gonna believe this, but that dog could talk."

"You're right," said Jenny, "I don't believe it."

"Are you saying the dog could actually talk like a human

being?" asked Carol, with scepticism that showed.

"That's right, he could actually talk like a real human being," said Tony, with a slight change in the tone of his voice.

"Are you serious?" asked Jenny, with a snicker.

I could see Tony rising to the challenge. His thick hairy arms dropped to his sides, his hands were fists, and his eyes narrowed. I'd seen this battle-mode transformation before.

I kicked Jenny's foot at the same time Solly kicked Carol. When Jenny turned to face me I glared at her. She got the message and said, "That's great. I never knew dogs could talk. That's truly amazing. Really, truly amazing."

Tony folded his arms over his chest again and nodded his head. "But only at midnight on Christmas Eve. Right, Solly?"

"Not just dogs," said Solly, "I think all animals can do it."

"Truly amazing," said Carol.

Tony took our order without writing it down and before long he placed clusters of the mini-hamburgers in front of each of us. He served the steaming coffee in white china cups that looked more like soup bowls with handles.

"I'd like to propose a toast," said Jenny, as she raised a cup of coffee with both hands. "Here's to Frankie the Foot, all the guys at the corner I've heard about, and Jamie's heroic talking dog...what was his name again?"

"Blackie!" we chorused, as we raised our cups.

"Here's to Blackie," said Jenny, as she looked at Tony.

The hamburgers kept coming until it was impossible to eat any more. I assumed Tony had been keeping track of the tab so I asked how much it came to.

"No-no!" said Solly, "this banquet is on me." He elbowed his way between Tony and me and held up some movie passes. "How many, Tony?"

"C'mon, c'mon. Get the hell out'a heah," said Tony, with a wave of his hand. "You bring in two pretty girls to this dump and they decorate the place for a while, you think I can charge you for it? C'mon, c'mon, get out'a heah."

"Thank you," said Jenny.

"You're very kind," said Carol.

"OK, you *mascalzone*," said Solly, "I owe you one."

"You don't owe me nothin'," said Tony, as he walked off to tend to the customers that had just come into the shop.

As we started out the door, Jenny and Carol turned and thanked Tony once more.

"Fa-git-about-it, ladies. Next time, leave the bums at home."

"How can he afford to do that?" asked Jenny, as we stepped out into the street. "Isn't he afraid he's going to get into trouble with the management?"

"Nah," said Solly. He caught my eye and started to laugh. "He's not gonna get in any trouble."

We stood around chit-chatting for a while and the girls exchanged telephone numbers. We shook hands all around and as we started on our separate ways, Solly offered to drive us home in the truck. We declined and Jenny and I strolled arm in arm to the streetcar stop.

"I had a marvelous first date," said Jenny, as she tilted her head against my shoulder and squeezed my arm. "Thank you for giving me such a good time. I don't want it to end." She turned, looked me straight in the face and added with a giggle, "You have the most interesting friends of anyone I know."

"You're meeting the ones that are not locked up yet."

The streetcar ride to her home was uneventful but pleasant. We talked and laughed and held hands until the day-dreaming conductor, eyes glazed, muttered under his breath, "Dexter

Avenue. Dexter Avenue and West Twenty-Fifth Street."

Jenny took my arm as we walked slowly down the darkened street that took us to her dark doorway.

"I had one of the best times of my life," she said, softly.

"So did I," I whispered. She wrapped her arms around my waist, placed her head against my shoulder, and snickered.

"You know," she said, with her lips close to my ear, "I never won anything before in my life and when I finally do, what do I win? A chicken! Can you imagine? A chicken! I can't believe it! Not a fried chicken, mind you, a chicken on a leash!"

"Could have been worse. Have you ever tried to walk sticks of pepperoni on a leash?"

Jenny made a sound of contentment. "If I had enough movie passes, I'd get you that Ford convertible that you love."

"Thank you," I said, "and if I had enough passes I'd get you that sapphire ring for your birthday."

We rocked in ecstasy. "May I kiss you good-night?"

"You don't have to ask permission," she whispered, her lips close to my ear.

My arms went around her small waist and I bent forward to kiss her. As we pressed our lower bodies against each other I could feel the irrepressible primal urge. There it was again, the source of my humiliation, pressing against her body. We were breathing in short audible gasps, squirming, when Jenny lost her balance and stepped between my feet to regain her equilibrium. Her thigh inadvertently pressed against the bulge that tripped the orgasm. As we stood clutching each other, trembling, I almost apologized but I wasn't sure Jenny realized what had just happened to me. I released myself from her arms, mortified.

"Thank you for a...memorable evening." I said, hoarsely.

189

"I will call you soon." I squeezed her hand, turned, and clomped a hasty retreat across the wooden floor.

On the lonely ride home, I sat at the back of the streetcar and slowly settled into a pool of guilt and shame. The broken blisters on my heels were painful. The stiff wing-tip shoes were dusty and scuffed. My pants were damp and on my sweater I found a small white down feather which I carefully picked off and blew into the air. It floated in the currents moving through the streetcar and settled on a seat further down the aisle. I thought of the irony of my saying "tiny little micro-orgasms" to Mrs. Lange and of my own mother's admonition: "Jeemie, don't bring dishonor to your family."

I found another white tuft on my sweater and held it up in the air between my fingers. When I let it go, it caught a current and floated down the aisle past the conductor who called out: "Clark and Fulton Road. Clark and Ful-ton Road."

We stopped in front of Costello's Grocery Store and I got off. Looking toward the eastern horizon I could see the orange glow of the steel mills. There was a faint smell of "the flats" in the air. The circuit was complete. I was home.

Chapter XVII

After graduation I was working for the tyrannical manager of a food chain store who harbored the notion that Adolph Hitler was directing his war as a campaign against him, personally, to disrupt his stranglehold on his employees. The Nazi leader was just learning to use slave labor. Our leader had been using it for years and was qualified to give seminars.

As long as jobs were "scarce as hen's teeth" and money determined your odds of survival, Mr. Kramer could practice his oppressive working conditions in the store with impunity. But now that the Fuhrer had launched his dirty little war, defense plants were springing up all over town with enticing starting salaries that threatened to suck up the available labor force.

To counter the danger, the store no longer required us to work long extra hours without pay. In addition, we were now offered two deli-sandwiches for lunch as a fringe benefit to promote corporate loyalty, but my days at Foyer Brothers Grocery were numbered.

I took advantage of the feeble incentive and shared it with an old neighborhood acquaintance who had recently elected to do penance at the Dairy Dell across the street.

I knew Richie from catechism days at St. Francis' but we never became close friends. After his first Holy Communion I only saw his pimply-face or his boil-riddled neck sticking out of the white lace collar of his altar-boy robe as he assisted Father

Gatto in the performance of masses every Sunday morning. The last time I saw him before he started to work across the street, he was kneeling, praying, and genuflecting at the altar for masses, weddings, or funerals.

Most of the neighborhood housewives felt Richie had a special relationship with God and treated him accordingly, but there were those of us who suspected he spent a lot of that time at the altar because he was a performer and liked the boost he got from being in front of a crowd.

Every workday at noon Richie and I met for lunch and completed the transaction we had come to expect. We went a step beyond Solly's movie-pass currency system and leap-frogged directly to barter. He gave me a jumbo-size dip ice cream cone and I gave him a sloppy cold-cut Wonder Bread sandwich.

We selected a shady area on the curb in the alley of the Dairy Dell and sat down beside each other with our bulging sandwiches and my dripping cone. With distended cheeks and food sticking out of the corners of his mouth, Richie took a long swig of the orange soda pop which we normally shared. He handed the bottle to me, and I noticed there were a bunch of sandwich particles floating in the soda. Watching the chunks of flotsam and jetsam slushing back and forth, I decided to go without liquid until I got back to the one-faucet dirty sink in the grocery's back room.

"So," said Richie, as he held the bottle of orange soda-pop in my direction and I held up the palm of my hand, "How do you make an elephant float?"

"OK," I said, as I unwrapped the wax paper from my sandwich, "how do you make an elephant float?"

"Easy. You take one scoop of ice cream, soda water, and add one elephant! Hee-hee-hee!" He went through a long repertoire of old jokes that he laughed at after each punch-line. I had learned from experience how to switch immediately to a catatonic state of mind.

While he was taking another swig of orange pop, and before he could start another joke, I reached into my wallet, took out a yearbook photo of Jenny and handed it to him.

"Wow!" he said, as he studied the photo. "That is some pretty dish. You goin' with her?"

I nodded.

"Um-um," he grunted, as he swallowed, *"That* is a beautiful girl. What's her name?" He handed the photo back to me.

"Jennifer Lange."

"Pretty name, pretty girl. How's your sex life?"

The question took me by surprise but in fact for the past several days I had considered discussing the problem I was having every time I took Jenny to her door after each date.

"I have a question," I said, licking my sticky fingers and wiping them on my handkerchief.

"It's a mortal sin," said Richie, matter-of-factly.

"Wait a minute. What do you mean it's a mortal sin. You don't even know my question."

"Sure I do. You're going to ask if pre-marital sex is a sin, right? It is and it's mortal."

"No, that's not what I was going to ask. This is more complicated than that."

"Holy Somoly! The girl's pregnant?"

"No, the girl's not pregnant. She's not that kind of girl."

"You got no problem then. So what's your question?"

"Now this is strictly on the QT, Richie. This mustn't go beyond this alley. It's between me, you and the lamppost. OK?"

"This is in strict confidence," he said. He tilted his head

slightly to one side like he was leaning against the wall of the confessional cabinet.

"Now..." There was a pause like he was considering saying, "Now, my son," but he didn't. "How may I help you?" he asked, in a hushed tone.

I lowered my voice to match his. "I remember at catechism Father Gatto said that the interrupted sex act is a sin. Right?"

"That's right, *coitus interruptus*," he said, solemnly, as he looked up at a cloud with his eyes narrowed.

"For cryin' out loud, Richie, I'm not sure, exactly, what constitutes the *beginning* of a sex act, let alone interrupted. For instance, when I kiss Jenny good-night, is *that* the beginning of a sex act or not?"

"I don't believe a kiss constitutes the beginning of a sex act," said Richie, with his eyes almost closed.

"Well then," I said, "let me ask you this. When I'm kissing her good-night and we're rubbing bodies together and we're both aroused, is *that* the beginning of a sex act?"

Richie thought for a minute. "I don't believe that's the start of a sex act either. I think God had something altogether different in mind. The Old Testament says '*thou shalt not casteth thy seed upon the ground.*' If you're not dropping your seed on the ground, I guess you're OK. I think they're talking about masturbating and stuff like that."

"Now, we're at the crux of the problem," I said. "This is kinda hard to explain...Rich...and embarrassing." I felt like I was standing stark naked at the altar-rail at midnight mass. "But...see...it's like —" In fits and starts, I described what happened each night in Jenny's doorway.

We sat in silence for a minute, then without facing him, I asked, "Now what I wanna know is...is...is...that a sin...or not?"

"Cripes no. That's not a sin. It's what-cha-ma-call-it... involuntary. It's like a wet dream. Ah...I think the key word here is...ah...ah...*intent*. You do not *intend* to have premarital sex with her. Am I right?"

"I think the key word here is *control*," I said, "my body *intends* to have sex with her. Boy, does it ever. But my conscience, my mother, *her* mother, God, Father Gatto and the Pope all say '*hold it right there!*' So, I control the intent. Problem is, some body parts are beyond my control and have a mind of their own."

"Just think of it as a dry run," said Richie with a laugh. "Or maybe a wet run would be closer to it."

"It's not even a wet run," I said. "It's more like a wet ride...a messy, humiliating ride, all the way home on the streetcar."

Richie stretched his legs. "It happens to everybody."

I felt relieved to hear him say that. "Thanks Richie. I appreciate your talking to me. I was beginning to feel like some kind of pervert."

"Hey...why don't you do what a lot of the guys do."

"What's that?"

"Put on a condom before you start that stuff."

I did not immediately grasp the significance of what Richie had just said. We sat together in silence as I contemplated the lightening strike. "A condom?"

"Yeah. Why not? If you put one on to prevent pregnancy, it's a sin. But if you put one on so the seed doesn't hit the ground, it's OK. Those are the rules."

"Holy mackerel," I said. "What a brilliantly, simple, and great idea!" I remembered the cache of prophylactics I'd collected from Frankie the Foot as a kid and had hidden in the orange crate in Mamma's coal bin. Suddenly, it looked like my doorway dilemma was resolved. "Jeez," I beamed, "what...a...

great...idea. Richie, you are a genius!"

We both stood up and stretched.

"Thanks again, Rich. I really appreciate your advice. By the way, this conversation is strictly between us. Right?"

"Good as forgotten," he replied. "Privileged information." He patted my shoulder and said, "By the way, speaking of geniuses, why are most fish very intelligent?"

"OK. You absolutely got this one coming. Why are most fish very intelligent?"

"Because...ready for this...because they spend most of their time in schools! Hee, h-e-e-e!"

As we walked away from each other I held my nose between my fingers and waved him away. Just before crossing the street, on my way back to work, I turned around. "Hey, Rich."

He stopped midway through the alley door of the Dairy Dell and asked, "What?"

"Why is a thumb tack on a seat like a jokester?"

"I don't know. Why?"

"Because they both can be a pain in the ass."

He burst out laughing and said, "That's good! That's good! I like that! I'm gonna use that one, I've been lookin' for new material."

Chapter XVIII

In the dim light of the musty cellar I pried open the sagging coal-bin door which had not been disturbed since the furnace had been converted to gas. I adjusted my footing on the irregular chunks of anthracite coal and carefully lifted pieces out of the way until I reached the buried wooden orange-crate that for years guarded the secret stockpile of "Frankie the Foot" condoms and other forbidden sex material. Overhead a mouse set in motion a shower of dust as he scurried across the dirt-laden furnace duct on his way to the safety of the foundation crevices. The stockpile was intact and well preserved.

I put several tin-foil sealed "rubbers" in my pocket for future use and slipped one between the dollar bills in my billfold. The oil-cloth package was returned to the box and the coal was carefully arranged until the crate was once again completely concealed.

With a pink shower hose, I had siphoned three gallons of precious "sticker B" gasoline from my father's dump truck into his '34 Plymouth without getting the anticipated mouthful of gas. A tucked-in blanket concealed the holes in the front bench-seat upholstery.

I finished dressing, picked up the handcrafted watercolor greeting card I had labored over for Jenny's birthday and headed for the kitchen.

"*Figlio mio*," said Mamma in her dialect, "you look very,

very, nice!" She paused in her stirring at the stove and let the long wooden spoon slide from her hand. My visiting sister Annie sat at the kitchen table dunking one of Mamma's large oatmeal cookies into her coffee.

"Honest t' God," said Annie, "you look so nice." She swallowed the last of the cookie and when she kissed me, she transferred a cookie crumb from her lower lip to my cheek.

"Hey, Mister Ladies' Man, let's see the card," she said, snapping a large cookie in two.

"I'll hold it from here. I don't need oily fingerprints all over it. I can't make another one."

"O-o-oh. A birthday card," said Annie. She squinted at the card and observed, "Asters and a sapphire. So your hot date Jenny's a September baby."

"You know these things?"

"All girls know these things," she said, matter-of-factly. She went back to her cookie-dunking and Mamma walked me to the screened door.

"Be careful, Jeemie," said Mamma, in her dialect. "Drive very, very carefully. Don't break my heart." She took my hands in hers, looked me squarely in the eyes and started, "Jeemie, don't...bring...dishonor —"

"Ma," I interrupted, "I know, I know, I know. Don't you worry." I took her face in my hands and kissed her forehead.

Out on the driveway, Papa stood in front of the car with one hand holding his well-worn pipe and the other hand tucked into his belt. He walked over to where I had rolled down the car window.

"Jeemie..." he paused, studied my face and said, "Jeemie, this is your first date with a car. Be careful." He started to turn away, had an afterthought, and leaned on the car window again.

"You are my son," he added, "and I'm very, very, proud of you. Remember...that the girl you're taking out...is somebody's daughter...and they are just as proud of her...as I am of you." He straightened up, tapped the bowl of his pipe against the palm of his hand, dumped the ashes on the ground, and said, "Don't forget that."

"I know, Pa, I know. Don't worry. I won't."

I gave a hearty wave to Mrs. Lazzarone's family whom I knew were maneuvering for position behind their curtained observation window.

I started down Clark Avenue with my mind immediately set on the problem that had been plaguing me ever since Richie came up with his condom suggestion. Where and when do I put it on? I had been plotting endlessly, but every idea I came up with seemed implausible.

When I pulled up to the curb in front of her house, Jenny was waiting on the porch swing. She came down the steps to greet me with her smile and outstretched hands. I couldn't believe how stunning this girl was, all dressed up.

"You look ab-sol-ute-ly beautiful!" I said. I took her hands in mine, and we touched cheeks.

"You flatterer you, you —" She led me toward the car. Then in reference to my stories about my former art teacher's understated compliments she tapped a make-believe cigar with her finger as her eyes moved from my head to my feet. "Not bad yourself, kid. Not bad."

As soon as we were settled in the car I reached into the glove compartment and sang "Happy birthday" as I handed her the card. She looked at the cover for a few seconds and her jaw dropped.

"Oh-my-God! The Aster and the sapphire! Oh, Jamie.

You remembered!" She opened the card and read the message inside. An arrow pointed to a small sketch of a snowman.

"This is solid lemon-ice," she read out loud. "P.S. I couldn't get you the asters or the sapphire but someday I will. I promise. Oh, dear. Oh, dear...I think I'm going to get weepy...I'm sorry...I tend to get gushy about things like this. What a sweet thing to do...and what a hopeless...sentimental...romantic... ninny I am!" She touched her eyes with my handkerchief and stuffed it back into my breast pocket.

"Now I've managed to mess up your carefully arranged handkerchief, too. Oh, dear." There was a pause, then she added, "Thank you, Jamie. Thank you so much for being so sensitive and for remembering." She leaned over and surprised me with a kiss on the lips. She had never initiated a kiss on the lips before. She pulled back to her side of the car and glowed as she studied the card again.

"Do you think your mother saw that?"

"Oh, I hope so! Listen," she said, as she touched my hand, "this is Sunday night curfew. I promised my folks I'd be home a little earlier tonight, so off we go to the Willoughby to satisfy your acquired taste for your favorite cuisine, ...*le grande 'amburger*...le grand ground cow!"

We finished our greasy meal at the Willoughby drive-in and when I opened my billfold to pay the check, there was the shiny circular condom packet to remind me of my unresolved quandary. It subdued the exuberance I'd been enjoying.

We drove to Puritas Springs Park on the outskirts of the city. I parked the car and we walked to one of the covered bridges that crossed the ravine that separated us from the park. We could hear the screams of the "Cyclone" roller-coaster riders as they plunged seventy feet down one side of the steepest ravine and came rattling up the other side before they leveled off and glided, flushed and gasping, back into the starting gate.

The bridge was crowded with coming and going lines of mixed military and civilian people. The two-by-six wooden hand rails looked textured. We ran our fingers over the hundreds of carved monograms, hearts and messages that had been painted-over with layers of dark green enamel. People who returned to the park after an extended interlude invariably searched out their sentimental messages and caressed the gouged marks on "Braille Bridge" with their fingertips.

"Here it is!" said Jenny, as she located the heart and pair of initials I had carved on one of our earlier visits. I had cut through the green paint to bare wood and the message stood out glaring and raw. She ran her finger over the carving.

"I love it," she said. "Some night I'm going to come down here with a saw and take this piece of rail home to hang in my room. See. Your art training paid off. It's a masterpiece!"

The midway that led to the dance pavilion had endless concessions and game stands. We smelled popcorn, hot-dogs and mustard, cotton candy, candied-apples and a lot of smells we couldn't identify. The barkers, the shouts and screams of people on the twirling, twisting, rising and falling rides, the huge engine that powered the Ferris wheel with its idling-racing-idling-racing rhythm, all blended into one overwhelming, cacophonous sound.

We left the midway sounds and lights behind us and reached a fork in the walkway. On the left was an octagonal building that looked like the shell of an abandoned carousel with a large sign hanging over the gaping entrance that read: "Penny Arcade."

A man roaming the aisles with a change-maker around

his waist had a white card stuck in his fedora hatband that read: "Change." I exchanged large denomination coins for a handful of pennies and gave some to Jenny.

"Oh, look over there," she said. "Madam LaZuma! I want my fortune told!"

In a glass case was a cast-metal torso of a woman dressed to look like a storefront gypsy. She wore a turban, lots of beads, rings, bracelets and her hands hovered over a crystal ball. Jenny dropped a penny into the slot and when the whirring sound stopped, a card came sliding down a chute to where we could conveniently reach it.

She took the card from the chute and read: "*Into each life some rain must fall.* I don't like that. Let me try again." She tried again and this time read: "*Seek and ye shall receive.* Now, that's better, Madam LaZuma. A lot better than winning a chicken. Which I didn't seek."

As we made our way toward the exit, dropping pennies into various slots, we encountered a glass case that was labeled: "Steam Shovel."

The two foot transparent cube was filled with pea-sized varied-colored candy to an uneven depth of about five inches. Scattered here and there over the hills and valleys of dextrose were assorted miniature toys and tiny replicas of cars, trucks, houses and other gimcrackery.

I dropped a penny into the slot hoping to maneuver a scooped prize over to the corner hopper when I spotted an imitation sapphire ring partially buried in the candy. A sapphire ring! Like the one I'd painted on her birthday card! I couldn't believe my eyes!

"I'm about to get'cha the sapphire ring I promised you!"

"What? Where?" she asked, incredulously.

"Right there. See. Right...there." I released the trigger and missed the ring by a full inch. I pumped penny after penny into the machine and eventually managed to hit the ring with each try but the ring was being driven deeper and deeper into the candy. With my pile of pennies dwindling, I did manage to get the ring partially into the scoop but it dropped out on the way to the hopper.

Jenny shook a clenched fist at Madam LaZuma and asked, "What happened to 'Seek and ye shall receive,' you dodo? We're seeking over here! We're seeking! When do we receive?"

I was running low on pennies and the change-maker was nowhere in sight. Jenny's eyes were fastened on the spellbinding ring. Her face was flushed.

I wiped my palms on my jacket and cautiously turned the crank that controlled the lateral movement until the ring was within an inch of the hopper. Slowly, slowly, I raised the scoop. It swung back and forth partway over the hopper with the ring hooked on one of the teeth. With riveted concentration we tried to force it to our will. The swinging stopped. I was about to touch the crank again when our breathtaking trophy spontaneously released and came clattering down the hopper. Jenny let out a shriek of joy and jumped up and down.

"YOU DID IT! YOU DID IT! You got me my sapphire ring! I *knew* you would do it! I just *knew* it!"

"Happy birthday, dear Jenny," I said. "Someday, it will be a real one." I placed the ring on her finger with unsteady hands. It fit perfectly.

"This *is* a real one, as far as I'm concerned," she said, glowing with affection. She held the ring out at arms length and a shiver of joy went through her body. "Seek and ye shall receive!" She turned toward the fortune teller, " Oh...thank you,

Madam LaZuma. And thank you, dear Jamie." She kissed me on the cheek and repeated softly, "Thank you."

As we neared the dance pavilion we encountered a persistent young hustler who fell into step with us and aggressively tried to stamp the back of our hands for a fraction of the pavilion admission price. I had to physically push him out of our way to get past him.

The dance pavilion was a dim cavernous single-story square structure. The obligatory multi-faceted mirrored sphere was hanging from the exposed rafters of the huge hip roof. A seventeen-piece band was playing "The White Cliffs of Dover" as the attendant stamped the back of our hands with what seemed like an inappropriate monogram.

"Why do they do this?" asked Jenny.

"If they used a PSP stamp every night," I pointed out, "pirates like that kid back there would ambush us in hordes and the pavilion would be out of business in no time. That's why the Aragon keeps changing its stamp on a regular basis."

"You know," said Jenny, "I never put that together, but that explains why the first night we met at the Aragon they used the Scranton Public Library stamp."

"That's right."

"Oh-h-h-h," she said, "that's...very...good."

The military personnel, which was quite commonplace by now, were well represented. The "WAACS" in their smart tan uniforms and over-seas caps were getting their share of attention from the soldiers. The sailors and marines were concentrating their charm on clusters of young civilian ladies.

The band was loud and compelling. We stepped onto the dance floor just as the band leader slid into a sensual trumpet solo rendition of "I Don't Want to Walk Without You."

We locked into a cheek-to-cheek embrace and shuffled slowly in time to one romantic, mesmerizing ballad after the next. No words were exchanged. I could hear Jenny breathing in my ear as we communicated our ecstasy with an occasional squeeze of the hand, a closer press of the bodies, a nuzzle. We had been transported to the surreal world that only young lovers in the *primavera* stage of their romance know. When the band took a break, we reluctantly allowed the real world to intrude and walked toward the concession stand.

"Oh look," said Jenny, "they have lemon ice. How about getting a bucket full and re-enacting that first night we met at the Aragon?" She mimed a handful of invisible lemon-ice thrown into my face.

"Listen," I said, as I feigned protecting my face with crossed arms, "I'll buy you some lemon-ice if you want, but I'm giving you a wide berth."

"Hey," she said, with delight, "don't knock it. I got your attention didn't I...Snowman?"

"You had my attention long before the ice shower."

"I'll never forget that night..." she giggled, as she gazed up at me, "...my Abominable Snowman."

As we finished our lemon ice and walked toward the exit for some night air, there was a sudden flash of light outside and the low rumbling sound of thunder.

"Uh-oh," I said. "It looks like we might get some rain."

"Looks like Madam LaZuma was right after all," said Jenny. "Into each life, some rain must fall."

"Madam LaZuma is not a fortune teller," I said, "Madam LaZuma is a weather forecaster."

"It's getting late anyway. Why don't we get going before it starts coming down," said Jenny, as she took my arm and leaned her head against my shoulder.

The crowds had thinned out considerably as we made our way out of the park hand-in-hand. The traffic on Brookpark was also light.

As we pulled up to the curb in front of Jenny's house there was an occasional sky-flash but no rain as yet had fallen. The house was dark but the driveway floodlight created a large semi-circular pool of light. I turned off the ignition and the testosterone compressor automatically roared into action as we went into each other's arms.

I hadn't resolved the condom dilemma, but right now, I didn't care. At least I would not be riding home wet on the streetcar. The streetcar. Of course! That's it! That's it! I don't have to contend with the miserable wet ride on the streetcar!

I broke away from Jenny, excitedly, walked to her side of the car, and opened the door.

"Come with me," I said, as I reached for her hand.

"What's going on?"

"C'mon," I insisted. I led her up the porch steps and planted her by the doorway. "Wait right here," I said, as I bolted back down the steps and dashed into the car.

I fumbled with my billfold in the dark, found the condom, tore open the package, and figured out how to use it. It was snug, uncomfortable, and tripped a swirl of high-tension emotions, the least of which was not the fear of making a fool of myself. I considered taking the thing off but the primal urge was overwhelming.

I was soon standing in the doorway with Jenny in my arms and the sheath in place. We kissed, hugged, contorted, and gasped. When the spasm occurred there was none of the awkwardness or wetness. The condom worked perfectly.

"Richie," I told myself, "you *are* a genius."

As the heavy breathing subsided, we exchanged the lingering caresses and kisses associated with reluctant departures, but when I went down the porch steps, I was surprised to find Jenny standing beside me. She took my hand and pulled me across the lawn in the direction of the glaring light in the driveway. As we rounded the corner of the house I dug in my heels.

"What the heck are you doing?" I asked, as the alarm bells went off in my head.

"Now it's my turn," she said, with exhilaration. "Come with me. C'mon."

"I can't," I said, with mounting apprehension, as the condom loosened its grip. "I really have to go."

"Come with me for just a minute," she said with glee, as she put her arm under mine and leaned forward toward the light that would expose my horrible dilemma.

"Jenny," I said, as the condom slipped further down my leg, "I really, really, have to go. *NOW!*" She got behind me and continued to push toward the light.

"This won't take long," she said, good naturedly. "My folks have been waiting for us to come home. My father is anxious to meet you. He has a surprise for us."

I wrestled my way out of her grip and as I twisted to head back to the security of the darkness and the car I could feel the weighted condom making its way down my pant-leg.

"Let go! Jenny, *please* let go! I *really* have to go! I'm *not* kidding! Jenny! Let go!"

From the other side of the circle of light I heard a voice and saw two figures slowly approaching. As Jenny got behind me and pushed toward her parents I could feel the condom slide slowly halfway down my pant-leg.

"Sweet Jesus, please help me!" I pleaded.

As we stood directly under the floodlight I felt the condom exit my pant-leg and hit the surface of the concrete driveway. I did not faint. With reflex action I put one of my big wing-tip shoes over the naked condom and sagged to the pavement in a crouch. As I feigned tieing my shoelace, I gathered the slippery condom into my hand and looked up at Jenny who was standing over me with a puzzled look on her face. I was visibly shaking but I managed to stand up on wobbly legs and buried my hand, with the moist condom in it, into my coat pocket.

"So you're the Jamie I've been hearing so much about," said Mr. Lange, with his hand extended. Jenny and her mother continued walking ahead.

I never looked at his face. Instead I stared at his extended hand like he was holding a loaded pistol. I reached out and noticed to my horror that the condom, which had stuck to my palm, was transferred onto his in the handshake! In slow motion, he turned his palm up to the light, looked at me, then stared at the condom and shook it back onto the driveway.

"You...monstrous...Italian...wretch —" He spit the words out with a twisted grimace that distorted his face as he wiped his hand on his coat. I stood swaying with my heart pounding, struggling for breath. "No...Mr. Lange...please...it's not —" But he had turned into the shadows and disappeared into the house. I reached down with great difficulty and put the glaring condom back into my coat pocket as Jenny and her mother strolled slowly back to where I stood, trembling.

"...wonder what on earth happened to your father?" I heard Mrs Lange say. There was an exchange that did not register with me and then the two women led me by my arms toward the darkness of the back yard.

"This is so exciting!" I heard Mrs. Lange say in an echo chamber. "Wait 'till you see what Mr. Lange has made for the two of you."

We walked through a grape arbor onto a closely cut lawn. Standing in the grass, in the light reflected from the driveway, was a white wooden double-seater glider swing.

Mrs. Lange ushered us onto the platform of the swing and I sat facing her with Jenny at my side. Jenny said something, then Mrs. Lange said something.

"...and Mr. Lange made this swing in his shop just for the two of you...." Her words drifted in and out of my mind. "He's been working on it...weeks...and Jenny hasn't been allowed to peek....Isn't...wonderful? I don't understand...happened to him. He's been...looking forward...like Jenny looks forward to Christmas morning."

I mumbled something unintelligible. There was a light, gusty sprinkle of raindrops and Mrs. Lange turned her palms toward the threatening sky.

"Oh my," she chirped, "I wondered if it was going to rain."

"I guess Madam LaZuma was right." said Jenny. "Into each life some rain must fall."

I was still struggling for breath when I suddenly started to hiccup violently.

"Are you all right?" asked Mrs. Lange, with alarm. "Are you having an asthma attack?"

"I'm sorry," I said, between hiccups, "but I really...I... *hiccup*...really, gotta go now."

I stood up and may have shaken hands before I stepped off the swing and walked down the driveway on very unsteady legs. As I approached the car I reached into my pocket for the cursed prophylactic. With my other hand I pulled the hand-kerchief out of my breast pocket and started to wrap it around the condom. I wanted to isolate it from my body as much as possible until I got home where I would dispose of it.

The condom fell from the tenuous hold I had on it and disappeared into the grass. In the darkness, I got down on my hands and knees and tried to feel it with my fingertips.

I desperately swept the grass with rigid, trembling fingers of both hands, again and again, but it was gone. My self-contempt and loathing burst into unbridled despair.

With the rain coming down in a steady drizzle, I stood up and steadied myself against the fender of the car. A shudder went through my body and I started to sob uncontrollably as I thought of the consequences of her father's discovery the next time he cut the grass.

I started the car, put it into gear and glanced in the direction of the house. Through my tears I saw Jenny standing at the edge of the light. She looked totally bewildered with her arms at her sides and her wet hair plastered to her face. In the glow of the floodlight, I saw the curtain of rain behind her quickly increase in intensity.

I pulled away gasping and hiccupping.

Chapter XIX

The uniformed policemen had scattered the coal and the remnants of Mamma's demolished coal-bin planks all over the cellar floor. The "bad cop" detective had me backed against the furnace and was finishing his latest tirade with: "You know this is more than contributing to the delinquency of a minor. *What we got here is...statutory rape.*"

"I did...*not*...have intercourse with Jenny."

"That's not what her father says. And...he gave us the solid, disgraceful evidence."

"It's *not* what it seems. Please...let me tell you once more—"

The "good" cop took over. "Listen, Jamie. Make it easy on yourself. If you tell us where the orange crate is, you're home free. You don't owe any loyalty to "Frankie the Foot." Besides, Mr. Lange is too well-connected politically. Now, your boy Frankie's a dead duck as a judge anyway."

Father Gatto, our no-nonsense priest, yelled from the shadows, "You and Frankie both goan straighta to hell! Guaranteed!"

I stood handcuffed at Mamma's back door where the police cruiser was flashing it's red roof-lights.

"Pig! Pig! Pig! Pig!" yelled the ravenous Lazzarone family chorus lined up along the fence like ecstatic vultures.

"Why can't I have my pants?" I pleaded, as two uniformed cops pushed me out to the popping flashbulbs.

"Jamie...Jamie," said a soft voice. "...Jamie. Hey...Jamie...."

I woke with a start, in a puddle of sweat, with my brother Ric standing over me gently shaking my shoulder.

"It's all right, Jamie. It's all right...it's all right...."

It was over three years now and every once in a while I had this recurring nightmare, just as Ric had his.

His nightmare started with the first horrible invasion wave that landed on Omaha Beach in Normandy, France, where pieces of red-hot shrapnel riddled his back. Heroic surgery saved his leg and his life and he was now making progress in an excruciating physical therapy program. But every now and then, since his homecoming, I woke him from his own re-lived hell as he convulsively twisted in his sleep in his own pool of sweat.

I was honorably discharged without going over-seas and was grateful I hadn't been maimed or worse. As a Marine fighting the Japanese in the islands, Vinnie had been contaminated with exotic parasites that ended his dreams of a football career. Some of my other neighborhood friends and one of the "lucky seven" never came back.

In the past, Jenny's parents had intercepted all of my messages and although it seemed hopeless, I mustered enough courage one night to call her once more. With a trembling finger, I dialed her number and was prepared to deliver a scripted "snowman" speech if I got past her parents but the operator said the number had been disconnected.

About a week later, I cautiously drove the vintage three-wheel Indian motorcycle I'd purchased for cheap transportation to the street on which Jenny lived and cruised slowly toward her house. It was a very disturbing experience. There was an obvious influx of new people that had infiltrated the area. The neighborhood, like much of Cleveland, had become transformed as indigent groups were lured from the countryside and rural neighboring states to the defense plants.

The shrubs on Jenny's street were shaggy and the grass between the uneven concrete driveway strips was weed-choked and tall. What used to be tree lawns was now hard-packed dirt and most of the houses desperately needed repair. The few that had been painted were gaudy.

I parked in front of Jenny's house. There were primary-colored parts of children's toys scattered throughout the former lawn areas, and a small mobile-home trailer was hitched to a rusting car in the driveway. I made my way to the chipped child-safety-gate stretched across the porch opening. A woman, usually described as swarthy, rose from the remains of the swing with a baby in her arms.

"Excuse me," I said, standing on the bottom step, "can you tell me if the Langes still live here?"

"Who?" The woman looked apprehensive.

"Mr. and Mrs. Lange."

"No," she said, with a smile. She began bouncing the baby again. "My brother-in-law Jiminez Garcia and me and my husband lives here. Jimmy an' his family lives upstairs. Me an' Alfonso lives down here."

"Do you know what happened to the Langes who used to live here?" I asked.

"No," she said, swinging the baby in an arc. "Jiminez buyed the house from...I don' remember...come back tonight. He could tell you." There was a silence as I tried to think of what to say next and she continued to swing the baby around her body.

"Oh!" she said with a grin, "I remember! The man's name was Harold. That's who Jiminez bought the house from an' made it two-family for us. An' the other people, who owned the house before Harold, what's their name? Lange? They went

213

with their daughter when she got married and went to live in Arizona. Maybe California or some place like that."

"You OK?" She asked, as I stumbled backward.

"Yeah...I'm OK...I'm OK...I'm fine," I said, like I'd just heard about a death in the family. "You...ah...don't know anybody that...ah...knows where the Langes moved to...exactly...do you?"

"No. Nobody. I'm sure Jiminez or Alfonso don' know, and poor Harold, God rest his soul, he died in the war."

That night Ric and I lay on our separate twin beds and for the first time I told somebody the whole Jenny story. When I got to the part about the condom and Jenny's father he started to laugh. He swung his good leg between the beds and set the atrophied leg next to it with his hands.

"God Almighty..." he said, "that is the saddest, funniest, love story I've ever heard!" He shook his head slowly. "Good-God-Almighty. Leave it to you, Jamie."

I swung my legs over to face him and made the blubbering sounds you make when you try to stifle sobbing and don't quite make it to laughing. Ric reached over and tousled my hair.

"Hey, brother. We've all been there, sooner or later. Never quite in your league, I gotta admit, but we've all been through *that* meat grinder. If it'll make you feel any better, since it's unloadin' time, here's one I never told anybody in the family and I don't want you to repeat this. It would kill Ma. But when I was stationed at Camp Atterbury, I met a USO girl at a dance...at a dance again...what is it about dances? Anyway, we fell in love. I mean, we-fell-*in-love*. We got engaged. Diamond ring, the whole bit. Just before I went over-seas I wanted to get married, so did she. I was *ga-ga* in love. But there was one little problem." He lit a PX issue cigarette and asked, "wanna guess?"

"You asked Ma for her blessing an' she went nuts."

214

"Nope. Ma didn't know I was about to get married. The problem was not Ma. The problem was the girl's husband."

"Husband? *Hus-band*? She was...like...still —"

"Yep."

"Holy shit! What the hell was goin' on?"

"It was a scam. These girls were camp followers who worked the camps. Once they became the GI life insurance beneficiaries of the guys goin' over-seas, it was *adios amigos!* Lucky thing my sergeant was gonna be my best man and recognized her. She'd been married seven or eight times already. Incidentally, a very, very pretty girl, but a real con."

"Looks like I have the same problem now, but this is no scam an' I don't know if I'll ever get over this one. It still gives me nightmares."

"Jamie, there's an old Italian adage that Ma and Pa use. Something like...*'remember to forget, but don't forget to remember.'*"

"Yeah. But like a lot of their proverbs and old country expressions, I never knew what that meant."

"Well, it's not like *'time wounds all heels'* and some of that other chicken counting stuff. They come up with some real brain food sometimes." He hobbled back to the edge of the bed and as he lowered himself to face me he cleared his lungs and put out his cigarette.

"When you were a kid, you got your finger caught in the sprocket of your first two-wheeler. Hurt like hell, gave you that scar across your finger. But you talk about the *fun* of your first bike, not the scar it gave you. It's a defense mechanism to remember just enough of the pain so you don't stick your finger into the sprocket again. If we didn't forget pain and remember pleasure, women would never have a second child."

"Ric, as I told you a long time ago, you are a pur-i-tty smart captain, suh!" I snapped a salute. "That's why you made two silver bars and I only made two cloth stripes."

"C'mon Jamie. You know that's baloney. You're a pretty smart guy yourself. Difference was, I landed in a unit I loved, and they cheated you out of the Air Force. I understand your resentment, but... that happens in the military."

"That happens in the military a lot, doesn't it?" I asked, as I fired up my resentment. "The military is an ass. A stupid... dumb...shitass."

"Whoa! Slow down, Jamie. Let's get back to the proverbs for a minute. We laugh at this stuff, but some of it's pretty profound because it's based on experience, not forecasting, which is the way most people interpret it. For instance...how about...*friendships are forged in fire?* The guys I went through hell with on Omaha Beach...they...ah...ah...ah...." Now it was his turn. He started to make the blubbering sounds, stifled the sobbing, but didn't make it to the laughing. "...the best thing to come outta the war...." He puckered his lips and nodded his head repeatedly as his eyes grew moist. "...those guys...are my buddies...*for life.*" There was a poignant pause, then he added, "Oh, shit. Just *remember to forget* — or, whatever."

"*'A woman's work is never done,'*" I added, quickly, "and I, for one, think that's irresponsible."

We laughed and reached across to shake hands. As we rose to a standing position, Ric hopped on his good leg to steady himself but lost his balance. He fell into my arms in an awkward embrace. Grinning, we tapped each other on the back and separated.

I didn't know how long the nightmare would keep recurring, but I was determined not to focus on the scar anymore. I plunged into a monetary feeding-frenzy to earn as much money as I could to build a nest egg for my career training. Seven days a week I drove a "gypsy cab" from four to eleven, while I worked the graveyard shift at an assembly plant on the east side of town. When I was rotated to the swing shift at Swanson's, I drove the cab from midnight to eight in the morning. Whenever possible I drove two cab shifts back-to-back, and cat-napped with my head resting against the seat-back between calls.

The recurring nightmare stopped.

I learned that my scholarship to the Cleveland School of Art was still active and decided to go with the less lucrative scholarship instead of the GI Bill of Rights. My resentment of the military was still festering.

Once school started, I attended classes in a state of euphoria from eight in the morning until late afternoon, continued to work nights at Swanson's, *and* drove the cab after school. It was a punishing schedule with little sleep and little time for social activities.

The drive and energy-force I discovered at the art school were not unlike what I had encountered at West Tech. The measure for excellence, however, was much higher, and the mature, motivated students continually raised the standards. The competition was fierce and most of the professors were clones of Paul Unger.

There was also a much higher level of sophistication in this older student body. Gone was the self-conscious embarrassment we experienced in Paul Unger's nude model classes. For four consecutive hours every Tuesday afternoon, we painted and sketched studies of a beautiful young nude model without associating her with lust. She might as well have been one of Paul Unger's plaster casts — sexually neutral. An evasive form to be captured on canvas, not on a bed.

One night, after an extraordinary day at the school, I sat in my cab, waiting for a fare, and contemplated the watershed events that occurred that afternoon. I thought about how irrational and wonderful conventional wisdom could be when it came to sex. In a few short hours, I had experienced the full range of the spectrum.

It started one day in life class. We had inadvertently arranged ourselves around the circular model stand so the male students occupied desks in a semi-circle and the women sat at theirs, on the opposite side.

When one of the sex-starved males on our side spotted the white panties of a female as she sat across the way, oblivious to how her skirt had inched its way up her thighs under her tilted desk, I got an elbow in my ribs and the curt, whispered message, "The one in the white sweater." Heads craned on our side for a better peek as the discovery was relayed from elbow to rib around our half of the stand. It didn't seem incongruous to us that we had to peer through the bare inner thighs of the standing model to glimpse the panties. Nor the fact that some were annoyed that the *nude* model was obstructing their view.

"Beaver hunting" ended as suddenly as it had begun. As we filed into the room this afternoon, trying to decide which seats had the best viewing potential, we became aware that every desk across the way had a 22" X 28" sheet of drawing paper taped from its edge as a modesty screen. Some of the men turned crimson. Some turned to each other sheepishly, and grinned. The rest concentrated on their work as if nothing unusual had happened. Except for the occasional tittering and secret whispers from the ladies side of the room everyone worked in silence for hours.

Also, this afternoon, when everyone had cleaned up and

left for the day, the model and I loitered on the second floor fire escape attached to the exterior of the building and enthusiastically discussed a variety of unrelated subjects. When the night janitor was leaving he leaned through the fire escape door and cautioned us to make sure the lights were out and the door was locked when we left.

At dusk, as the only occupants left in the darkened building, the model and I were still having a great time discussing high philosophies and low absurdities of life. She confessed she was the one who had alerted the vulnerable ladies and at one point had considered sitting across the way from us on one of her breaks and letting her robe slide off her spread legs. There were many pensive pauses in our exchanges, as well as many explosive giggles.

Eventually, she was out of cigarettes and crumpled the empty pack into the pocket of the robe she wore around her naked body.

"This has been so much fun...Jamie? You did say your name is Jamie. Right?"

"That's right, Cindy." As the outdoor light continued to dim, we stood up and stretched on the narrow landing. As her arms dropped back to her sides, she lost her balance and I grabbed her to prevent a fall. We stood facing each other in a loose embrace, staring silently into each other's eyes. The message was clear. We tightened our embrace and kissed. And kissed again. The testosterone compressor came on automatically and I covered her face and neck with kisses as we made our way back into the darkened room. We lay on the model stand with enough diffused sunset afterglow coming through the clerestory windows to create a soft seductive aura around her beautiful face. In this light her body resembled white alabaster.

When it was over, she said, "I wish I had a cigarette."

"Let's go to Dean's on my bike for a bite and Pall Malls."

"No," she answered, as she got dressed. "It's too beautiful and special a night for rushing. Let's walk."

We faced each other in the narrow booth at Dean's Diner, finished our dinners with minimal conversation, and Cindy flashed quick little smiles between puffs on her cigarette.

"What is it?" I asked.

Her head cocked to one side and her smile spread into a gentle grin. She tapped the ash off her cigarette and stared at the residual smoke rising from the ashtray.

"Was that your first time?" She asked, quietly.

Our eyes met and flitted from side to side.

"First time this week," I blinked, with embarrassment.

She put out her cigarette and reached for my hands under the table as she continued to scan my eyes, tenderly.

"Well, first time on a model stand," I offered, lamely. I looked down at the smoldering cigarette in the ash tray.

"I loved it," she said quietly. "In a way it was for me too. I haven't wanted to be with a man for the past five years." She squeezed my hands and her eyes got moist. She pinched her mouth together then said through quivering lips, "That's when I lost my sailor-boy."

She took my arm, in the relative darkness, and we walked back to the school without a word.

"Thank you, Cindy, for a very memorable evening," I said, when I took her to her car.

She nodded her head and drove off.

When we encountered each other in the classroom the following week she diverted her eyes and showed no sign of recognition. Eventually the model's schedule was rotated and almost everyone was pleased to get our rotund black female model back again because Matty could hold difficult poses with minimal breaks.

I never saw Cindy again but she would always remain a special person in my life because of her critical influence in my maturation process. She had gently released me from the vise-like grip of repression Mamma and the church had imposed and sustained all through my formative years. Opening the floodgates of sexual restraints turned the tide on other old-world taboos as well, and I acquired an assertiveness and confidence that helped reorganize my priorities and brought my goals more into focus.

When I told my tradition-locked mother I was moving to my own apartment, she responded with the expected shock, histrionics and hand-wringing because no one in our family, or ancestry, had ever left the homestead before marriage. Mamma's primary concern, understandably, was the ramifications. She feared that once Mrs. Lazzarone spread the news of what her renegade son was contemplating, the humiliation would be unbearable. I felt guilt-ridden, of course, for creating such a predicament for Mamma — until God intervened.

The Lord works in mysterious ways.... The thought of higher education in this ethnic neighborhood was so remote it was beyond the realm of comprehension. In fact, like the majority in this immigrant community, no one in Mrs. Lazzarone's family had gone beyond grade school. Except for the neighborhood icons, the family physician, the priest and the teachers, most of us had never met anyone who had gone to college...had never even *seen* a college.

In one of her probes into the personal life of the fledgling St. Francis priest, Mrs. Lazzarone learned that he had been restricted to the seminary campus in his Jesuit training. She interpreted this as an honor that was earned with merit chips and penance. She knew he was sworn to celibacy and things like that, but the campus confinement probably promoted him to a higher position in the heavenly hierarchy.

It went without saying that for Mrs. Lazzarone, all college students went into the same icon hopper. When she learned that I had been "chosen" to live on campus "at the college" it indicated an elevation in status and I was glory-bound to become "a doctor, a lawyer, a priest or some kinda big shot. That's for sure."

In her opinion, not only did my family gain instant prestige but by the process of osmosis, *she* also acquired stature simply by being a "celebrity's" neighbor. This turn of events was better than if a councilman had moved-in next door.

"Suck-up" over-the-fence chats with Mamma became a regular occurrence. Many times when I made my irregular visits home, Mrs. Lazzarone would lean out of the back door or window with a cheery greeting. I kept my reserve and waved my limp Duke of Windsor wave in return.

This unexpected turn of events could be summed up with one of Mrs. Fantonetti's theological proclamations. *"Miracolo!"*

Chapter XX

I rented a room in a huge turn-of-the-century mansion within walking distance of the school. The Victorian manor house was occupied exclusively by art students. No restrictions. No supervision. Low rent. Low morals. A sorority house on either side. This 23-year-old philanderer had discovered a jackpot at the end of a heavenly rainbow.

Schinkel's, like the Hilton Hotel, was named after its off-premises landlord, but if you told anyone in the university complex that you lived at the Hilton they probably wouldn't roll their eyes like they did when you announced your residence was "Schinkel's." Actually, I didn't find heaven at Schinkel's as much as I found a suburb of Sodom and Gomorrah. When I was introduced to the rows of sorority houses on the nearby Case-Western Reserve Campus I quickly learned the true meaning of the biblical phrase "Carnal Wickedness."

The 40-foot-long basement level room I occupied had a mural full of cupids over a bench-seat at one end. A white Italian marble fireplace was built into the long outside wall. The salmon, beige and white Tudor planked walls made the room bright and hospitable.

Some of the converted bedrooms scattered throughout the house had their own bathrooms. The rest of us shared a communal shower and kitchen that were also located in the basement, just down the hall. It was not unusual for traffic to stop in and socialize unless I had hung out my elegant doorknob "Do Not Disturb" sign which had been stolen from the Hilton by the previous occupant of my room.

Eventually, the debauchery and the three-day-parties with their "22 bottles of beer on the wall" got repetitive and boring and I became more reclusive to concentrate more on my demanding school projects which now took precedence over all other activities.

The serendipitous course of events extended to my transportation requirements as well. The motorcycle was brutal in inclement weather and just as my search for an affordable substitute began, I stumbled onto and purchased for ten dollars, from a fraternity down on Juniper Road, a lifeless Model T Ford Sedan that was identical to the car my brother Ric had driven in the thirties when we careened around the streets of Cleveland the night before The Big Raid.

I towed the graffiti defaced carcass to Mamma's garage, rebuilt the engine with Ric's help, and worked out a deal with Mr. Alger's "Clark Avenue Collision Body Shop." They'd paint the car, I would paint all the signs they needed, complete with their own unique syntax. The one in the parking area read: "No Parking — Collision Only."

They used the stunning Rolls Royce lacquer color combination of black for the top and fenders, a rich subdued ochre for the body. The car that was once an embarrassment in my life was now an antique, a sensational status symbol.

The two university "hangout's" were located not far from the campuses. The Black and Tan Club offered soul food, jazz, and an occasional big-name colored celebrity. "The Silver Lira Bar and Grill" offered a theme ambiance, an Italian menu, and lounge musicians.

Before my old high school buddy Vinnie Grosso had joined his older brother, who owned the original establishment, "The Silver Lira" languished as a neighborhood bar and bocci court. When Vinnie took over the helm, he purchased and incorporated the adjacent two-story building, converted the more isolated part of the acquired addition to a family oriented restaurant, and added a small kiddie swimming pool next to the bocci courts. This section was intended to give the place ambiance and respectability.

The "real money," however, was made at "The Grill." It had a small dance floor, intimate atmosphere, drinks, and a cover charge, which Vinnie waived for me and my friends. I also had a coveted reserved space under a light near the entrance, where I parked my vintage car to support the artificial pedigree aura he had created.

Vinnie had grown a handlebar mustache, a barrel chest, wore a vest, a gold watch chain, and parted his hair in the middle to set the dress standard for the waiters. The pretty waitresses wore high collared puff-sleeved blouses, hair piled into buns on top of their heads, stiletto heels, and hems brazenly high above the knees.

His PR instincts were razor sharp. Whenever he sensed it was required, he would leap over the bar with baseball bat in hand, crack the head of a rowdy, pay the photographer he had planted, supplied the dramatic picture to the reporters drawn to the place by the radio scanners, and settled the affair through his political ties. The notoriety assured a long list of nightly stand-by reservations. When I took my dates there, I was ushered past the waiting-line of impatient customers.

After months of maneuvering, I finally had a date with Magnolia McBee, the magnificent southern belle who graced the sorority house next to Schinkels. For this coming event I combined the best elements from my basic date-packages; a hand-painted card, the Model T, all the "Silver Lira" amenities, and the coup de grace — Rocky River Park.

The day before the date, I went to set up the props in this Hollywood setting, an ideal stage for a romantic tryst. I wrapped my battered guitar in an old blanket and buried it under a pile of branches and leaves to be retrieved effortlessly in the moonlight when the opportune moment was at hand for my serenade. This one-man off-Broadway sleight-of-hand production, with its hidden roses and other props, needed no rehearsing. I'd done it to perfection many times before.

At the appointed hour, I left the Model T in our driveway and walked the short distance next door with my custom-made card in hand, a bounce in my step, and my inspired syrupy southern salutation, complete with practiced drawl, on the tip of my tongue.

A sorority sister opened the door enough to stick her head through and announced that Magnolia was too sick on her bed to come to the door. As I stood there blinking, she slipped out onto the landing, closed the door carefully behind her and put her hand-cupped lips to my ear.

"This is strictly off the record. Understood? I think this is awful, but here's what's going on."

It didn't register the first time around so I asked her to repeat the message. It didn't make a whole lot more sense the second time around but I thanked her and started back to my place, completely undone.

"Well, I'll be a son of a bitch." I walked a few more steps across the lawn slapping the card into the palm of my hand. "I'll-be-a-son-of-a-bitch," I repeated, as the rage and humiliation combined to percolate the blood pressure required for a full blown temper tantrum.

It seems that Billy Eckstine, the colored folks counterpart to Frank Sinatra, was doing a one night stand at the Black and Tan and Miss Magnolia elected Bradford Ellison to escort her to this auspicious event.

Yeah, yeah, yeah. I knew Brad. He was the shit who was doggin' it around the campus with his bright red Studebaker convertible that his big shot lawyer father bought him and he was polite and all that shit. He's still the goddam bad-ass black bastard who stole my date! Can you imagine the fuckin' balls? Dating a white girl? *My* date!

"And you, you pretentious-treacherous-white trash-whore! Won't your red-neck hee-haw parents turn their anal sphincters inside out..."I let the fury roar unchecked. This level of emotional release was new to me. Sure, Miss Magnolia Maggot was the trigger, but this intense anger had been building up, layer upon layer, throughout the repressive years.

I hung my "Do Not Disturb" sign on the door knob in the hall, locked the door, dismantled and oiled the working parts of my Spanish Star pistol to prevent a misfire, and slammed the loaded cartridge-clip into the gun-handle like I intended to punish it.

I was surprised by a light knock at my door. Nobody had ignored my privacy sign before. I stood frozen with my chest heaving, staring at the door, listening. Instead of the expected retreating footsteps, I got a louder, more persistent, repeated knock. When I opened the door a small attractive girl with the disarming face of The Little Match Girl stood there clutching a clipboard to her chest.

"Are you Jamie?"

"Yes."

"According to the papers you're selling your paintings before the galleries can hang them on their walls, right?"

"I'm doing OK," I said, with my lungs working like a bellows that rhythmically fed the puckered exhale that rustled her bangs. "If you don't mind, I'm very, very, busy —"

"And you're the one teaching a figure drawing class at the Cooper School of Art. Right?"

"Yes. Listen," I said, gasping, as I narrowed the door opening, "I really don't have time —"

She pushed past me and leafed through her life drawings. She was a freshman at the Art School, she explained, her name was Mata something or other, she was having trouble with these drawings, and, oh, she lived in the room above mine. And, oh, what was the gun for?

"You're not going to shoot the colored guy?"

"What are you talking about? What colored guy?"

"I watched the whole tableaux construct itself, piece by piece, like a living erector set, from my upstairs window where I work and sometimes see things."

"You didn't come down here for help at all, did you? You're here to fill-in the gossip gaps. Right? Mrs. Lazzarone?"

"My name is Mata, not Mrs. Hoo-hoo. No, I'm not here for help. I'm here to prevent something stupid. I'm here to tell you the colored guy didn't arrange the date and Scarlett O'Hara didn't plan this to kick your butt. You're too insignificant in her self-absorption. She needed him for something and that's as far as she could think...up to arms length."

"You know these things?"

"All women know these things. Billy Eckstine. The Billy Eckstine concert."

"What?"

"The Billy Eckstine concert. Scarlett knew she needed him to get into the Black and Tan. You're too white for the limited seating. Sure, it's a feather in his cap. Pretty girl. She'll get him in, he gets her in. There isn't a girl within a 20 mile radius that doesn't know about the concert but they just wouldn't be found dead with a colored guy. This has nothing to do with you at all. Bet she didn't even remember she had a date with you. Now. What are you gonna do with the gun?"

"Listen, Miss Know-it-all —"

"Mata, as in Mata-Hari."

"Listen Miss Mata Know-it-all. See that target hanging under the cupids back there? At times of acute stress or frustration, when my ego and my psyche have been hammered to the size of a rat dropping, I fire off a full clip at the target. It makes me feel all better and it scares hell out of the cupids. Now, if you don't mind —" I was re-directing my rage toward this brass-balled upstart, prepared to shout her out or throw her out of the room physically, if I had to. I could see she sensed the impending onslaught.

"Tell ya the truth," she said, enveloping herself in the little match girl persona, "guns scare me too. I wish you'd put that thing away." Her strategy gave me a great idea.

"Nothin' to be afraid of. Come 'ere." I patted the bed next to where I was sitting and tried to coax her to fire into the phone books stacked on an end-table against the wainscoting, ten feet from where we sat.

"The gun's cocked and ready to go. Just aim at the phone books...like this...and...fire —" I knew this ploy would send her running out of the room screaming.

The explosion rattled everything in the room that was

not nailed down. The bullet penetrated the phone books, gouged a path in the painted wainscoting, ricocheted off the underside of the bookshelf above the phone books and still had enough energy to traject back to where we sat, slap her smartly on the forehead, and drop onto her lap looking very much like a penny that had been squished on a track by a streetcar.

We leapt up together and as I followed her around the room spouting ineffectual reassurances about the mathematical odds of that ever happening again, she spun around to face me, hands on her hips.

"All right! All...l...l....right!" she yelled. "Now you've symbolically shot the southern belle, the colored guy, and scared heck out of me and the cupids. Now...has your masculine psyche grown bigger than a rat dropping? And...do you want to shoot Miss Goody-goody-two-shoes again because she's the only eyewitness to your humiliation?"

I couldn't believe how this kid had taken control of this situation. With her bangs and her waist-length hair, she could put on Mary Janes and play an under-age Hollywood Alice in Wonderland. But she thinks and acts like a mature woman. I walked to my door and wedged it open.

"How old are you?"

"I'm not jail bait, if that's what you're asking."

I flushed and apologized. "Listen, Maggie —"

"Mata," she corrected. "M-a-t-a. Mata, as in Mata-Hari."

I dropped my chin to my chest and as I massaged my temples I said, "I'll-be-a-son-of-a —"

"— gun," she interjected, "expert son-of-a-gun who'd like to get back at Miss Magnolia Charmschool but doesn't know how." She had a nice giggle. We laughed and exchanged preposterous revenge plots that we thought would be fitting for

Magnolia's unforgivable transgressions.

"No, wait," said Mata. "I've got it! She is supposed to be sick in bed with the vapors. Right? Well, what could be more embarrassing to her or satisfying to you than to confront her *with* the colored guy *at* the Black and Tan? You're already dressed and I can be in a jiffy."

"Hey!" I said, as she started to scurry out the door, "You forgot why you came here. Here's your drawings." Sheepishly, she took the sketches from me and I added, "Why are you getting involved in this whole dumb thing?"

"I want to ride in your neat car."

We were chugging up Mayfield Road two blocks before the Black and Tan Nightclub and all the parking spaces on both sides of the street were already jammed shut as far as the eye could see. Throngs of fans spilled beyond the police barricades into the street to engulf the cars they hoped would offer a glimpse of a celebrity.

As we inched forward behind a limo, an officer who had been attracted to the Model T was joined by a second uniformed car buff and then a third. As they walked alongside my slowly moving vehicle we discussed the merits of the car and the odds of finding a parking space.

I was stopped opposite the court area in front of the club, when the police went into a huddle with a group of colored men in tuxedos who had come out of the club entrance.

The police cleared a path and waved us into the center of the court. A cop was shouting at me through my rolled-down window and gesturing but I could not hear his voice over the screaming horde. When the police cordon protecting my car finally broke ranks, I could see that the crowd was dispersing and focused on gaining entrance to the club.

We learned from a policeman that Billy Eckstine had exited the club long enough to take a series of publicity photos using my car as a background prop. We never saw him. We also learned that because Mata could not produce any identification to verify her legal drinking age, we were banned from the concert. I arced the car around the court, dodging stragglers, as we made our way back onto the street.

"Oh, I'm so damned mad!" said Mata. "I'm not jail bait! I'll sue! Where is your gun when we need it! Come on! Let's shoot our way in!"

I knew going into this improvised escapade that the odds of actually getting into the club were pretty remote, so I actuated the back-up plan and retraced our drive down Mayfield Hill on our way to "Vinnie's" for a more tranquil evening of privilege and good Italian food. As we approached "The Silver Lira," it was apparent that the back-up plan was also in trouble. Like the Black and Tan melee we had just left, there were teeming people and police also around Vinnie's entrance. But this swarm was pouring *out*, not trying to get in, and the police were aggressively over-powering individuals.

As the flashbulbs popped, a line of disheveled men with their jackets pulled over their heads for anonymity were being guided into the rear doors of the police van parked in my reserved parking space. I recognized one of the men with a coat over his head as Vinnie. This was not one of Vinnie's PR stunts. This looked serious. An ambulance made its way through the gathering curiosity seekers.

"Let's get the hell out of here!" I said to Mata. We raced to the other side of town to Willoughby's Drive-in. After we calmed down and ate, I decided to drive to Rocky River and retrieve my hidden guitar. Maybe serenade Mata, maybe go back to the safety of my room to suck my thumb and sulk.

When we got to the park, the soft breeze was comforting, the full moon was casting a bright light and the water was making a pleasant burbling sound as it made its way through the huge, smooth boulders.

"Let's take a walk," I suggested, as I stepped out of the car.

"I don't know," she said, "I'm not sure about this."

"Com'on," I assured her, "It's OK. I just want you to see this place. You've earned it. I won't make a pass. I promise. Give you my word."

"And you'll take me home when I want to go?" she asked, suspiciously. I made a cross over my heart with my finger.

It could not have been a more romantic setting as we sat on the huge familiar rock absorbing the mesmerizing sights and lulling sounds.

I checked my bearings, reached into the shadowed crevice on my side of the rock for the planted guitar, but couldn't locate it. After several more bearing checks and sweeps, I swung my legs over the edge of the rock and dropped into the shadow to widen the search area. There was a muffled snapping, tearing, wood sound as my foot, with my full weight on it, went through the top of the guitar and continued through the resonance-board. I extricated my foot from the tangle of strings and splintered guitar wood and covered the pile of scrap with leaves and twigs. To paraphrase Vinnie's metaphor: This lovely day had lengthened into a giant second-hand suppository.

When we got back to Schinkel's I took Mata to her door but we never touched. Not so much as a handshake.

"Well," she said, as she stood halfway into her doorway, "Thank you for a wonderful ride in your wonderful car...and the tour of the underworld...and for sharing the moonscape.

I'm sorry Miss Parasol didn't get her come-uppance, but it was lots of fun, anyway." She waved the "bye-bye" gesture, started to close the door, and hesitated.

"By the way," she added, "from what I know about Miss Gone With The Wind, she set this whole thing up. The colored guy never knew what hit him."

"I know that," I said. "I don't know Brad Ellison all that well, but from what I hear, he's a very decent person. Everyone speaks well of him. My stupidity, not his."

"And another thing," said Mata, from her narrow door opening, "your doorknob sign should read, 'Do Not Disturb. Violators will be shot!'" She grinned, waved, and shut the door.

Chapter XXI

I made a very interesting discovery. When an irresistible force meets an immovable object — they become interchangeable. Mamma was a hardened block of intransigence, and I was "a chip off the ole block."

Distorted bits and fragments of my art school escapades somehow made their way through the grapevine into Mamma's kitchen with unpleasant results. Very nice girls I had brought home to meet the family she now referred to as "that tramp..." or "that dirty tramp..." and nothing I said or did seemed to appease her. Month after month the schism grew until about two weeks after my only date with Mata, I went to visit Mamma and the reception was uncommonly cool. She did not return my greeting, left the stove where she'd been stirring with her back to me, and returned from another part of the house to carefully place two folded newspapers on the table in front of me, without saying a word.

"The Mayfield Monitor" showed a photo of me in the Model T engulfed in a sea of humanity with Billy Eckstine standing with one foot on the running-board, grinning, in a striped blazer, waving a boater. The only visible white faces were me and the policemen. I somehow was wearing a cop's hat so I looked like Mr. Eckstine's chauffeur. The headline over the photo read, "Billy's Back!"

"The Cleveland News" photo showed the men with their

coats over their heads parading past my car as they were being led to the paddy-wagon in front of Vinnie's. Mercifully, Mata was a silhouette. I was not.

"That dirty tramp —"

"Ma...Ma...Ma....Don't start on me."

"You bring dishonor to your family!" she yelled.

"Oh, please!" I yelled back. "Not that same old crap again."

"Your behavior is a disgrace!" she bellowed, in her dialect.

"Ma...let me tell you something," I growled, as I paced the kitchen. "I'm not your baby anymore and just because I won't do *exactly* what you, your mother, or your grandmother wants me to do, doesn't mean I'm a disgrace! We're not in Capurso! We're in America now!"

"Do you know what people are saying about you?...Do you? Do you have any idea?"

"I don't give a goddam or a good shit what your dago friends are saying about me!" We were both so startled by my vile profanity, the room suddenly went silent. When Mamma recovered from the shock, she stomped to the door in a rage and held it open.

"You? You who almost killed me when you were born? You talk to your mother this way? Get out! Get out now! And don't come back until...I will not tolerate...will not tolerate such a filthy mouth in my house. Get out of this house! Now!"

I swept up my Homburg hat, charged out of the kitchen, and slammed the door forcefully behind me.

She and I had growled at each other many times before but the fury usually subsided with the two of us sniffing and circling each other stiff-legged with our ears flat back and our tails twitching nervously. Like the "capo" pecking order confrontations I had witnessed on the corner as a kid, when the

236

growls changed to snarls and teeth could be glimpsed through quivering lips, someone almost always yanked the choke-collars before any serious damage could be done. But this time, Mamma and I had inadvertently drawn figurative blood and didn't know what the next step was. So we improvised.

The battle lines were drawn; she on the west side of town, me on the east, with the Cuyahoga River defining the combat zones. After about two months of silence on the two fronts, a peace emissary, in the form of my sister Annie, called and tentatively offered a willingness to negotiate peace conditions.

The last time she called I had presented a declaration of independence and demanded an apology from my mother. This time I misread her gesture as capitulation and upped the ante.

"Jamie, you know, and I know, Ma loves you dearly. But ain't no way she's gonna apologize. C'mon, for cryin' out loud. She's your *mother*. You owe *her* an apology. Is it gonna kill ya?"

"All right. Tell ya what. She can skip the apology altogether an' go right to the begging for forgiveness. And that goes for anyone else who agrees with her stupid Capurso ideas."

"Jamie. If you grow up and come to your senses, call me."

I gradually did regain my senses as waves of guilt and familial attachment washed over me and I felt the irrepressible tug to make amends. But misplaced pride and my new-found independence combined to create a counter-force too powerful to acquiesce to reason. Month after month the silent face-off continued until I gradually started to consider the uncomfortable possibility of a permanent estrangement. Whenever I sought support from my friends for my position against my family, they wisely remained neutral. I made myself block my family problems and in this state of suspension was able to cope with day to day concerns encountered at the school.

One of the annoyances at school was the lack of feeding facilities for students. Each day at noon a bunch of my classmates and I would pile into the Model T and drive to a small delicatessen near Mayfield.

Napoleon said, "An army marches on it's stomach." Our returned war heroes marched back to class when their stomachs were satisfied, not when the school told them to. As a result, classes after lunch started when enough stragglers had been collected. I recognized this weak link in the curriculum flow as an opportunity waiting to be exploited.

I went to the large Star Bakery maintenance garage, a block away from Mamma's house, where I had once noticed a short-chassis bakery truck. It had been moth-balled for the duration of the war and was now obsolete, well maintained, and priced for quick sale.

I walked into the Dean's office at the appointed hour with drawings of the modified truck, made my visual presentation and ended my proposal with this clincher: "This, of course, solves your lunch problem with absolutely no cost or obligation to the school."

With a hearty handshake, he approved the plan and agreed to reserve a place in the parking lot just opposite the side entrance for "Jamie's Lunch Wagon."

The health department erected the next hurdle. All food that was not pre-packaged and sealed, like my sandwiches and coffee, had to be prepared in a commercial establishment that had a health department approval certificate for a minimum of two consecutive years. For most people, this obstacle would have been the death knell. Not me. I was one of Mr. Unger's Lucky Seven and felt confident I could find a matching set of snow-flakes if I put my mind to it.

When I described my lunch-truck dilemma to Kristin Borge, a fellow student, she introduced me and my problem to her father who owned a deli-grocery in the village of Independence on the southern out-skirts of Cleveland. Mr. Borge and I liked each other from the start and I was grateful and indebted to him when he assumed the role of mentor.

The redesigned lunch truck was crisply painted and converted to a mobile cafeteria. The ladies referred to the rig as, "cute as a button."

Once my career as food aficionado was launched, my new daily schedule started with my alarm sounding at 3:30 am. The routine started with a drive through the deserted dark streets to the west side of town, following a route that eerily traced the path followed by Ric and me as kids in the Model T.

Each morning, with a truckload of guilt and longing, I passed Mamma's dark house on my way to the Star Bakery where I purchased freshly baked Kaiser sandwich rolls. Then hurried to the dairy where I loaded the milk tubs, went on to pick up and pack the ice cream products in dry-ice, bought the sealed snack packages, and completed the circuit in Independence, where I made up a variety of generous deli-type sandwiches under the tutelage of the deli-master, Mr. Borge.

"You've never heard of Sweden House coffee before?" he asked. That kind of question introduced the opening of the daily lessons I learned about the specifics of food handling. But more importantly, I learned about business acumen generally. The lessons always ended with this admonishment: "No compromises if you're serious about this business."

When he felt that I'd served my internship, he gave me a key to the store with the warning, "And don't disturb my beauty sleep unless the store's on fire. I owe it to my beauty."

The lunch truck was an immediate smash. Although I usually pulled into my allotted parking space before the school officially opened each morning, I was sometimes late to class. Men in business suits, secretaries, and students from surrounding campuses were already waiting in a long line for "take-out" when I arrived.

Mr. Borge was a fine imaginative gentleman and successful entrepreneur but he was never satisfied with the status quo and kept raising his own goal sights: *"A business is like a greenhouse plant. If it isn't growing, it's dying."*

When the deli business was polished enough to become a money-making machine, he turned it over to his wife and enthusiastically concentrated his energy on the large stone and timber mansion he had mulled over and finally purchased to convert into an authentic Danish Smorgasbord. The magnificent structure, located in the next village down the line on Route 21, sat nestled in a virgin forest at the end of a long, elegant driveway that was lined with handsome blue spruce trees.

In order to keep the Smorgasbord restoration process from lagging, Mr. Borge had announced through flyers, and newspaper ads that the opening date would be Christmas Day. It became apparent as we approached that date that even with intensified efforts we'd have trouble meeting that deadline. So we recruited more art students with construction skills as well as design training to join the race.

Mr. Borge had fenced in the area between the barn and the tool shed to pen 12 majestic geese he intended to serve as an authentic Danish treat throughout the Christmas season.

On one of my trips past the pen to the rubbish heap behind the tool shed, I confirmed my suspicion that although most of the birds were getting bigger and sassier by the day, one was getting thinner and strange looking. On another trip I noticed it was bleeding here and there and staggering. I learned from those at the house who knew about goosely things that this was the goose selected by the flock for sacrifice in a grisly "pecking order" ritual.

Mr. Borge recommended we not move it to safety because the ritual would start afresh with a replacement victim.

With an armful of debris left over from the grand opening Christmas decorations, I stopped at the pen to pay my respects. Pressed against my side of the enclosure was the doomed goose rapidly approaching his pathetic fate with the rest of the gaggle boisterously feeding on the other side of the enclosure. When he raised his wobbly neck out of the mud into which he had collapsed, I impulsively took a large bow-tied red ribbon from one of the Christmas gift boxes I was carrying out to the rubbish pile, and dropped it over his head and secured it to his neck. Pandemonium ensued. Flailing birds fell over each other, shrieking and pressing hard into the corners in a desperate attempt to get as far from the terrifying monster as possible.

For the first time in weeks, the ostracized bird dragged himself to food and water with the frenzied flock giving him all the space he needed.

The rehabilitation process continued day by day until the former sacrifice strutted cockily in wide circles with an entourage of females in his wake. All he lacked was a cigar and a derby. Ironically, with his wilted red-ribboned talisman, only he and one pet mate survived the Smorgasbord oven to raise a family for the following year.

This survivor of fowl-play had bluffed his way to the top of the totem pole. *Capo dei capi* — shades of Clark and Fulton. Vinnie, whom I hadn't heard from for some time now, had once said: "Everybody's just about where they ought to be in the scheme of things."

When the Christmas Day Grand Opening came, there were well dressed patrons in the *Hugge*, the reception area, waiting to be seated in the splendid dining room. Unfortunately, despite our efforts, we were not ready to receive them.

We had worked through the night to iron out the glitches that develop for any opening, and like all openings, there are always last minute, frantic emergencies. This was no exception. We made repeated dashes into the village for one thing and another and were getting concerned with our stone-faced, restless customers who were just holding, no longer sipping, their instantly topped cups of tea and coffee in the waiting room.

There were small rooms off of the main dining room that offered authentic Danish appetizers and beverages. Like any buffet style dinner, the plan was to invite the guests to serve themselves as often as they wished. Uniformed waiters and waitresses would stand by to assist.

When the first customers were finally released into the restaurant proper, many of the couples crowded into the various rooms to acquaint themselves with what was available. They walked around and gushed over the three-tiered seafood table with its sparkling ice, pointing out the pickled herring with onion rings, tiny Danish shrimp, sliced *Frikadeller*, and smoked salmon. There was one potentially embarrassing problem in this room that no one had, as yet, discovered.

It was me.

I was trapped under the table, concealed by the long, floor-length skirt of the tablecloth. I had been making last minute plumbing adjustments under the table when Mr. Borge inadvertently let the impatient customers into the dining area.

It would not be prudent to crawl out from my hiding place with my three days growth of beard and grubby coveralls so I resigned myself to wait quietly until the coast was clear.

The last time I was in a similar predicament, I was a kid under a dark door-stoop with a dusty black dog who wasn't talking and it was also, ironically, Christmas Day.

Finally, after what seemed like an interminable period of time, I checked all around, could see no more shoes showing under the voluminous tablecloth, grabbed my tool box, and beat a hasty, crawling-in-reverse retreat...right between the legs of an elderly woman who was now standing with a plate full of food, straddling my body like we were playing "horsey."

She screamed, threw her plate into the air and as she staggered backward, grabbed the lip of the deep triangular ice-loaded tray above me for support and managed to dump buckets of shaved ice on my back, neck, and head. She instantly transformed the room into what looked like a diorama of the Antarctic. The elderly woman collapsed into one of the two occasional chairs flanking a small antique table that supported a ceramic lamp.

Once I was safe on the other side of the kitchen door, I stood up and brushed ice from my hair and body as rivulets of ice water made their way down my spine and into my shorts. I tilted my head from side to side and tapped ice out of my ears.

"Hello, Jenny Lange," I said to myself, "I didn't recognize you, but, here you are...you've done it again!"

I could hear the hysterical woman trying to convince the members of the staff that had gathered to calm her, that there was a "huge, scary snowman like-thing under the table!" Mr. Borge comforted and reassured the elderly customer as he escorted her gently from the room. The hired help moved in quickly with brooms, buckets, towels and squeegees.

The rumor that made its way from room to room was that a magnificent ice sculpture of a polar bear or a snowman had fallen from one of the tables and disintegrated on the floor. Luckily, they added, no one was hurt seriously, even though it had struck a woman on its way to the floor. They weren't sure if she had caused the accident or not.

After I showered, shaved, and got into my waiter's uniform, I went downstairs and assumed my post next to Kristin in the dining room.

"I hear a good place to hide from little old ladies is under the seafood table," I said, without looking at her.

"Especially if you feel guilty and the little old lady is the mother you haven't talked to for a year," she countered.

I was startled by her response. This was the first time one of my friends had broached this sensitive subject since the fracas had occurred.

"It so happens," I said, "that the little old lady was a customer, not a mother." I continued to survey the diners with a false attitude of indifference even though I was eager to pursue the topic in the hope that Kris was about to suggest a face-saving resolution to the impasse. When she showed no sign of picking up the conversation, I added, "So you think I'm the one...should... apologize. Even though I'm right and she's wrong?"

"You know, Jamie," she answered, "on one of my rare visits to your house, your mother said to me, once, in her broken English, 'People never seem to remember the good things you do in your life, but they never, ever, forget the bad.'" She smiled a crooked smile and scanned the tables. Then she added, "Customers and mothers are always right."

Chapter XXII

Judging by his uncanny good luck, Mr. Borge seemed to have a cadre of Guardian Angels who had been individually trained to act on specialized assignments. One, for instance, seemed to have nothing better to do than to ensure that the traffic lights changed to green as he approached an intersection. Another, a gifted celestial CPA, must have been directing his business decisions.

Mr. Borge was considering consolidating his assets to create a pool of ready money to nurture his thriving and expanding Smorgasbord. As he contemplated the merits of the maneuver, he was unaccountably approached by an eager buyer pressing to purchase his deli-grocery in Independence for cash. The deal would not be consummated for a few months but when it eventually happened, "Jamie's Lunch Wagon" would be severed from its nerve center. This unanticipated development must have caused *my* angelic watch-dog crew to scramble.

I had first refusal on his L-shaped lot that was separated from the Deli by a narrow side street. When Mr. Borge adjusted his liberal terms to accommodate my affordability, I was launched onto the next plateau of my food business career and everybody on my team "up there" probably let out a collective sigh of relief. The site I decided to build a drive-in restaurant on was strategically located near the Ohio Turnpike.

Because the land purchase had depleted my resources, it became necessary to do as much of the actual physical construction as possible, myself. I acquired a lot of rudimentary building information from local libraries, then pestered contractors, foremen, sub-contractors, and supply yards, to learn as much as I could about site layout, electrical and plumbing code requirements, block construction, and all the rest.

For months, after school, I raced out to Independence, to *my land,* and hit the ground galloping with my primitive pick-ax flailing at the solid shale base to prepare the ground for the coming foundation footing. Eventually, I succeeded in pouring enough hand-mixed buckets of cement into the footing cavity to form the foundation for the cement block corners I'd use as benchmarks to construct the masonry walls. When I ran unavoidably past sundown, any excess mortar was troweled onto the edges of the cement blocks and tapped to the level of the taut guide strings by the light of the truck headlights.

One sunny Sunday afternoon, standing proudly on *my land,* at the rear of the truck, I had pulled out two long adjacent drawers, turned them upside-down, and returned them part way into the cavities, to form a makeshift field table.

As I rolled out a floor plan and weighted the corners down with small stones, a glistening black two-seater Jaguar sports car, top down, crunched over the gravel and stopped close to where I was standing. The young man wearing leather driving gloves and a patched-elbow tweed jacket, turned off the ignition. The action appeared to simultaneously immobilize both him and the car. He sat motionless with a frozen smile that exposed white, even, teeth surrounded by a neatly trimmed Van Dyke beard.

"How can I help you?" I asked, with my senses on alert. He stepped out of the dream machine without answering, peeled off his gloves one finger at a time, folded the jacket neatly and laid it on the car seat. He then took off his herringbone sport cap and arranged it deliberately on the folded jacket. With his hands on his hips, he looked directly at me and shook his head slowly from side to side to indicate he was disappointed that I didn't recognize him. He walked past me to look at the rubble on the other side of one of the low walls, and as he removed his sunglasses, still grinning, said, "This place looks like the final resting place for second-hand suppositories."

"Well...I...will...be...a...son...of...a...bitch!" I said, as we laughed and walked toward each other with open arms. We locked in a tight embrace, slapping each other on the back, turned, caught our balance, then continued our turning, rocking, and slapping. We stopped waltzing each other around the lot and sat down on a couple of cement blocks.

"Yeah, goddamit, sure, Vinnie," I said, to my childhood and high school buddy, "like I'm supposed to recognize a new hairstyle, parted on the side, without the handlebar mustache, 30 pounds lighter, no baseball bat...oh, shit...I'm sorry Vinnie, I wasn't thinking —"

"Hey, it's OK. It's over. It all turned out OK. This is my courtroom persona, designed by one of my lawyers. Makes me look more respectable, dignified. And it's probably gonna be me for a while. Weren't you impressed when I pulled up?"

"Well, I gotta admit —"

The lawyers had used his bank account for a *piñata*, he explained, got beat up pretty good, financially, but they did keep him out of jail. On the night of the tragedy, one of his planted photographers got a shot that showed a close-up of the victim's hand swinging a beer bottle and Vinnie's hand swinging a baseball bat. The question the jury deliberated was, "who was the aggressor?" The verdict, finally, was justifiable homicide, with one guy dead, the other almost broke and 30 stress-pounds lighter. I did my drive-in show-and-tell and as I flipped to the floor plan he stopped me and went back to the site plan.

"It's an "L-shaped" lot. Is that barn back there yours?"

"Yeah. It's great. I use it to store my building supplies."

"Oh, shit, Jamie. You may be a great artist or designer or whatever the hell it is that you do, but you're one crappy business man, I'll tell you that much."

"Whataya mean? I thought I was doing pretty good."

"Good, my ass." He shook his head and ran his hand through his hair. "That barn or this rubble restaurant makin' any money for you? No. They costing you money in taxes? Yes. That's good business? Bullshit! Your gonna do this on your own resources, right? Hey, the no-legs guy who begs downtown in front of the May Company, *he* relies on his own resources. You think maybe *he's* gonna own the May Company some day? Yeah, sure. If he keeps his nose to the grindstone, right? Bullshit! This world, my dear Jamie, is one big friggin' shell game!" Now he was in his element. He got up and started to pace back and forth in front of me.

"You know, Vinnie, you should become a bible-thumpin' minister or a philosopher. You've got more damn advice —"

"Hey, ole buddy," he said, "at the rate you're going, that son-of-a-bitch *is* gonna own the May Company before you make a dime with this thing. Wake up for Christ's sake. *NEVER... NEVER!...EVER!...*risk your own money on a business venture. *NEVER!*" When he reversed his direction at the end of his accelerating three steps, he did an about-face that was digging a shallow pit at the end of each run.

"After a hundred years," I said, "you finally look me up, and this is what you came to tell me? I don't know what I'm doing? You know what...*ole buddy*...somehow I've managed to get this far without your —"

"Hey, Jamie! I'm only trying to help. Learn from my experiences, my mistakes. Look at me. The sons o' bitches cleaned me out." He pulled his empty pants pockets out and tugged at the cloth for emphasis. "You think I'm gonna get behind that fuckin' bar to try and make it up? Bullshit! The bank's paying for this one. I'm gonna borrow right up to here. *And*, I'm gonna _earn_ money on *their* money, not pay interest. Matter of fact, you can get in on this one. I'll borrow more than I need and loan you whatever you need to finish this Egyptian pyramid, interest free. No interest. Won't cost you a thing."

"And why would you wanna do that, Vinnie?"

"Because I buy my booze and beer in quantity, *big* quantity. You let me use the barn, rent free, to store my booze, I'll loan you what you need, interest free. Zappo! That's it. You're in business."

"And you're gonna do this outta the goodness of your heart, right?" Vinnie stopped pacing, sat down on the cement block next to me and lowered his voice to a level of intimacy.

"Look, Jamie, you do whatever the hell you wanna do. Go back to begging in front of the May Company for all I give a shit. You go try to borrow by yourself, they're gonna have your great-grandchildren paying off this mortgage. My own collateral will cover what I need to borrow. That friggin' car right there would do it, without the bar and grill. Which, by the way, is free and clear."

He leaped up, took several steps, turned with one thumb locked into his belt, the other hand jabbing a finger at me.

"No...no...no. Wait," he said, excitedly, "I know what. You tell me what you want for the barn rent money — I'll double it!

No loan. Every month. Money comin' in to finish this mausoleum. Cash on the barrel head! Your beggin' days are over, Jamie, baby!" He sat down next to me again. With his arm around my back he tugged me toward him repeatedly and added, "Hot damn, Jamie! Happy days are here again!"

When I didn't respond to his exuberance, he stopped the sales pitch dead in its tracks. We sat quietly next to each other, lost in our thoughts as we raked miniature Japanese gardens in the pea-gravel with our splayed fingers. When he had reorganized his strategy, he tried the intimacy approach again.

"It's just that the more collateral I slam down on the desks of these shylocks, the more it speeds things up. With the deal I've got going, I need this money *now*. For you, it's a formality. Collateralize the loan and forget about it. Look, I'll even put in a bulletproof clause for ya. Let your lawyer look it over—" He laid out a very logical plan and ended with, "If something goes wrong, it's my ass, not yours."

"Vinnie, why do you need *this* barn? Why don'cha get something closer to your business? Why come all the way out here?"

"Because even with me paying you twice the rent it's worth, if you go with the rest of the deal, it's still half of what that kinda storage would cost me in the city. It's called 'moving the shells around in the right order,' my boy."

"Vinnie, thanks for the offer. Let me think about this."

He swaggered to the car, dressed himself in his English gentleman's costume, leaped behind the wheel with the same agility he had as a high school athlete, put the roadster in gear, and said over the growl of the engine, "Make the contract for a five-year lease with one-year advance payment for a security deposit. More, if you think you need more." He waved and I turned my back to the spewing gravel.

Although I normally didn't get many visitors out on the lot, a couple of days later I was sitting on the ground with my back propped against the shading low wall of the drive-in when another car pulled up between me and the interstate traffic. This visitor startled me a lot more than Vinnie did. When my father, whom I hadn't seen for over a year, got out of his dilapidated Plymouth, my brain sent mixed signals to my body. My interior mechanism instantly hit the emotional turmoil button, while the exterior shut down completely.

Papa got out stiffly, shaded his eyes from the glaring sun, and studied the building I was putting up. Neither of us looked directly at the other. In incremental steps, he worked his way to where I sat staring at the ground, lowered himself next to me without a word, then tapped, packed, and lit his pipe. Minutes went by as he puffed away in his solitude.

"You can pick...your friends...but you can't...pick...your... family —" The words following each puff sounded as if he was interpreting the balls of smoke wafting against my right ear like they were Indian smoke signals. "...what you get...is what you got." Uncharacteristically, his affected diction sounded like an amateur poet doing a reading for other amateur poets in the back room of the local library.

We sat for another minute in silence and when it was clear he was finished with his transmitting, I pulled the pencil from behind my ear, held it like I was holding the stem of a pipe, and responded between exaggerated puff sounds, "you can't pick your family...puff, puff...but you can pick your nose, puff, puff, and what you get, is what you got."

I had never heard my father howl with laughter before. I shrieked with joy and collapsed to one side, purging the tension until I was weak.

"Every family needs at least one *mascalzone*." he said.

"What, exactly, is a *mascalzone*?"

"A smart-ass," he said, groaning to a standing position. The response tripped off another round of howling. I had never heard my father expose this coarse side of himself before.

He extended his hand to help me up and said, "C'mon son. Get up. We've got a building to finish up here." I took his firm grip, stood up, and we embraced with tears running down our cheeks. He put his arm around me and we walked inside the roofless drive-in. "Now," he said, as he pinched his nostrils together, "tell me what you want me to do."

"No, Papa," I said, gulping back the overwhelming feeling of love and security I'd felt even as a kid each time Papa came to my rescue. "I can't tell you what to do. You know that. I'll show you what has to be done. Then *you* tell *me* how we're gonna do it."

He took his measurements, wrote notes to himself, and we worked out a schedule. As I was rolling up the plans, I described Vinnie's business propositions.

"Bring me the deed to this place, the contracts Vinnie draws up, all that stuff, and I'll run it past Mike DaFutte. Let's see what he thinks about it."

"Who's Mike DaFutte?"

"Our neighborhood ombudsman. He's a cop, studies law at night. Just like his brother Frank before him."

"We talking about Frankie the Foot? Oh yes! Frankie!"

"That's right. Sure, you know Frankie. He's a big time judge now. Helluv'a nice decent man. They both are."

As if to accentuate and cement our new relationship, that was the second profanity, diluted, I'd ever heard uttered from my father's lips.

My reconciliation with Mamma was arranged by my omnipotent father and took place in the same setting traditionally reserved for Christmas. The dining room table overflowed with the same Christmas banquet, but instead of carols, the gathered family sang joyous Italian street songs, accompanied by relatives playing their string instruments in the kitchen. To emphasize the unqualified importance of the reunion, Mamma never covered her hand-made lace tablecloth with a bedsheet.

After school and on weekends, my father, brothers Ric and George, and my brother-in-law Jerry, joined me in the building frenzy. Now that the feud was over, Mamma packed lunches for us and sometimes she and my sister Annie joined us for on-the-job picnics. The familial bond was never stronger.

The following spring we decided to open the completed soft ice cream portion of the building to the public. Without fanfare, we simply hung an "open" sign under the "Dairy King" road sign and were in business. As the first passers-by who made the discovery formed a ragged line outside our serving window, I checked myself in the back-room mirror, adjusted the white overseas-type serving hat and straightened the clip-on black bow tie. The white shirt and lab coat had been repeatedly starched and pressed by Mamma until the outfit felt as if it had been fabricated by the same people who had produced the stainless steel equipment and walls that made up this spotless, sterile, glass and metal room. We looked like we were prepared to perform emergency appendectomies if the need came up. Emotionally, I felt I was in the wings of the Met stage, together with my butterflies, waiting for my cue.

Appearances was not our only concern. As with all grand opening events, Murphy's Law was being strictly enforced. The freezer repair man still hadn't determined what made the funny noise. The cone-drying machine was not working properly so that instead of crispy, snappy cones, we had cones that changed shape when you picked them up. As the day lengthened, so did the list of malfunctions.

The representative who had installed the frozen custard machine six hours before our opening could not demonstrate the vital round-the-rim technique of dispensing the extruded soft ice cream because the necessary mix had not arrived until long after the demonstrator had left the premises. The procedure, he cautioned, was critical, and would determine the difference between profit and loss.

"How may I help you, sir?" I asked, in a voice that betrayed my calm demeanor. The man in the business suit who had been waiting patiently at the head of the growing line rattled off an impressive list of exotic-sounding concoctions as if he was practicing a Berlitz foreign language lesson. I followed his gaze to the wall behind me and discovered a dazzling display of colorful posters that promoted a sumptuous array of dairy dishes that we apparently offered.

I turned my back to him and for the very first time faced the Dairy Maid machine. I tried to mentally work out a strategy of how, exactly, I would assemble the three ten-cent and three 20-cent cones, the only things on his confusing order I could possibly attempt to put together.

I snapped up a cone from the pile to my left, put it under the nozzle, pulled the activating handle with my right hand, and was pleased to see the frozen white cream extruding out of the stainless steel faucet-shape like toothpaste being squeezed out of a giant tube.

Once around the rim, perfectly. The second coil ring was wider in diameter than the first, the third was even wider.

The result was a wobbly coil-built soft ice cream bowl shape. I got the same result with the second try. On the third attempt, part of the coiled-bowl collapsed onto the rigid bare wrist attached to the hand that was garotting the cone and my confidence followed it into the disposal bin. With image no longer a concern, I nervously piled blobs of the stuff into each cone.

"I wouldn't do that if I were you!" came a shout, from behind me. I turned to see my customer stooped and peering through the screen that separated us. "No! No! Don't do that! Look at the gauge!" The gauge needle was deep into the red zone. "You'd better stop that *right now* or you're gonna be in *big* trouble soon!" came the repeated loud warning.

I turned to face the audacious voice. He had raised the screen and poked his head inside between the vertical tracks holding the screen that raised and lowered like a guillotine. I followed his glare to my sister Annie who was standing on a stool behind the machine pouring another gallon of cream into the hopper.

The machine growled, rumbled and started to tremble. The sound quickly changed to the freight train sound everyone interviewed after a tornado describes, and the Dairy Maid hopped up and down like a Mack truck doing jumping-jacks. As we all watched in awe, it extruded a steady, pulsing, rectangular column of ice-cream, the dimensions of the hopper, straight up toward the ceiling. Those people were right. It does sound like a freight train.

The unsupported white column collapsed to the floor with the clattering cover, and a second column formed and grew.

"Hit the cut-off switch!" bellowed the voice behind me. "Hit the cut-off switch!" Annie and I, transfixed and confused by the spectacle, looked up at the second growing block of ice-cream like we were watching a spectacular display of fireworks. We didn't move.

The side door burst open, the man leapt at the machine hitting buttons on the control panel and turning valves as the second block splattered to the floor. The machine shuddered to a stop and fell silent as though the stranger had delivered a karate-chop knockout blow.

As embarrassed members of my family stumbled out of the wings with mops, buckets, shovels and other paraphernalia, I contributed my droplets of sweat to the mess. The accommodating stranger took charge of the clean-up with the authority of a Chief Bosun's Mate. When we were back to emergency-room standards, he smiled and introduced himself as Mark Richfield, neighbor and competitor.

"Competitor?" I asked as we shook slippery hands, "As, like, you run one of these places?"

"Yep."

"I haven't seen another short-order place between here and Cleveland," I said.

"Exactly. My place is on the east side of Cleveland, but I tried to get this piece for my second Dairy Queen franchise. Would'a been convenient. I live right down here." He pointed toward the end of the short side street we were on. "Your bid got the land, I got the envy."

He called cheerfully to his wife, Wilma, who was watching the proceedings through the screen. She came in and I learned in the congenial introduction that she rotated as manager of their east-side Dairy Queen and they had come to my place to get the provisions for their son's birthday party, which was already in progress at their home, a few doors down.

On my insistence, Wilma rounded up the young excited

revelers and seated them at the umbrella tables out front. This party was on me. Mark and Wilma donned white coats and I watched him repeatedly and flawlessly demonstrate the roll-around-the-rim technique. Each cone came in at *exactly* the critical three ounces on the small delicate scale.

Wilma satisfied the people in line and still managed to take out relays of trays to the squirmy tadpoles at the tables who ate the ice cream concoctions as if they were in a contest.

Apparently, I still hadn't used up all my chips with my guardian angels. For most of the following week, the Richfields and I collaborated to put the place in order and my neighborly mentors gave me a crash course in management essentials. Although I still hadn't mastered their level of dexterity, by the end of the week I could do a commendable job of the roll-around-the-rim trick.

By late fall Wilma had assumed the role as my co-manager on an hourly basis. Each morning she drove her son to school and successfully managed the drive-in with a stand-by staff of locals, while I completed my own academic commitment. My school had installed a line of coin-operated food-dispensing machines in the corridors to replace the defunct Jamie's Lunch Wagon. No big loss. I'd hitched my new wagon to a bigger, brighter, shooting star.

One morning, I was paged at the school with the urgent message to call the drive-in immediately. A very excited Wilma at the other end of the line was almost incoherent. Before I drove out, I calmed her down enough to learn that although we were accustomed to beverage trucks rumbling back to the barn at all hours of the day and night, this morning, shortly after a caravan of three trucks had backed up to the barn, all hell broke loose. Federal agents, local police, and God knows who else, had converged on the trucks, wrestled the drivers and their helpers to the ground in handcuffs and invaded the drive-in with drawn guns. She handed the phone to the local police chief who said simply, "Mr. LaBianca, you'd better get down here as fast as you can." Prior to this, whenever we bumped into each other, he'd always called me Jamie.

By the time I got out there, the place looked like a Billy Eckstine concert in progress. I had to park behind the hardware store, walk across the highway, and wade through the milling mix of lawmen of every description and gawking onlookers. Inside the drive-in, a pale Wilma introduced me to a team of federal agents who immediately started a bombardment of perplexing questions in such rapid-fire order that in my bewilderment, I had no time to gather my thoughts to answer. As the questions turned to threats, I was able to convince them that I had nothing to do with what they kept referring to as "the contraband, the incriminating evidence they needed," and my relationship with Vincent Grosso and the barn was strictly that of landlord-tenant. I didn't bother him; he paid his rent and didn't bother me.

They served me with a sheaf of legal-looking, court order documents, another round of threats, and with a finger thumping into my chest, reminded me that I would be called as a material witness. They then filed out to join the hyperactive forces at the barn.

As I looked up from the perplexing documents I held in my trembling hand, Wilma, with tears running down her cheeks, turned to Chief Bartel and said, "Can't you do something to help here?"

"I'm very sorry, Jamie," said the local police chief. "I don't think you had anything to do with all this, but I do have to enforce the law. You have until noon on the twenty-first to evacuate this building. The locks will be changed, and after that you will be arrested for trespassing or breaking and entering if..." He walked to the door, turned and said, "I'm really sorry, Jamie. Better get yourself a good lawyer. Right away."

"Goddam you, Vinnie! You son-of-a-bitch! How could you do this to me!" Although I uttered no sounds as I walked out onto the side road, my violent deaf-mute gestures expressed my inner feelings clearly.

After I caught my breath and collected my scattered thoughts, I concluded from life-long experiences with Vinnie that he had not perpetrated this latest outrage with evil intent. He probably deluded himself, once again, with his over-blown sense of confidence and invincibility. Without malice aforethought, Vinnie, the alchemist, had transformed my pot of gold at the end of the rainbow into a chamber pot.

My father made a flurry of frantic phone calls to arrange an emergency meeting with Frankie the Foot's brother Michael, the neighborhood ombudsman who had gone over all of the papers my father had delivered to him that afternoon.

Michael had marshalled all of the legal forces at his disposal, including his brother the judge, and was now ready to report his findings. My father and I sat on the other side of his large desk crowding the basement rec-room which was serving as a temporary office until he received his impending law degree. A quaint-looking needlepoint sign on the wall behind his chair read, "Blessed Are The Troublemakers."

"OK," said Michael, after the proper exchange of niceties, "here's the poop. I got good news and bad news. No choice. You get the bad news first. This is a great case for me to cut my teeth on! Perfect!" He rubbed his hands together and added,

"Still pro bono, of course, but some lawyer's would pay to get this case. Very unusual circumstances. Every level of law enforcement is involved. The Feds, the Locals, jeeze, anybody in-between that's wearing a badge is in on this. I can't believe —"

"Michael," I interrupted, with my chest muscles tightening, "do I still own a drive-in? Am I going to jail? What the hell is going on? Please get to the point."

"No! No! Wait! You gotta hear this! No, you're not goin' to jail. But get a load of this. Your buddy Vinnie is somethin' else. He beat the homicide rap but gets hit with a wrongful death suit by the guy's family and loses. Ah'right? Now, all this time he's running a kick-back racket down at the bar and grill...what the hell's the name of his place?"

He started to shuffle through papers. My father put a match to his pipe, puffed twice and tapped the pipe embers into an ashtray when he realized how quickly the cramped room was filling with smoke.

"What...the...hell...is...it...called?" muttered Mike.

"The Silver Lira," I said.

"Yeah. That's it. The Silver Lira. Anyway...where was I? Oh, yeah. Vinnie has a kickback scheme cookin' with his booze truck drivers. The distributors stole truckloads from the warehouse suppliers, sold the booze at the...the Golden —"

"Silver Lira," I reminded him.

"Right. I don't know why the hell I'm blockin' that damn place. Anyway, they launder the money there. Then, a disgruntled driver turns informer, goes to the Feds, and spills the beans. The Internal Revenue Service, the guys who got Al Capone on the same charge, stake out *your* barn, where the contraband is stored, and just as they've got an airtight case and are moving in for the kill, the wrongful death decision is leaked and all of the affected parties go nuts. But the bank moves in like a banshee, ahead of the others, leaving the rest of the vultures a step behind, waving papers in court for their piece of the road-kill. They'll be battling in court for years, but this time the bank wins this free-for-all."

"So, I'm dead. I lost my drive-in for sure."

"Yeah, Jamie. I'm afraid that part is true. This has nothin' to do with the barn. That's a whole separate federal IRS tax-evasion problem and the most serious one for your pal Vinnie. I wouldn't wanna be in his shoes about now. No doubt about it. He's going to jail. He's broke, the dead guy's family owns the, the...friggin' Golden Bar and Grill and the bank owns your drive-in because you collateralized Vinnie's bad loan. What a kick in the ass, Jamie...your place will go up on the auction block because, although the odds of this happening were pretty remote, who would'a guessed all this other shit was going on."

"And the good news is...I'm not goin' to jail. That's the good news you've been saving for last?" I asked, as I roughly squeezed the fingers of one hand with the other.

"Mr. LaBianca. You wanna tell him this part?"

Papa was putting a match to his pipe, raised his pinkie finger to point to Michael, and continued the pipe sucking without responding.

"Well," said Michael, "I'm not taking any credit here at all. This is all your father. When he brought me the original deeds for the L-shaped lot, he noticed Lot Number Two was in *Mrs.* Borge's name, not the old man. So, at your father's suggestion, we offered only Lot Number One to the bank for collateral, and they bought it."

"Holy shit!" I said, as I leapt up, "Are you kidding me? I still own Lot Number Two?"

"Yep. And it gets better. Mrs. Borge had been negotiating to long-lease the lot to the post office. Your father acted as your surrogate counselor and...and...ta-rrr-aaa..." he said, with a musical flourish, "...we-have-a-long-term...*commitment*!"

We were all standing and stomping our feet in the smoky room, exchanging wide grins, handshakes, and back slaps.

"Long after that drive-in becomes a pawn shop, the post office will be paying you a cost-of-living adjusted rental fee...you'll be doing better than if you'd hung on to the drive-in...unless the U.S. Government goes under. Jamie, you may not know how to pick your friends, but you sure as hell did pick the right family. And, exactly the right father!"

On the giddy ride home, I lay my weary head against the seat back. Exhilarated Papa drove as he recited an Italian proverb in his dialect.

"What does that mean?"

"It means..." he said between puffs on his pipe, "...you can pick your friends...and you can pick your nose...but you can't pick your friend's nose."

When the laughing subsided I asked, "I know that's pretty profound stuff, but where did that come from, exactly?"

In his Italian dialect, again between puffs, he responded, "What am I...an ear...nose...and throat specialist?"

Chapter XXIII

I entered my studio through the back door. The note attached to the pull-chain on my overhead fluorescent lamp read: *Jamie — see me as soon as you get home — URGENT!!!*

The relentless IRS attack on Vinnie for tax evasion had intensified, and Mike DaFutte, who represented him pro bono, had intimated that this mess no longer involved just back taxes and monumental fines. The note implied there had been a serious development.

Mike's office, on Clark, was in a store front that Vinnie and I had helped convert to a light, airy, respectable looking law office. Walls of books, the whole thing. He wanted this office, here, on Clark, he said, because he needed more ombudsman experience in the neighborhood trenches before he accepted the secure position offered to him by the prestigious downtown law firm of Dayton, Dayton, and Haynes. The prospective career move had been discreetly arranged by his brother, the Honorable Francis A. DaFutte, a.k.a. Frankie the Foot, whose foot was about to cross the threshold into the pious chambers of the Supreme Court of the state of Ohio.

I sub-leased the back room from Mike to help defray the cost of our shared transitional domiciles. The arrangement worked out just fine. A plasterboard wall separated my apartment/studio from Mike's office. In addition to having the only toilet in the place, I had a shower, a washtub, a refrigerator, and a hot plate, on my side of the wall. My windowless room was three times the size of the law office, had a rear exit door to the parking area, and enough fluorescent lights hanging from the exposed rafters to give anybody a solid body tan if they turned on all the lights at once and walked around naked for fifteen minutes. A burn or freckles if you were fair skinned.

When his father died and their house was sold, Vinnie was suddenly homeless. We brought in a second small bed into my living quarters for Vinnie, and improvised a temporary separation between us with a clothes line and blankets. Cardboard boxes of personal items, once scrupulously separated into assigned areas, tended to get lost when Vinnie's father's unmarked boxes were added to the inventory.

I cautiously opened the door to Mike's office and heard Mike saying to someone, "...yes, I understand, but I believe there's more to it —" I closed the door carefully and retreated quietly into my workspace.

I allowed some time to elapse, carefully opened the door a crack and listened. I realized Mike was on the phone, not sitting with a client. When I poked my head in, he frantically motioned for me to enter.

He stood up, cradled the phone between his shoulder and his ear to free his hands, and scribbled one large word on the legal pad on his desk: IMMIGRATION. He held up the pad for me to read, grimaced, and pointed to the phone pressed against his ear. His eyes rolled toward the ceiling.

Mike was listening intently, but occasionally he broke the silence with "Yes, sir. No, sir." and finally, "Thank you, sir, I will do that." He hung up, yanked open the top desk drawer, and started thumbing through his little black book. He stopped and turned to me.

264

"Jamie...listen...I'll be with you in a minute. That was the INS, the immigration people. They're gonna deport him! Holy-jumpin'-Jesus! I can't believe this! I-simply-do-*not* believe this...Holy jumpin' Jesus!"

I stared at Mike as he fidgeted at his desk, opening drawers and slamming them shut. He put the phone to his ear and started to dial.

"They're gonna deport who, Mike?"

He held up a finger to silence me and said into the phone, "This is Mike DaFutte, may I speak with Mr. Haynes, please." Then, after listening for a short interval, he added, "Would you have him call me as soon as he comes in. Tell him it's urgent. Thank you, Laura." After he hung up, he hissed through gritted teeth, "Son-of-a-*bitch.*"

"They're gonna deport who, Mike?"

"Vinnie. They're gonna deport Vinnie." He leapt up, raced past me to the shelves of uniform looking law books, and carried one to his desk.

"Mike. Am I hearing you right? Deport? How the hell can they deport Vinnie? Legally? And to where?" This was worse than getting a breezy report from a surgeon, leaving an operating room, that starts out, "It's bad folks, but I'm in a rush —"

He slammed the book shut and as he returned it to the shelf, he said, "Italy. Back to Italy. Jamie, have a seat."

He led me to the conference side of his office and I settled into one of the six low-slung, upholstered, contemporary Danish chairs that surrounded the large glass-topped coffee table. Mike handed me a cup of coffee and sat down in the chair opposite me.

"Jamie," said Mike, as he swiped the beads of sweat that had collected above his upper lip, "you grew up with Vinnie, know him about as well as anybody can, like a brother, almost. Even though he inadvertently got your ass in a sling, you still forgive him like a brother would, right?" He kept his eyes focused on me as he sipped his coffee. The cafe curtains and potted palms concealed us from the sidewalk traffic, but I cautiously looked over my shoulders before I answered.

"I know that preamble, Mike, and you look like a mortician about to console the bereaved family. What in the name of hell is goin' on here?"

Mike crossed his outstretched legs at the ankles, and rested the lower heel on the edge of the glass table. Without putting down his cup, he tossed the folded morning paper across the table. There it was, that damn file photo of Vinnie pulling his coat over his head as he was led to the paddy wagon. And, behind him, my Model T stood in its full glory.

"These reporters know more secrets about Vinnie than you do. Vinnie and I talked and he wanted me to discuss this with you before you read about it in the paper." Mike unconsciously ran his eyes along the full length of the cafe curtains strung on the shiny brass bar, put his cup down, leaned toward me with his elbows on his knees, and locked his fingers.

"Vinnie Grosso came to our neighborhood when he was 20 months old. He almost had another brother. The miscarriage killed his mother. His older brother was running another bar in Florida and was killed in what looked suspiciously like a mob execution. Now his father dies of prostate cancer and, although Vinnie and his father were never very close, he was his only living relative. Vinnie is now totally alone and his moving in with us is a start, but this is a very bad time for him. He may look like he's laughing on the outside, but he's hurtin' like hell on the inside."

He drained the last of the coffee from his cup, set it down on the table, then stared into the bottom of the cup, like he was reading tea leaves.

"Before his father died," he continued, "I formed an irrevocable trust so we could pay off the small mortgage after the sale of the house and lock Vinnie's small inheritance where the IRS can't get to it." He paused, followed the shadow of a passerby walking on the other side of the curtain and tapped his lips with his locked thumbs.

"Vinnie Grosso was born in Italy."

I threw back my head and laughed. When I looked back at Mike, his expression hadn't changed.

"Mike...what the hell are you talking about? Is this some...kinda —" Mike didn't stir. "You're not shittin' me are you?" He shook his head. I got up and walked across the room to the needlepoint "Blessed Are the Trouble Makers" sign and the American flag propped up behind his desk.

"Wait a minute, Mike, wait a minute. How the hell can this be? He was in the Marines, for Christ sake."

"An alien who has come to stay, while he resides in this country, is subject to the laws of this country and not to those of his own country, and may be conscripted —"

"...his father was a citizen," I interrupted.

"Never naturalized. Come back here. This really gets unbelievable. You ain't heard nothin' yet." He threw his arms straight up like he was stretching and broke into a big grin. "Any celebrated defense lawyer in the country, maybe the world, would kill to have this case, and...*bam*! It falls into *my* lap. It's gonna catapult me into the major league...or, I'm gonna end up with a long, year-'round wool coat on a downtown street corner with a cup full of yellow pencils in my hand."

I sat down at the coffee table again. Everything below my eyebrows puckered as I rubbed my shiny forehead with my rigid middle finger. "You're tellin' me this gets worse?"

"Jamie, every friggin' law enforcement agency in the country is gonna be in on this before we're done...maybe even the recruits at the Police Academy." He threw up his arms again and said, "And it's *mine! All mine!* Get a load of this. Vinnie...Jesus, I can't even believe this myself. Vinnie rents private rooms above the family restaurant once in a while to the Chicago Giancana outfit and they meet up there with the New York Gambino bunch to get their story straight before they all go down to an occasional Youngstown summit. Everything's normal. Undercover cops are in place as waiters at the feasts. Vinnie collects his rent. Doesn't wanna know from nothin'. Nobody bothers nobody. Then Vinnie, with his obsession for female parts, puts a one-way mirror on the medicine cabinet in the ladies room, complete with camera and —"

He stood up, turned the "closed" sign toward the street, locked the door and motioned me through the door that led to my quarters. He turned on the light in the "kitchen" and led the way to my studio.

As we walked through the rubble we referred to as our living quarters into my immaculate studio, Mike stopped short. Nobody crossed over into my studio area without permission. Nobody. He stopped and turned to me.

"Je...per...per...how the hell do you ask for permission to do something in Italian?"

"E permesso," I said.

"Right!" he pointed to my work table and with a gesture of supplication asked, "E permesso?"

"Prego."

We pulled stools up to my worktable without turning on any of the studio lights and Mike got serious.

"Jamie, this is...what's Italian for absolute silence?...Oh, screw it. This information is protected by lawyer-client privilege. Me and Vinnie are safe. They can't touch me and can't make him incriminate himself. But...they *can* subpoena you. *You* can get into deep doo-doo. Under oath, you either tell 'em what I'm about to tell you, or, you run the risk of a charge of perjury. Then they'll put the squeeze on you to get to him. Vinnie wants you to know what's going on. OK? Your choice. You wanna know, or not?"

"What about my family. They gonna be OK?"

"We've got that all covered. The city replaced the rotten galvanized pipe feeding water to Mrs. Lazzarone's house from the main line in the street and tried to bamboozle her into paying for the repair. Their responsibility. I took care of it. In return, when the federal agents canvass the neighborhood she's gonna see to it that the feud between you and your family is still going on. You haven't seen them for years. She won't be as efficient as when she had her party-line phone, but she'll get the job done. She loves being included in a conspiracy."

"Mike...that lady is a little nuts, you —"

"Trust me. They won't bother your family. Now...where was I...OK, they tore apart Vinnie's house before we sold it, and since we're all under surveillance, we lead them on a wild-goose chase once in a while by strolling through the locker room at the bus terminal. By the way, my phone's probably tapped, so any private calls are made from Miller's drug store. Since Vinnie's living with us now, my sources tell me this place gets hit next. I'll know when."

"Jesus, Mike. This is scary. What are they looking for?"

"Once I tell you, Jamie, you're in it up to your neck. Incidentally, for good measure, Vinnie could be on the mob's shit list, too. Maybe not. You sure you wanna know?"

"Vinnie may not be a real brother to me, but at least a first cousin by now. Family, as Mamma said to us a million times, *onore della famiglia.* Don't dishonor the family. Yeah, Mike. If Vinnie's goin' down, I'm goin' down with him."

He shook my hand and said, "OK. Now, lemme see, where the hell was I?"

"The women and the one-way mirror."

"Right. OK. Let's see. Oh, yeah. So now he's getting his jollies by taking pictures of ladies with their pants down. But that ain't enough. He gets one of those audio 'Electronic Memory' things, wire something or other. What the hell are those things called —"

"We had the account at the agency where I worked. It's a Webcor Recorder. Ran a fine wire, about the thickness of a fat human hair, from reel to reel. Or, as they preferred to say at the agency, 'spool to spool'."

"Right. Anyway, things are goin' really nice. So Chicago and New York are having one of their big pow-wows up there and the two big Capos' want to talk top-secret stuff but they're not talking in the big room because it might be bugged. Same with the men's room. So what do these two super sophisticated, cautious, powerhouses do? They're gonna outsmart everybody by duckin'...now get this...*into-the-ladies-room*! Come-into-my-parlor-said-the-spider-to-the-fly! Heh-heh-heh! Son-of-a-bitch! Can you believe this?"

"Holy shit! And Vinnie's got this all recorded?" I said, as I stood up, with my hands cupping my ears.

"Not only that," said Mike, "the son-of-a-bitch has some

photographs of the two biggest mobsters, from the two biggest families, from the two biggest cities, forming an alliance in one of the smallest crappers in the country...and he's right there, *right there*, to get it all!"

"You know," I said, when we stopped howling, "this really would be really, really funny if it wasn't so goddam serious and scary. But, for top o' the line, leave it to Vinnie!"

"Jamie, let me tell ya something. As a cop, I ran into some real corkers —" He started to laugh hysterically again, and so did I. "...some real fuckin' corkers in my time...but... this...Vinnie...takes the cake!" He collapsed onto the stool convulsed with laughter. When he collected himself, he said, "But, you know what? I love 'im. I just *love* this guy. If you don't take him as a brother, *I'm* gonna."

He went on to describe how Vinnie, in the space behind the one-way mirror, made himself 2X2 contact prints with a home developing kit and had bare-ass pictures of most of the women in Cleveland, including wives of big time politicians and cops who met the syndicate paymasters there for their fat envelopes. When the shit hit the IRS fan, they raided and searched everything remotely connected with Vinnie, and although Vinnie had hidden all the stuff, except the critical wire, in a defunct sewer drain, they found it. "I can tell you from experience," said Mike, "they almost always do."

"Anyway, that's when they found the Mafia rogues gallery shots. Right there, amongst all the other bare assholes. The floor of the crapper was being mopped when the big bosses decided they wanted to go in. So, before the two Capos' yanked the charlady out, she spreads newspapers on the floor so the powerhouses won't slip. Nice considerate touch. And they give her a nice considerate tip."

Vinnie's snapshots, Mike continued, which brought the FBI into the case, showed the talking heads having a tete-a-tete standing on a newspaper headline that firmly established the time and place of the meeting. Unfortunately, some of the shots also showed the wire recorder in the foreground, on this side of the mirror, and it's this captured conspiratorial conversation that the FBI desperately needs to smash these powerful underworld families. Without the crucial recordings, they couldn't go before the Select Committee on Intelligence with a bullet-proof case. Anyway, Mike said, with the wire recordings as his ace, he'd been negotiating with Immigration and the FBI, but the best *quid pro quo* they were offering was the Federal Witness Protection Program.

As Mike was finishing his story, someone banged on the back door. I got up, stumbled to the riveted steel door, paused with my hand on the knob until I got Mike's nod, then cautiously let Vinnie and two bulging brown paper sacks of groceries in. I locked up behind him and turned on the fluorescent sun. The cross light accentuated the stress lines forming on Vinnie's face. The bags under his eyes and the creases coming down past his mouth made him look tired, and older. He put the real food away and spread the packaged junk on the hollow-core door we used for a dining table.

"You guys want coffee with the donuts?" asked Vinnie.

"Just one more cup," I said, "and you can call me Mr. Coffee Nerves, like I'm not nervous enough, suddenly."

Vinnie looked at me, then at Mike, then at me again.

"Oh, you know the whole story?"

"Yes, I know the whole story, you dumb shit, and I'm not surprised. I knew from the time you used to watch Eleanor undress every night when we were kids, that your peep'n-tom obsession was goin' to get you into hot water. As far as the other part of the story is concerned, I always suspected you were an alien, but I thought you were from Mars, not Italy."

"Same thing," said Mike, "I...whoops!...there goes my phone. Settle down...settle down. If it's more trouble....Shit, how can there be more trouble?" Mike stepped into his office and closed the door behind him.

"Speaking of phones," said Vinnie, "did you notice there's a guy repairing the phone on the pole out there for three days running now? A Rolodex mind with only one card. Are these guys subtle, or what?"

He compacted the two grocery bags and pitched them like basketballs into the cardboard trash box, raised his arms in a sign of victory, and went to the toilet.

"Incidentally," he said, as he stepped back out, "it occurred to me just now. One guy's getting deported, one guy graduates with honors from the art school and ends up painting pictures two doors away from where Daisy painted her lamp shades, and the third guy graduates with honors from a big time law school and ends up in a storefront. If you ask me, none of us is doin' very good."

"I can't speak for Mike," I said, rocking on the back legs of the spindle-back chair, "but as for me, I'm obviously getting closer all the time to my lifetime goal. Two more moves toward Thirty-Third Street and I start painting lamp shades 'to order, while you wait.'"

Mike came back in and said excitedly, "It's comin' within 24 hours. Brace yourselves. If the Keystone Cops hit during the night when I'm not here, call me. Don't tell them anything, and don't resist. And let's start makin' promises to St. Francis, Father Gatto, and God."

"Mike," I said, "one of the bastards is on a pole out there, they may hit at any minute —" I held out my arms like I was stopping traffic. "I know what to do...I know what to do. Give me the goddam wire. *Quick!*"

"Jamie —"

Vinnie's swearing, when he was in your presence, was contagious. Even I caught the bug.

"Shut the fuck up!" I snapped, "I'm not just standing around with my finger up my nose yelling '*CAR!*' Give me the goddam wire and go up front. Lemme handle this."

Mike came back from the front with a plastic-wrapped small package flecked with potting soil. "Jamie, you gotta let us in on this. What the hell—"

"Goddam it, Mike! Anything I come up with is better than the roots of the potted palms. As a former cop you should know it's the first place they'll look. Yeah, sure, you had this buried *deep.* Remember, my ass is also on the line here. Now, get outta here. Both of you. Nobody but me is gonna know where this gets buried until after they're gone. I don't want three sets of eyes giving them unconscious clues."

When the deed was done, we sat around the coffee table up front and they both pressed for a hint.

"Mike," I said, "when we were kids hangin' around the corner, your brother Frankie taught us a thing or two. I'm not about to use his famous cigarette ash contest, or any of his other great magic tricks, but I'm thinking the same way. I ask myself...'now...what would Frankie the Foot do in a situation like this?' And it comes to me! I'm not gonna tell you how, yet, but I will tell you this much, I'm gonna kick their asses and they're gonna thank me for it."

That night, after Mike had gone home to his apartment,

Vinnie took down the blankets between our beds and we talked.

"You know, Jamie, if I hadn't been there when you kicked the shit out of Cookie Occarro...*and he thanked you*, I'd be shittin' in my pants about now. But, I have confidence, I trust you...and Mike. And Mike. I wouldn't say this to anybody else, but ever since my father died, something snapped in me. I feel...I don't feel like invincible Vinnie any more. Actually, I'm scared shitless. Jamie, what the hell am I gonna do in Italy if they boot me out? Huh? The sons-o'-bitches! I ruin my life in the Marines for them, an' this is how they show their gratitude? No, goddam it. I'm goin' for broke. I want the money they'd give me in the Witness Protection deal as a pension. I want full citizenship, a social-security card, and for what they did to me in the Marines, maybe burial at Arlington cemetery, with you next to me...whether you're dead or not."

"Better yet," I said, "with the whole world snapping at your heels, why don'cha become the unknown soldier? OK. Enough of this bullshit, Vinnie, let me ask you something. You think the mob...by the way...what the hell was going through your head that made you rent those rooms to these hoodlums who give all Italians a bad name?"

"All that bullshit started with my brother Buddy, not me," said Vinnie, defensively.

"Anyway, you think the mob isn't gonna put two and two together when the wire shows up at the Senate Select Organized Crime Hearings, and they see you buzzin' around town, living like a king, after all the newspaper talk about invincible Vinnie Grosso getting the boot?"

Vinnie let his head drop back and studied the exposed scissor-truss rafter directly above him like something interesting was going on up there. He took a deep breath and as he brought his head forward, he exhaled a low sustained sigh that ended with a whistle.

"Me and Mike have gone over that already," he said. "There were undercover cops at those meetings serving as waiters. Everybody there suspected that. *They* coulda made the recordings and the pictures. Me? Let them deport me for show. Lots of coverage. I'll marry an American girl as a pensioned, retired, federal employee, and I'm clear. So...you're not gonna tell me where the wire is?"

"Vinnie, let me ask you something. When did we learn how Frankie the Foot's scams worked?"

"When they were over."

"Exactly. And for a good reason. Fewer people, fewer slip-ups. You know, I went through this deja vu once before in my life. Remember the big raid? Almost exactly like this. Complete with the Model T parked outside. Exactly like this. We beat the bastards then, we'll beat 'em again. Hey, if we can beat Lincoln and West High and Cookie Occarro, this is gonna be a piece of cake. I'm not tuckin' you in with a bedtime story outta Mamma's fable book, but, trust me. It's gonna work out. I hope you have nice dreams."

"You know what, Jamie? For the first time in a long time, I just might." He rolled over with his back to me, "I...just...might."

They hit at 4:00 am. By the time Mike got there, the INS, the FBI, the U.S. Department of Justice strike force, and swarms of other guys wearing navy-blue baseball caps and jackets marked "U.S. Marshall" had poured into the place. Three men sat us down in widely separated chairs to prevent collusion. Considering the situation, they were surprisingly civil and polite during the interrogation process.

The rest were going through everything. Everything! There

were ladders propped against the overhead trusses, while others examined the cement-block wall, carefully, for tell-tale signs of fresh mortar. The bastards even tore out the bottom side of our hollow-core kitchen table. They waited until sunrise to go through the Model T. The shouting, the din, and the smell of tense, sweaty, bodies was like a locker room after a victorious championship game. At exactly 8:37 p.m. that night, the last blue uniform was gone.

The place looked like a tornado had passed through a mobile-home park and then backed up for a second pass because it had overlooked something. Vinnie was collapsed on one bed, Mike was on the other with his arm draped across his eyes. I was buoyant and brewing coffee.

"You guys want coffee with your stale donuts?"

"It's finally over," said Mike, "thank God Almighty, it's over. They won't be back. That's it. We won!" He leaped to the floor and yelled, "We won, goddam it! We won!" Vinnie propped himself up on his elbows to enjoy the jubilation.

"Jamie," he said, "now I know how Carnera felt when he beat the piss outta Sharkey. By the way, I really don't give a shit, but the only thing missing here was a thank you from the bastards. Otherwise, you kicked the shit outta Cookie Occarro all over again, goddamit!" By now, Vinnie and Mike were waltzing around the room between the piles of snarled-up clothes and tipped-over cardboard boxes. *Daisy, Daisy, give me your answer do / I'm half crazy —*"

"So, now what, Mike?" I asked, as I cleared what was left of our violated table and put out the coffee cups, donuts, and bags of greasy crunchies that had escaped the raiders' wrath.

"Well, now the *real* fun starts. We're free and clear. No more threats, no more harassments. They'll come begging, now, on *our* terms. The hearings are coming up. They're runnin' out of time. Vinnie, you can ask for anything you want...anything. You'll get it. I'll do the negotiating. Now, Jamie, how 'bout it? You gonna tell us?"

"Sure. But not here. This place is probably bugged by now. Don't ever bring up the subject again in here. Ever. Let's go get a hoagie or somethin' at Gagliotti's."

As we walked down the darkened street, Vinnie tapped Mike on the arm and pointed to a store and sang, "'Daisy, Daisy, give me your answer, do —' When he gets good enough, this is where Jamie's gonna paint lamp shades."

"That's right. And on every one, I'm gonna paint 'Blessed are the trouble makers' over a picture of Vinnie Grosso."

We got to Gagliotti's, the only storefront with lights on at this time of night, entered the empty shop, and slid into the corner booth furthest from the kitchen. From this vantage point, we could survey the entire customer area.

"The usual?" asked our cheerful waitress.

"Yeah, Palma, but for a change, can you serve us on clean plates," I said, to supply the tweak she had come to expect.

"Hey," she said, with her good-sport smile, "if you want it like home...eat at home." She reached the kitchen door, turned, and flashed her smile again.

"Don't raise your voice," I cautioned, as we sat in the booth waiting for our hoagies. "For Christ's sake, let's not blow this thing at this stage."

"Jamie," said Vinnie, trying to contain himself, "you-are-truly-a-fuckin'-genius."

"Here, here," said Mike, as he raised the salt-shaker in a toast, "how the hell do you say, 'bigga victory' in Italian?"

I raised my fist and said, *"Veni, vidi, vici."*

278

"You know," said Mike, "At one point, before they came, I was pushin' to find out where the hell you could possibly hide that reel and you said you were gonna hand it to them, and they were gonna hand it back and thank you. That's when I really started to get...how do you say *nervous* in Italian?"

"Shitta inna da pantsa," said Vinnie.

I motioned them into a tight huddle with our heads almost touching over the narrow booth table that separated us.

"Your brother Frankie," I said quietly, "once told us something on the street corner that stayed with me. *The best place to hide something is out in the open.*' I never knew what he meant by that. I thought about it a long, long time when I went to bed as a kid. Then last night, I see Vinnie's father's fishing rods propped up in the corner and it comes to me. Bam! That's it! That's it! Son-of-a-bitch! That's it! Thank you Frankie! Thank you! So I take the wire from the Webcor spool and wind it onto the fishing reel, tie a nice feathery lure on the end of it, and put the rod back in the corner with the other two. The wire line that used to be on the reel is now a tangled mess in your father's fishing box."

"The fuckin' fishing reel! Three banged-up fishing poles propped up in the corner with all the rest of my father's junk. Right out there in the open! Jamie LaBianca, I could kiss your ass! Ass, yes. Lips, no. You're the one that deserves a bunch o' trophies in the showcase at Tech. Gee-Gee was right. It's times like this I wish my name was LaBianca. You sure you're not related to Tony?"

He and I laughed and filled Mike in on our inside joke as the waitress put the bulging hoagies before us.

"And...and...I'll be goddamed if he didn't do it again!" said Vinnie, as the waitress walked through the swinging doors into the kitchen. "I was right there to see it happen with my own eyes an' ears." He was flushed and rocking back and forth.

"See what?" asked Mike, as he tucked a dangling piece of cappacola ham back into his mouth.

"I was right there when Jamie hands the rod and reel to the agent who put the handle through the portable fluoroscope, the same kind we had at shoe stores when we were kids. Remember? The guy hands the rod back to Jamie and...so help me Christ...he *thanks* him! Jamie just made a goddam fool o' the guy, kicked his ass, really, an' the son-of-a-bitch *thanks* him! He-fuckin'-*thanks*-this guy!" He pounded the table and buried his head, laughing, into his folded arms.

The waitress brought the second round of dripping hoagies and cokes and when she was gone, Vinnie's revved-up emotions collapsed and suddenly shifted to sober-somber.

"You know," he said, rotating the bottom of the coke bottle against the table top with his fingers, "I don't remember my father ever doin' a goddam thing for me. Ever. But now, when the chips are really down, and my very life is at stake, he comes through...and together with Jamie here, the...two of 'em..." he choked on the emotion, lips quivering, "the two of 'em get together...an' let's not forget Frankie the Foot, here...they all get together...and save...my fuckin'...." He started to cry.

Then I did. Then Mikey.

Chapter XXIV

The only newspaper carrying the Vinnie Grosso deportation story was the Parma Heights Bulletin. Almost everyone else, by now, had lost interest. The major Cleveland papers had tried to milk the last few drops out of what had unexpectedly become a bonanza, by dredging up the manslaughter charge yet one more time.

The attempt was accompanied by the pivotal "beer bottle and bat" photograph with caps that read: "Death or Deportation, You Be the Judge". This last-gasp attempt didn't generate one single outraged "send 'em back where they came from" letter to the editor. The reverse human interest approach with neighbors proclaiming, "he was always such a nice, courteous boy," met with the same flabby response and the story slid off the back pages onto the presses of the suburban weeklies.

Mike's legal strategy was to keep the story alive as long as possible to impress everyone in Chicago and New York who needed impressing, that Vinnie Grosso, who had secretly gotten everything he wanted from the Feds, had nothing to do with the crucial wire-tape recording now being studied by Kefauver's Senate Crime Investigation Committee in Washington, D.C. and New York City.

"Jamie," said Mike, "looks like I'll be spending more and more time out of town, so if you'll do me a big favor, I'll put an extension phone in your studio and maybe you'll act as my secretary when you're puttering around here and I'm not. You don't have to wear a dress or lipstick."

Just before he stepped out into the glaring sunlit parking lot, on his way to another round of significant downtown meetings, he turned and added, "by the way, Missie, Vinnie will be sleeping at my place when I'm gone to keep an eye on things, so, we'll see how this musical beds arrangement works out."

When Vinnie, for the sake of convenience, became Mike's permanent room mate, Eddie "Brat" Bratenahl, my co-worker at the litho company moved into the vacated bed.

Brat and I had answered the same McCallister Lithograph Company "help wanted" ad when I was in my third year at the art school. He started as a full time point-of-purchase cardboard engineer apprentice and I was accepted as a part time illustrator and p.o.p. engineer.

We were of an age, both had an unexploited aptitude for solving cardboard packaging and display problems, and eagerly absorbed all of the technical skills we could from the in-house Grand Guru of the cardboard display world, with the unlikely name of Stanley Stemmer.

The three of us complemented each other and after graduation, I shucked all my other attempts at making money and joined their forces full time as a mongrel illustrator/engineer.

At one point, over my strenuous objections, Mr. Burchfield, the vice-president in charge of a large chewing gum manufacturer's account, ignored most of my best designs and made his presentation for a major campaign with selected tried-and-true, and in my opinion, dull, solutions for what could have been break-through designs.

Not only did the sales pitch bomb as I had predicted it would, we lost the account. Ultimately, we were called into conference by the president, who unleashed his fury while he paced the room. Most of the rebuke was directed at me, personally, because I was identified as chief designer in this project. After that, my relationship with the company authorities, especially with Mr. Burchfield, was strained.

I not only got mad, I got even. I had elegant business cards and stationery printed, called myself Daisy Display, in honor of Clark Avenue's distinguished lamp shade painter, sent out an impressive query letter to the same chewing gum manufacturer, and got an appointment.

I walked into the palatial downtown branch office and made an eye-opening sales promotion with the designs that had been rejected at McCallister's, and topped the boffo presentation with my *coup-de-grace*, an animated 10 X 12 snappily decorated poster of a smiling swimmer. It was designed to jiggle in the aisles of buses, subways, streetcars and supermarkets that used cross-current climate control.

My wide-eyed swimmer, hanging from a chandelier over the conference table, did her act better than I'd ever seen her perform before. The invisible air-conditioner currents rolled the eyes from side-to-side, rhythmically, in concert with the tongue which repeated the action over her sparkling teeth.

The grey-haired executive, who thought he'd seen it all, was fascinated, his pendulum eyes locked onto the swimmer's. He stood up slowly and muttered, "Well...I...will...be...damned."

He leaned into the office intercom, got seven or eight more gaping people, including two secretaries, to join the wonder, took it down several times to demonstrate the simplicity of the design, and shook my hand each time he introduced me to another of his fellow officers. "I want you to meet...." He studied my business card and continued, "...Mr. James V. LaBianca, who is successfully representing Daisy Display."

Getting the major account for Daisy Display transformed my life. My studio became "the land of the midnight sun" as the fluorescent lamps burned well into the wee hours, with Brat and me bent over the cutting table working frantically to meet the outlined deadline schedule.

Mike had cleared our big-time contract, accepted the accounting responsibilities for Daisy Display and like Brat, was hired on a percentage-of-the-profits basis.

Oddly, I felt a subtle sense of guilt because I won the account and my employer had lost it. But why? Hadn't I tried as hard as I could, as I had on many other occasions, to convince Mr. Burchfield he was headed for another disaster? And weren't my designs retrieved from his wastebasket *after* he lost the account? This was the St. Francis perpetual guilt program at work.

The following Monday, just before our lunch break, Mr. Burchfield called me to his office on the intercom. As I approached his door, Brat stepped out of his office, leaned over to my ear with a cupped hand and said quietly, "He knows the whole thing."

When I got back to the workroom, Brat and Stanley "Steamer," our mentor, were eating their machine-dispensed sandwiches with their feet propped up on the cutting table.

"Got the boot?"

"Nope," I said as I tore the plastic off of what looked like an old railroad-diner sandwich, the antithesis of a deli sandwich. Two slices of Wonder Bread enveloping a meat-color stain.

"*No-o-o-o?*" they chorused.

"Nope." I described how Mr. Burchfield had been warm and ingratiating. Even exposed the large gaps in his overbite when he attempted to smile. And, on top of that, he offered me the title of Production Manager with a ten-percent raise.

They looked at each other, then at me, and Steamer asked, "You? Production Manager of this place?"

"Nope. Manager of the main office design department in New York," I said, with a haughty look on my face.

"New York!" they harmonized.

"The dirty slimy bastard!" said Steamer. "Jamie, I've been around here long enough to know what's goin' on. You're the best designer we've ever had around here. Now, why would old butt-ass ship you off to New York? Why...? Because the others won't go along with firing you, that's why. Even with the bubble gum disaster he hung around your neck, you've brought in enough winners so they won't fire you. So what's he gonna do? He's gonna kick you upstairs or make life so miserable for you, you'll quit. The dirty, slimy bastard!"

That night, after our usual take-out deli dinner, Brat, Mike, Vinnie and I sat around our battered kitchen table in our "war room," eating fried crunchies with cokes as we carefully listed my options after the explosive events of the day.

"I'm with Yogi Berra," said Mike, "'when you come to a fork in the road, take it!' This could be an opportunity in disguise. Stick around to help Brat with the heavy lifting on the gumball job, then go up to the "Big Apple" and see if it's rotten to the core. It's not as if you're burning bridges behind you. Brat can handle Daisy and I'll take care of business and any renegotiating that might come up. With my New York contacts, I'll even find you a cheap apartment. If it doesn't work out, pack a couple o' cockroaches in a match box and come-on back. We'll have hot coffee and stale donuts waiting."

"I'm with Mike and Steamer," said Vinnie, "Obviously, Scrooge is pulling off the old switcheroo shell game. I've told you enough times, the whole friggin' world is one big fuckin' shell game. But so what? Long as you know it. If you don't make a move, you're about where you ought'a be. Make a move, you might go up the totem pole. It's not as if this is a crisis. Whatever happens, we four Mouseketeers stick together. Right?"

"What'a ya think, Brat?" I asked.

"Sounds good to me." As we shook hands, Brat added, "Let's win this one for the Gipper. Or is it Jipper?" He threw a salute that started with his thumb on his nose and said, "Give my regards to Broadway."

After all the arrangements had been made, there was one last consideration; transportation. I had walked several times to the car dealer on 25th Street, trying to convince myself I needed the breakthrough, true pillarless, hardtop convertible Ford Victoria, for my first long distance trip. I circled the car like a lecher and was tempted to go and plunk down the down payment but the list price of $1,925.00, as it had on all of my previous trips, sobered my lust like a bucket of cold water splashed on my dozing Depression-mentality.

On my way back to the studio to start the contemplation process all over again, I took the shortcut through the service area as I had done many times before. But this time, a very funny thing happened.

As I was about to exit through the large, open, overhead door to walk past the rows of new inventory parked in the sunlit lot, I focused on the tan tarpaulin mound in the corner. I had seen it before but hadn't noticed the patch of three inch white sidewall tire peeking out from under the front corner of the dusty canvas that covered the car shape.

The car next to the canvas mound was over a pit with a squinting mechanic waving an extension cord underneath it.

I hunkered down and asked him if it would be all right if I sneaked a quick look at the car under the canvas.

"You can do better than that," he said, "You can tie a rope to the bumper and haul the damn thing the hell outta here." The original owner of this place, long before his time, he explained, when this place was still a Chrysler/Plymouth dealer, bought it during The Big War. The son has been trying to dump it, he went on, since Pop died, but, no luck. "We sure need the space more than we need this albatross," he said.

When I lifted the corner of the tarp and peeled it back over the hood, my heart almost stopped. God Almighty! Good-God-Almighty! This truly was one of Mrs. Fantonetti's *miracolos!* This was the same Ford Jenny Lange and I had admired and sat in on our very first date!

"Thank you Jesus! Oh...thank you, thank you, thank you, Jesus! You can forget about the lottery now!"

The son's asking price for the car was $800.00. Using Mamma's best West Side Market haggling techniques, I dickered the price down to $425.00, including a full tank of gas. A cluster of mechanics gathered around the car to discuss its merits. One extended a congratulatory hand and said, "It sure is a purty little thing. Congratulations."

As I drove slowly down Clark with the top down, heads turned and I waved my back-o'-the-hand, limp, Duke of Windsor wave. Nostalgia washed over me and although I could feel the presence of Jenny sitting next to me in her tennis whites, I longed to share this maiden voyage with someone else who would be just as thrilled. I pulled into Mamma's drive, loaded Mamma, Ann, and Mrs. Lazzarone into the seats and off we went to Willoughby's like four giggly, high-spirited teenagers, out to conquer the world.

In New York, Mike had lined up a one room apartment for me on 80th and Amsterdam. It had a lumpy bed, a small toilet next to a small alcove that contained a fridgerette, a sink, and a plywood surface that served as a counter-kitchen table. The plywood lifted off to expose the bathtub. The ensemble must have been crammed together before the walls went up.

My first day in the dingy, dim, hallway, I met Mr. Butler, my falling-down-drunk alcoholic neighbor who proudly announced, when he introduced himself, that he was a direct descendent of ancestors who had fought at Bunker Hill. He knocked repeatedly on my other neighbor's door. Mr. Butler surmised they wouldn't come to the door because they were two sensitive, lesbian, folksingers.

After a couple of weeks of adjusting to the corned beef and cabbage and onion smells in the halls, the faint sound of a 24-hour-a-day radio, the long delays for hot water, the resident cockroaches, the slamming doors at all hours, the 3:00 a.m. hallway arguments, the rudeness, and the lullaby of traffic noises and sirens, my room buzzer buzzed. I certainly wasn't expecting any visitors but pressed the first white button, with no result. The second button brought the Spanish accented voice of the Super saying, "Me-stair La...Bunko? Telephone."

I galloped down the four flights of stairs to the wall phone next to the Super's door, picked up the dangling receiver and heard Brat use the code name, "Gee-Gee?"

"Gretchen Goering, speaking."

"Jamie, I didn't want to call you at work with this, but Steamer was right. Burchfield set you up. He got you outta here to replace you with a young, pimply-faced relative. What's happening with you?"

"Well, what you're telling me doesn't surprise me. The

plant where I work is a dirty, greasy, turn-o'-the-century brick factory. I'm the production manager, all right. Trouble is, there's no design department. The so-called designing is done on Madison Avenue. These guys are still using the same old dumb p.o.p. patterns that came with the factory —"

"That explains where the shit they hand us here comes from," interjected Brat.

"Exactly. Can you imagine? I don't know how they stay in business, year —"

"What Madison Avenue? You said Madison Avenue."

"Well, McCallister has a financial interest in an art agency on 57th and Madison that is supposed to come up with the campaigns, but Matt Yuska, our plant manager, says they're only interested in glamour media stuff...no cardboard."

"Actually, that's nice to hear. Why don'cha start to steer some of the display stuff toward Daisy? We can handle it."

"Not yet. Matt's seen what I can do and he's trying to set me up in the agency. He'd love to see me inject some fresh blood into this thing. If it happens, I'll be in a better position to see what's...whoa...whoa!"

Suddenly, our building superintendent's door banged open and a bristly, shaggy eyebrowed, snorting man in a dirty undershirt put his full 300 pounds behind the belly that was ramrodding a large trash-filled cardboard box through an un-yielding door frame, on it's way to the curb.

"Comin' through!" he yelled, as he charged toward me. He looked like an escaping prisoner-sweathog who'd been held captive in the cellar.

I dropped the receiver and leapt onto the steps, out of the path of the run-a-way box car. When the train passed, I picked up the receiver. "Brat? You still there?"

"Yeah. Jesus, what the hell was that?"

"That...my friend...was a New York welcome wagon that just came through. Lemme tell ya, Brat, this place is a shit hole. For safety, I park my precious car in a private garage. Matt's arranging a meeting for me at the agency. If I get the job with a substantial raise, soon, so I can afford this place, fine. Otherwise, I'm comin' home. I take it things are still OK at Daisy since I talked to you last?"

"Oh-yeah. Don't worry about us, we're doin' fine." We finished chatting and he signed off with, "Well...that's about it. Take care, Tiger. Good luck...and, hey...keep those cards and letters comin'. Ya hear?"

I made my presentation to four of the Madison Avenue agency's officers. I had learned to incrementally raise the surprise level carefully with each original three dimensional mockup I placed before them. When I got to the last, a variation of the smiling swimmer with the rolling eyes, they all stood up, pleased, and applauded lightly. Mr. Vanderlane, the president, continued to watch the rolling eyes with the fascination of an infant in a crib, hypnotized by a slowly rotating mobile.

"Well...I...will...be...damned," he muttered.

My newly designated work area in the Vanderlane Agency took up a small space in a corner of the "bull pen" which was shared by six other illustrators. In this makeshift, trial basis, work area, with limited elbow-room to cut out and decorate my prototypes, I managed to crank out golden eggs that were selling at the unprecedented rate of seven or eight out of ten tries. The previous success rate in this agency was approximately ten percent.

A partial translucent glass wall was hurriedly built across the end of the bull pen that had floor to ceiling windows overlooking Madison Avenue. A prominent, gold leaf, "do not disturb" sign was painted on the entrance door to my new, separated studio.

It was the not-too-well-concealed intent of the administrative board that behind my new glass barricade my meditative hatching process was to be protected at any cost. "Hold the mayo, but let's keep those golden eggs a-comin'!" Mike DaFutte's decision to write the contract opting for a percentage-of-the-profits, in lieu of a salary, was a stroke of genius. Most of the old timers did not take kindly to the conspicuous rewards lavished on this uppity new kid on the block.

One afternoon, a man quietly opened my door, without knocking, slipped in, and carefully closed the door behind him. I had never seen this man before. He wore a white shirt, bow-tie, thin hair combed over his bald pate from his right ear over to his left, and had ruby rings on his stubby pinkie fingers.

"Listen, LaBunko," he said, as he leaned against the entrance door without introducing himself, "I'm here to speak for everybody in this place. There's something —"

"Won't you please sit down?"

"No. I prefer to stand," he said, through clenched teeth.

"How can I help you?"

"You can help me by coming to your senses. You sit here in your cocoon, oblivious to what damage...you sit here showing-up everybody... makin' us look like loafers. Well, you listen to me you better-than-thou young punk —" He then described how I was rocking the boat, how I was affecting retirement, my threat to families, kids, the national debt, and why I had to slow w-a-a-y down.

When he left, I wondered what would happen if I did not

comply with his directives. Would they send in a couple of wizened octogenarians with fedora hats, sunglasses, and brass knuckles to make me see the error of my ways?

Because it would afford me more time to make contacts for free-lance work, I decided to "get along" with my co-workers by stretching the solution time allotted to agency projects from several hours, to several days. To overcome the boredom that developed between jobs, I spent a lot of time looking into the plate glass windows of the brassiere factory on the third floor level directly opposite us. When I wasn't actually being productive, just pretending, I evaluated the dazzling female models sashaying back and forth on the runway in their flimsy underwear, in front of prospective wholesale buyers, and me. I was often tempted to hold up a large score card, like an Olympic figure skating judge.

I suspected that the major pique harbored by my associates was not based on economics, but was related to my glass wall. This unanticipated calamity apparently deprived these guys of their primary reason for coming to work each day.

I soon came to appreciate the privileged class. I was a *nouveau* member, luxuriating and ogling, like some rich, retired old geezer, poolside, in Miami. You wanna talk perks?

Like Vinnie always says, at any given point in time, everybody's just about where they ought to be in the scheme of things.

Chapter XXV

Important potential customers are sometimes lured with expensive box seats to macho sporting events such as baseball, football or hockey. But figure skating, I learned, adds perverse excitement when a pampered prospective client, with his wife seated beside him, surreptitiously tries to capture the voyeur's thrill of catching close-up glimpses of the female skater's tantalizing panties with his high-powered binoculars, each time the gliding ballerina stretches for the back of her head with her skate blade. High-class art school beaver hunting.

My glass-lined studio had the most perfect luxury box seats imaginable. My clients did not sneak looks. They gaped at the near-naked models across the way openly, without fear of consequences. They even exchanged daring waves.

An enthusiastic client once held up a makeshift sign that read: "We were made for each other," and the coy model responded with her own scrawled message: "You dirty old man." The model's smiling and waving friends, also scantily dressed, joined her in a line-up at the window. My co-workers, gaping through my open door, threw their grudges to the wind, stampeded into my studio, and faced them like they were forming a hootin'-hollerin' Pickett charge.

After that, the hostility and psychological skirmishes directed at me and my glass wall from the bullpen boys gradually diminished, so I selectively rationed invitations to my box seats. But total capitulation occurred only after a few seasons had passed and the bow-tied enemy came to realize that I had the ultimate weapon in my possession. The climate control thermostat for our zone of the agency was located on my side of the glass wall. The war was over.

One day, I was tapping my right temple with a pencil eraser, contemplating how many naked angels can dance on the head of a pin, when there was a light knock on my door and a pretty young girl entered. Without a word, she left a folded note on my desk, and with a "bye-bye" gesture, closed the door behind her. The note read: "You dirty old man." I sat bolt upright and looked repeatedly across the street for a waving model. At lunchtime, she was back, leaning on my desk.

"You don't remember me, do you?" she asked.

"Sure I do," I said, grasping at straws, "I just didn't recognize you all gussied-up with a gorgeous dress, high heels —"

"Wrong, wrong, wrong. I'm not one of those gorgeous things from across the street, but thank you." She rolled her eyes to heaven, put the back of her hand to her forehead melodramatically and said, "How quickly they forget. I'm the Madonna of the Rocks. Remember? Schinkels? Black-and-Tan? Hit in the forehead by a near fatal bullet —" As she went on counting the memory fragments on her fingers, I stood up with my mouth gaping and walked toward her.

"God Almighty. Are you...Massa? No, no —" I stood directly in front of her and sputtered, "Not...Maggie. Wait. Wait...."

"Mata," she said, "Mata, as in the infamous spy, Mata-Hari. All growed up and still ignoring your 'Do not disturb' sign." We embraced, swayed, patted each other's backs and gave the euphoria free rein.

"Mata. Mata." I said. "You'll have to admit, that's a very...

how can I put this, delicately...a ver-r-y unique name."

"In your circle of friends, maybe. But not in the rest of the world. In Spain, they even named a door after me."

"A door?"

"Yes. Even you have heard of...ready for this?... Matador."

"Oh...God. Your humor hasn't changed, but you sure have."

I held her at arms length and studied her. "I just can't believe this. You're absolutely stunning. What ever happened to Alice in Wonderland? And how on earth did you get here?"

"It's a long story, of course, but I'm working in the front office. I had no idea you worked here until your name crossed my desk on a memo yesterday and I thought to myself...wait a minute..." We excitedly described what had happened since Cleveland and I brought her all the way up to Vinnie's deportation and how I came to New York.

"Incidentally," she said, "You don't have a gun in here, do you?" She covered her forehead with her hand.

"No, no." I assured her. "These days I own a crossbow."

At noon, we took our lunches in my brief case to Central Park where we couldn't help interrupting each other with pent-up questions, additions, and outrageous memories.

As we sat on a huge rock that supported an equestrian statue, she unwrapped her second crustless water-cress sandwich and said, "Tell me something. Are we doomed to meet forever more on rocks just because we started this way?"

"I don't mind," I said, grinning.

"Actually, I don't either," she said, "but there's two things I'd like if we're going to keep meeting on huge rocks like this."

"What's that?"

"A full moon and a 'Do not disturb' sign of my very own. You don't still have that wonderful old car that was the smash of the art school and the Billy Eckstine concert do you?"

"Yep."

"Wow! *You do*? I want that too! Gotta have that car!"

Thereafter, we met everyday for lunch at the base of the statue. Everyday, that is, until one night pranksters cut a hole in the top of the pigeon-spattered bronze statue, filled it with water, and drilled a hole in the anatomy so the horse peed for days. It was a prank worthy of the Lucky Seven at West Tech.

After that, we went to a nearby bench. When winter came, we ate our lunches in my studio with the faddish vertical blinds shutting out the scene that no longer interested me.

Our mutual attraction continued to soar and we made every effort to see each other socially whenever possible. During office hours we communicated with coded messages and fabricated reasons to visit each other. Once, when the coast was clear, I followed her into the ladies room to plant a "bent over" kiss. In the evening, we took identical courses at N.Y.U. and before long we had accumulated enough credits for a degree of Bachelor of Science in Education in the field of Fine Arts.

One Thursday night, after class, we boarded the Houston Street train after enduring yet another excruciating English Literature session with Dr. Foley. We walked to the end of the car which had the smaller number of reeking bodies and lolling heads and settled into our seats.

At the other end of the car, one of the bodies layered in overcoats, a stocking hat, and a long matted beard, separated himself from the other pile of discarded humanity. He rose in increments, facing us, and steadied himself with his face a few inches away from one of my swaying "refreshing" swim-girl posters suspended from the car ceiling. As the derelict tried unsuccessfully to follow the pretty girl's rolling eyes and tongue, he formed a smile that slowly expanded into a big grin. The exposed isolated teeth matched his yellow eyeballs, exactly.

With the grin now frozen on his face, he moved his head and tongue slowly from side to side in an attempt to lock onto the motion. When it became apparent he was not going to accomplish the task, he stared, out of focus, at the briskly swaying poster and said, hesitantly, "Ah...will...be...damned."

He turned his face, with the drooling mouth, and filthy-looking beard, toward his stacked buddies, lost his balance, and collapsed, more or less, into the space he had occupied earlier.

"Well," said Mata, "You just won-over another customer."

"When I see first-hand evidence of my powers of persuasion," I said, "a surge of power goes through my veins. Right now, I feel like a Svengali."

Mata nudged me and pointed to the other end of the car. The young man with the black mustache and bandanna who'd gotten on at the last stop, made his way directly to my poster, studied it for a while, then squeezed the top and bottom together so he could peek into the space where the pendulum card with the eyes printed on it was suspended. He sat near the animated poster and stared at it with fascination. Mata stared at him with fascination. I stared at Mata.

"Oh! Jamie! Look!" said Mata with alarm. She took my arm and pressed close to me. The two black ladies sitting near us got up and moved to seats beyond us. The man who'd been hanging on the strap near us also crowded into the diminishing space at our end of the car.

I had never been in this predicament before. The young man who had been studying my swinging poster earlier was standing in the aisle at his end of the car with a long switchblade knife gleaming in his hand.

I went rigid, wondered if the door behind us that led to the next car was locked, and frantically searched the walls for an alarm cord as we slunk down in our seats as much as we could to avoid his focus.

The man with the knife and the bandanna braced his back against the enameled pole opposite my poster and reached over to slit the tape that was holding the bottom edge shut. He raised one side of the sandwiched poster faces to expose the two eyeballs printed on the round pendulum card, hanging inside from parallel vertical strings.

With one downward slash, the eyeballs were hanging on separate cards and when he closed the sandwiched poster, the eyeballs moved across the dye-cut eye openings independent of each other. The illusion was remarkable and much more effective than what I had done.

Bandanna Man grinned with satisfaction, snapped the knife shut, tucked it away, sat down, and beamed at his accomplishment. The ladies who had scurried to seats behind us were giggling uncontrollably and the man who had joined us in our space now made his way from pole to pole toward the other end of the car to get a closer look. Still within earshot, he said, "Well-I'll-be-a-goddam-son-of-a-bitch!"

The train lights blinked and as we glided into the light of a white-tile subway station, Mata leaped to her feet.

"God! Jamie...I missed my stop! C'mon! C'mon! C'mon! This is the 79th Street stop! Your stop! The door! Hold the door!"

As we stepped onto the cement platform, the subway door closed and the train rustled track debris as it disappeared into the black tunnel. "You OK?" I asked Mata, who looked shaken.

"Thumping heart, but I'm fine. Let's just get out of here. I could use a double shot of caffeine about now. Is that White

Tower at 79th and Amsterdam still open at this time of night?"

"I'm quite sure it's open 24 hours. The quality of the food and service change with the quick-turnover help. At times, when I see the servers, I think I'd have a better chance of surviving the subway third rail."

We climbed the stairs at 79th and Broadway, next to the Bretton Hall Hotel, and considered using their ultra swanky coffee emporium. Mata felt self-conscious about the way we were dressed so we decided, instead, to check out and maybe risk the White Tower.

There it was, radiating in a glory undiminished by time. The shiny white brick with the black mortar facade, the stubby tower on one side of the roof-line parapet. An exact duplicate of the White Tower restaurant near the Garden Theatre, in Cleveland. The only thing missing was Tony Giardello.

As we sat on our stools drinking our bowls of delicious coffee, I told Mata about Tony Giardello and the movie pass currency system devised by neighborhood businessmen in Cleveland during the Great Depression.

I told her how Tony had the 8:00 p.m. to 4:00 a.m. shift at the White Tower, how he brought his own trays of hamburgers and buns from home in the trunk of his car. How he then served *his* hamburgers to the swing-shift steel workers from 10:00 p.m. until midnight, and switched back to White Tower hamburgers from midnight to 2:00 a.m.

"And he had no problem with conflict of interest?"

"None. As far as he was concerned, he wasn't, afterall, *stealin'* anything. He was just using their place for a little while to augment his puny salary with his own paid-for hamburgers. And...he wanted to honor his friends by occasionally serving them...free of charge. Or, sometimes, a couple of movie passes."

"Well," said Mata, as she made her way to the exit door, "I guess I have no choice. After what happened on the train tonight, there's no way I'm going back to my place at this hour, alone. Incidentally, that was good coffee. Do you have any movie passes to pay with?"

As we walked down Amsterdam arm-in-arm toward my place, Mata looked up at me and asked, "What was your plan of action for that guy with the knife on the subway?"

"Easy," I said. "The guy obviously had intuitive cardboard engineering skills. If he had approached...any...one...of...us...I would'a offered him a job."

"See how it works out?" She raised and kissed my fingers.

We reached my apartment, scrubbed down, and just as we were settling in for the night, the buzzer buzzed.

"Me-stair La Bunko. Telephone."

I picked up the dangling receiver, instinctively faced the super's door and prepared to sidestep any oncoming train.

"Hello."

"Gee-Gee?"

"Gretchen Goering, speaking."

"Jamie. Listen. It's me. Vinnie. You got paper and pencil?"

"Hey! Vinnie! No. I don't. Holy shit. What a nice surprise. Somethin' special's gotta be goin' on? You wouldn't be calling at this ungodly hour unless —"

"Jamie, I don't have time to bullshit. I'm at Idlewild to change planes and in a few minutes I'm finally off to Sicily to convince King Umberto that Mussolini is really dead. Yeah, I know, like you and everybody else, I thought this whole damn thing was dead, like Mussolini. Well, it's not. But here's what you need to know right now. I'll be meeting my girl in Dubrovnic, Yugoslavia, at the Hotel Argentine... across the

Adriatic from Bari, Italy. That's gonna be my home base."

"*Yugoslavia?* What is this? An Italian kid in Yugoslavia?"

"I *used* to be Italian. After I show my face around Palermo for a while, and Mike says its OK, I'm coming back, whenever, walkin' backwards and wiping away my footprints with birch branches. My port of departure will be Bari. My last official domicile will be Dubrovnic. My last name? Who the hell knows. Maybe Twiller. Would that make me a former Italian?"

"Vinnie, holy shit, let me go upstairs and get a pencil."

"No. No time. You'll be hearing from Mike. He's got all the dope. I'm calling to say good-bye, but also, I forgot to tell Mike he may be hearing from the girl I've been waiting for all my life. She's an instant-translator, speaks five languages fluently, and moves between the UN and American embassies around the world. She would work perfectly for Mike. Perfectly. Write this down...shit...you don't have a pencil —"

"Vinnie, let me run upstairs —"

"No. No time. Just remember this name. Stephanie Twiller. T-W-I-L-L-E-R. Very English. Ver-r-y conservative. Really, really, nice girl. Got me jumpin' through hoops. Won't allow me to swear. Can you imagine that? That's like not allowing the waves to touch the shore. For Christ...oops...gotta watch that."

"What ever happened to your other heartthrob, Vera?"

"Vera is a nice kid...not too bright, and no passion. I got'ta have passion. Makin' love to Vera was like makin' love to a log. When you make love to a log, you know *you're* having fun, but you can't tell if the log is...what? —" He turned away from the phone, talked to someone, came back and said, "Listen Jamie...I gotta go. Mike will fill you in."

"Vinnie, wait. Quick, one more thing I hafta know. God knows when I'll be seeing you again, and there never seems to be a right time to ask because you never...I'm almost afraid to ask. What...ever happened to Gee-Gee?"

"Oh, hell...Jeez. Gee-Gee? You remember the little store next to her father's bakery on Denison? She took over the little store, lives upstairs with her husband, and downstairs she does a roaring business specializing in decorating wedding cakes. Spectacular, high class, high-society stuff. Did one for the Mayor's son. Listen, Jamie, I really gotta go now, and if Italy invades Ethiopia again, don't go blamin' me, you *malscalzone*."

He hadn't hung up yet. I could still hear the distinct background airport sounds.

"Vinnie? You there?"

"Yeah, I'm here. Jamie, listen. This is hard for me to say ...uh... son-of-a-bitch —"

"Vinnie, you take care...I love you like a brother —"

"Me too," he said. Then he was gone.

There was a scuffling behind the super's door and the doorknob started to rotate. I slammed the phone onto its hook, scrambled out of the way and raced upstairs.

Chapter XXVI

Mata and I were getting weary of the New York scene. Weekend trips to the Hampton Beaches helped, but we decided that with Christmas approaching, it would be a nice change to go home for the holidays and surprise the families, whom we hadn't seen for three years.

We headed north to her home in Buffalo at night to avoid the traffic. As we raced toward the North Pole in my "Old Faithful" Ford convertible, it kept getting colder and colder. We progressively added layers of clothes culled from the luggage, including babushkas, but it didn't help. By the time we got to Buffalo and parked in front of her house, Mata looked like a pile of laundry sitting next to me.

"You look like one of those West Side Market ladies in that babushka," I said.

"I beg your pardon, madam," she responded, as we got out to unload her luggage. "We *both* look like Siberian refugee sisters. That day's growth on your face makes you particularly attractive, Katrina."

Encumbered with armloads of gift packages and luggage, we cautiously made several trips over the crunching snow to the darkened house. When all of her things were safely inside the front door, we exchanged lingering caresses and I walked back to my car. As I pulled away from the curb I blinked my headlights twice and she repeated the signal with the living room light-switch as she peered through parted curtains.

Five days around the kitchen table in Cleveland, eating Mamma's wondrous treats with relatives telling all the old familiar anecdotes and drinking anisette, recharged familial bonds and stirred tribal security. Uncle Nick talked, more than sang, his annual Italian Christmas carol parody and his "friendships are forged in fire" speech, was feeble and flawed, but nobody, of course, corrected him. Cousin Angie belted out her Italian folk song, still by rote, to an audience that had been thinned by time. New faces like Ric's former VA therapy nurse, now his fiancee, were gradually replacing the empty slots.

The farewell "hug-'n-kiss" line that formed in Mamma's kitchen made my departure for Buffalo emotional and difficult. All of the ladies wept and as I embraced the men, they seemed a little bit shorter, except for my younger brother George, who buried my face in his chest. Papa did not weep, but when we touched cheeks I could feel his stubble quivering.

On the return trip to Buffalo I met Mata's parents. As we faced each other for the first time, Mata's smiling parents made an immediate, favorable impact. When Mata introduced me, her mother stepped forward, as if to embrace, then took a step backward and extended a hand, flustered.

Her father, an attractive man who towered over me, shook my hand and slid his other hand around my shoulder as he led me into the living room.

"Come in, son, come on in. With the amount of space you take up in Mata's letters, we feel like we already know you very well." Although both parents were native Hungarians, her mother's accent was barely detectable, her father had none.

Their large, attractive home reflected their upper-middle-class status. The interior looked like it had been assembled by an expensive in-house furniture store decorator. Her mother's European addition to the decor was the crocheted antimacassars covering the armrests of the stuffed furniture.

After a round of niceties, Christmas cookies, and Tokay wine served in small Waterford glasses, the ladies retired to the kitchen to make the final arrangements for the trip back to New York. Mata's father and I remained in the living room where I learned he had been chief research and design engineer for Westinghouse and numerous national steel companies but was now semi-retired as an internationally known consultant. Since we both wore our passion for innovation on our sleeves, we quickly had an energized conversation going.

When the car was packed and we stood at the front door ready to leave, Mata's father took my extended hand in both of his and shook it repeatedly. Her mother stepped forward, close enough to embrace, and this time, she did. Parting, once again, was indeed sweet sorrow.

"Your parents are wonderful people, Mata."

"Thank you, Jamie. That pleases me very much. Did you see my father's eyebrows raise when my mother actually hugged you. That kind of affectionate lack of reserve is usually foisted only on kissin' kin."

"Well," I said, "Now I *really* feel honored." We entered the freeway on the outskirts of Buffalo and made our way east.

"Do you know what?" said Mata, as we drove toward New York City, "I stopped in at Buffalo State Teachers College and I'm qualified to teach in New York State. I need to take a few courses but not immediately. And do you know what else? I looked on the bulletin board in the placement office and there's an art teacher job open in Patchogue, on Long Island. No stress. Boating. Fishing. And a lot closer to the Hampton's beaches."

"So what are you saying?"

"I'm saying that I hate New York City and this sounds like the job I've been training for all of my life."

"And...what about me?" I asked, after a period of silence.

"You hate New York as much as I do. You open a studio out there and get free-lance work. You've proved yourself. They need you...as much as you need them." Once again, we withdrew into our thoughts.

"You're serious about this aren't you?" I asked.

"Yes," she said. "It's time to make a move."

"And...what...about...us?" I asked, quietly. We drove through the night for a while with the engine droning in the background. She turned in her seat, and studied my profile.

"We get married," she said.

So we did just that. The simple civil ceremony legalized our relationship but did not alter it in any way. Our families back home made little adjustment squeaks when they received our unconventional announcements but as far as we were concerned, we were committed and married long before the law said that we were.

We moved her things into my room at Mrs. Wallace's and it quickly became apparent that the space was not adequate for two adults and their belongings. While I continued working at the Vanderlane Agency and accumulated an expanding list of free-lance clients, Mata, with latent organizational and accounting skills that hadn't surfaced until she started to work in the front office, quit the agency to conduct my business affairs and to hunt for an affordable apartment that was located within a reasonable distance from my workplace.

She soon discovered that the apartment task was formidable. Because rent controls were still in place in New York

City, an underground brokerage business developed that was virtually impregnable unless one had inside information from personal contacts. The relentless search became interminable and appeared hopeless.

"You know what?" said Mata, one evening as we faced each other over the meal she had prepared.

"What?"

"I'm really, really, getting to hate this place." I knew the look. I knew the tone.

"And?"

"And..." she said, as she moved her glazed baby carrots around on her plate, "I checked, and the art teacher job in Patchogue is still open. I'd like to go see what it's about."

"Fine," I said.

"Fine?" she said, with a surprised look that indicated she had been prepared for a debate.

"Fine," I repeated. "Patchogue is not too far out on the island. We can use a break. Set it up and we'll take a ride out there."

"Hallelujah!" she shouted, as she raised her arms in a victory salute. "We are freedom bound!"

Mata arranged for an interview for the position of junior high school art teacher in Patchogue. After the meeting, which went well, she rushed down the front steps of the school, and jumped into the car with a handful of folders and stapled sheets of material she had picked up. "Oh, God, Jamie. This is where I want to be. Wait until I tell you...this is *so* great! You are going to be *so* envious!"

As she burbled on, we explored the small city on the bay and the more we looked, the more interesting it became. It was not far from Manhattan, was quiet, and offered privacy without isolation. The stone covered beaches did not compare with the extraordinary beaches of the Hamptons, but they did offer access to the water. We parked on the long picturesque pier, which was an extension of South Ocean Avenue, and admired the flotilla of fishing and pleasure sailboats moored there.

On our way back into the center of town we cruised slowly past the junior high school where she hoped to work and I impulsively turned onto tree-lined Amity Street. Mata interrupted what she was saying about the merits of my considering teaching as a career and pointed through the windshield.

"Oh! Look at that. Isn't that...a beautiful...old house."

The two story Victorian structure was unoccupied and in a state of disrepair. The lawn was choked with tall weeds and the lathe-turned elaborate fence, running the length of the brick sidewalk was almost bare of paint. The sign on the gate read: "For Sale or Lease."

We walked cautiously onto the wrap-around veranda and peered into the windows at the rooms furnished with antique furniture and stamped metal ceilings. At the rear of the large lot, which was dotted with shade trees, we discovered a rectangular one story building. Unlike the main house, this 30 x 60 foot workshop was in excellent condition. Opposite this structure, forming a gravel court area, was a charming six-bay carriage-house that also needed restoration.

"Get a load of this," said Mata at one of the numerous shop-building windows. The interior was dusty, but bright. Six large tilted drafting desks were arranged in two rows and large work tables were scattered through the shop. The far wall, with the fireplace opening, was made of large irregular shaped granite stones. We looked at each other with amazement.

"Can you believe this? It's *perfect* for a studio!" she said, excitedly, "absolutely perfect!"

Mata was on the short list of applicants for the teaching job and each time she was called back for yet one more interview or meeting, we spent time at the house, which we now referred to as "Schinkel II" to commemorate the large rooming house in Cleveland where we first met.

The corner coffee-shop owner told us the place had been on the market for several years but because of the size and restrictive covenants, was considered a white elephant by local realtors. He also told us the shop behind the house had been a thriving civil-engineering business run by Mrs. Beardsley's only son Calvin Charles. She died at the age of 97. When Calvin died, the business disbanded. The out-of-town heirs contested the covenant that severely restricted any shop-alteration, but it was supported by the courts.

In the meantime, Mata continued her futile SODA rounds for apartments. SODA was her acronym for Society Of Desirable Apartments. She looked up from the realty ads she was circling in red and looked in my direction, coyly.

"Why don't you join me tomorrow. I want you to experience what *real* New York belligerence and rudeness is like."

We met for lunch and afterwards made the rounds for apartments together. I was appalled at the degree of brutal insolence we encountered. "Is this the kinda crap you've been putting up with all along?" I asked, after an exchange with a landlord that almost came to blows. Mata nodded, and I stewed over the incident for the rest of the day.

"You know what SODA really stands for?" I asked Mata after supper, as she did the dishes in our tiny sink.

"What?"

"Society Of Demented Assholes. I've had enough. I didn't want to get your hopes up, but this thing today did it. I've been discussing the old house with Mike, who's in Cleveland, and he put me in touch with a lawyer friend of his in New York —"

"Wha...a...at?" She turned from the sink and dried her hands as she sat down opposite me at the small table by the bed. "Say that again."

"I've been hatching a plan but I didn't want you to get excited until I was convinced it might really be possible. That Patchogue house is just three blocks east of the commuter train station into Manhattan. The shop is perfect for my studio needs, there are three suites in the place —" She covered her mouth with her hands as more and more white showed in her eyes.

"...and if you get the art job, you'll be within walking distance of South Ocean Avenue and the school." She let out a squeal of joy and covered me with kisses.

"Oh God! I can't believe this! I don't care if I get the job or not. Let's do it! *Let's just do it!* Oh, Jamie, I've been secretly dreaming about that place ever since I first set eyes on it. We can re-do the suite of rooms at the back of the first floor for ourselves. The parlor and dining room that flank the entrance vestibule... oh...wait...look —" She opened an art portfolio flat on the floor and scattered around some floor plan sketches she'd made.

"Here...here...look. We could live in the back here, over-looking the studio...Daisy Display II...like it? I love it! The front parlor and the dining room that are separated by the entrance vestibule and staircase we can rent as professional offices —"

I stood up stiffly from where I'd been kneeling beside her.

"Whoa! Whoa. I had no idea you were spending your days doing this. Holy crow, Mata, slow down. I think you may be getting carried away here —"

"Society...Of...Demented —" she enunciated with exaggeration, as she looked up and brushed the hair from her eyes.

"OK! OK! OK!" I said. "Just let me think about this."

"There are three furnished suites," she said eagerly, "a bath and a community kitchen that are strategically located between the three second floor bedrooms. Get Brat and his wife to join us and they can move into one of those suites. Instead of shipping business to Cleveland...consolidate...bring Cleveland here! Ya...hoo! Ya-a-a...hoo!" She skipped around the room, snapping her fingers and singing, "Mine Eyes Have Seen the Glory of the Comin' of the Lord —"

"You know you're nuts, don'cha?" I said, as I felt myself being swept up by her enthusiasm. "We'll probably end up broke but at least we'll be charter members of SODA. Society of Deranged Adults." In the middle of our sparse room we clutched each other in an embrace that sealed our future, for better or worse, for richer or poorer.

"To quote my lunch-truck mentor, 'A business is like a greenhouse plant. If it isn't growing, it's dying.'" When I pulled away from her hard kiss, my upper lip hurt.

For several months, thereafter, Schinkel II looked like it was encased in a swarm of worker bees, and from the nerve center, the first completed suite of rooms we now called home, Mata supervised the massive renovation like a possessed queen bee. One small rented-truck load of personal possessions, and suddenly, our tiny, dreary Manhattan room, the wailing folksinger neighbors, and the hall-phone train wrecks, were a thing of the past.

All of Mata's carefully constructed plans were galloping along, way ahead of schedule. If the completion of our personal living quarters was any indication, this place was going to be a showplace. Two walls of floor to ceiling windows in my office overlooking the Daisy Building flooded the room with glorious daylight. Like every other elegant alteration decision Mata had made, the narrow vertical casement windows had been carefully selected and tastefully customized so the overall effect did not compromise the integrity of the old building.

Things were going along better than our wildest expectations. Of course, no matter how well thought out are the best laid plans of mice and men, there's always glitches. Nothing serious, mostly, but occasionally, improvising is required.

For instance, I pulled into the court area between the carriage house and the studio, where Mata had carefully laid out a series of brick walk areas; the apron in front of the garage doors, connecting brick paths, etc. The six swarthy bricklayers were immobile and sunning themselves on piles of bricks. The foreman, the only Portuguese in the group who spoke English, was standing in the shade of the carriage house overhang, leaning against a garage door, his hardhat tucked under his arm.

As Mata ran toward my car, she looked disheveled, very excited, and was shouting incoherently.

I stopped her forward movement with my hands on her shoulders and rode over her tirade with, "Whoa, hold it! Hold it! Now...wait...wait.... OK. Now, tell me what's going on."

"What's going on?!" she shouted, "I'll tell you what's going on. What's going on is these jerks have wasted most of the morning taking a siesta, that's what the...hell...is going on!"

"And why on earth are they doing that instead of working for a day's pay?"

"Because I want to make a few changes in the design and..." she started to get weepy with frustration, "they won't talk to me! They turned their backs on me!"

I caught the eye of the foreman with the toothpick sticking out of his rows of white teeth and he motioned for me to follow as he walked a short distance from the group.

"You see, Me-stair Labunko, it is a thing where we come from, that a man must not, *cannot*, take orders from a woman."

He put the toothpick back in his mouth, shook his head and repeated, "It is *imposeebla* that a man can take orders from a woman." He put his palms together in a gesture of supplication and said, "She is a *ver-r-ry* nice lady, and we respect her very much...*assa lady*." He took out the toothpick, waved the stem in the air like it was a miniature flag and said, "but not assa boss. *Never!*"

I went to Mata and explained that we were bucking a cultural taboo. Together, we hatched the solution and walked back to the foreman.

"OK," said Mata, "I will tell my husband what I want done, then he will tell you, and you can tell your men. Is that OK?"

The foreman spit out his toothpick and burst into a big grin. "Now you haff the answer to save face! You are good people!" he said, as he gave me a bear-hug and touched my cheeks with his.

And so we walked around the site making adjustments in Mata's brick designs with Mata telling me, me telling the foreman, and the foreman relaying the message to the happy work force walking close on our heels.

"Now," said Mata, as we walked toward the house, "if I remember right, the latest woman in Vinnie's life is an instant-translator. Right? After what just happened here, am I suddenly married to one myself?"

"What I'd like to know is," I said, "when these guys take their marriage vows, do they say 'I promise to honor and obey her *assa woman*, not *assa boss* ?'" Snickering, I added, "With their attitude, what happens when a woman cop gives them a traffic ticket? Or, they're facing a female judge? Or—"

"...Or," cut-in Mata, "when they dance with a transvestite, who leads? C'mon, enough silliness. Let's go inside."

When the exterior had been totally restored to its original magnificence, the fertilized and watered landscape came to life. The grass came in lush and green and shrubs flourished so the gaps between plants closed, touched, and no longer looked like prize-winning specimens on display at the country fair. We could now look at the approaching winter without apprehension, and the pillars of the community felt the time had come to start their inevitable "let's share the glory" visits.

First came the newspaper articles with accompanying "before and after" shots. These space-fillers prompted the walking tours. The local historical society, after repeatedly complaining that we were desecrating holy ground, closed the summer season with a wide angle group photo posed on our front steps. When the posturing was over, they filed past me with limp hand shakes. Their president, Lucy Armbruster, brought up the rear with an extended hand and a plea for a donation.

The other line that formed were the creditors. I stoked up the fires under Daisy Display until they were so red-hot I was beginning to scorch my fingers and lose control. Like the Sorcerer's Apprentice, the jobs just kept coming faster and faster, until we had such a steady stream of packages being exchanged between Daisy-NY and Daisy-Cleveland, via Greyhound bus, that we were on a first name basis with the drivers, and were eligible for special bulk rates.

Brat quit McCallister's and together with his nephew and two other learners, was running the thriving Clark Avenue branch. Steamer, biding his approaching pension time, joined them every night and on weekends. He had two nephews of his own standing in the wings.

As soon as Steamer was eligible for retirement, he took over Daisy Display and Brat was bumped up to the East Coast. He loaded his pregnant wife and belongings into a U-haul truck and led the caravan of cars driven by his nephew and the two apprentices to Patchogue where Brat and Sheila moved into one of our upstairs suites. The revved-up learners rented rooms nearby but ate in our communal kitchen.

With Brat and Steamer taking the brunt of the pressure, Mata and I could escape more often to our modest beach cottage in Springs, just outside of East Hampton, at the eastern end of Long Island.

As Vinnie used to like to say, "The whole friggin' world is one big friggin' shell game." So far, with a whole lotta luck, I've managed to keep an eye on the pea. So far.

Chapter XXVII

Mike DaFutte, who was now in his element, and hitting his stride, got so busy he could no longer personally tend to our accounting needs, so he put us in touch with one of his New York rising star associates, a young accounting and investment Whiz Kid named David Shapiro. David, to our great joy, moved into the suite of offices flanking our front entrance staircase. The handsome mahogany panelled offices and resource area Mata had decorated were on the left, the conference room on the right. His secretary/receptionist had her desk in the large entrance vestibule which was decorated to look like a pleasant parlor/waiting room.

David, who quickly became our trusted friend and confidant as well as a super financial advisor, often called us into his conference room before he acted on any of our major business decisions. He patiently attempted to explain, in lay terms, the confounding Alice in Wonderland tax and financial advantages available when you walked through the looking glass into the world of number crunching, where, apparently, one could make money, legally, by losing money.

I acquiesced to his superiority in this area and when he urged us to incorporate, Daisy Display became Daisy Enterprises, Inc. We soon diversified and expanded by opening a small ad agency two doors down on Amity Street.

It wasn't long before Daisy Enterprises, Inc. was taking

quantum leaps to the bank and we owed most of our boosted affluence to the gold-standard touch of David Shapiro and Mike DaFutte whose meteoric rise in the world of politics and finance got him featured in most of the money magazines. I was doing better than I could have imagined in my wildest dreams but compared to Mike, I might as well be Vinnie's no-legs guy in front of the May Company.

Mike had started as Deputy Auditor General for New York City, ostensibly, to investigate irregularities in city departments. While he raked through the muck of city politics and saw the extent of the corruption, he assembled a very impressive private group of former FBI investigative agents, forensic physicists, medical experts, and auditors, who collaborated under one roof. They called themselves *The Cerberus Group*, after the mythical 3-headed guard dog.

Their primary function was to protect municipalities and large corporate organizations against law suits, industrial spying, and corruption. When it became apparent that the unique investigative services offered by these expert court witnesses were saving their clients millions of dollars yearly, the demand exploded and *The Cerberus Group* soon had comptroller offices in Cleveland, New York, Los Angeles, and New Orleans. His Washington branch opened international doors and Mike soon was a frequent flyer to his offices in Rome, London, and other capitols around the world. If Mike wasn't suddenly the richest man in Ohio and New York, he was so close to it, as they say, you couldn't tell the difference.

After several days of heavy-duty meetings in New York, Mike arranged to come to Patchogue to settle some matters with David and agreed to stay overnight in our carriage-house guest bedroom.

When we picked him up at the train station we almost didn't recognize him. I couldn't remember when I'd seen him last without a silk suit and tie but there he was, in blue jeans, sneakers, sunglasses, and a sweat shirt with a silk-screened message on his chest that read: "Blessed are the Troublemakers." The message was enclosed in a balloon-shaped figure that was emanating from the mouth of the blindfolded Goddess of Justice and Law, holding up the scales.

Mata had David, Mike, Sheila and Brat over for dinner and served them her prized stuffed eggplant specialty. After desert, when we were all caught up on the water cooler gossip and jokes, Sheila went upstairs, Brat went back to the shop to have his after-dinner cigarette and put the ongoing projects to bed, and David went to Bellport, the next town over, to stay with his parents. Mike and I retired to the living room.

While Mata finished the dishes in the kitchen, Mike and I put a match to the logs stacked Indian-fashion in the large opening in the fireplace and in no time the flames were roaring up the flue. When Mata joined us she was surprised but pleased to see the entrancing blazing logs, which had lain dormant for several seasons.

"Oh!" she said, as she settled next to me on the couch. "Isn't that a nice sight!" She poured a mild after-dinner drink for each of us.

"I was just saying to Jamie," said Mike, "like everyone else, I can't get over what you two have done to this house. It really is one of Mrs. Fantonetti's what-cha-ma-callits...how do you say miracle, again, in Italian?"

"*Miracolo.*"

"That's it. This place certainly qualifies as one of Mrs. Fantonetti's *miracolos.*"

"Let's give due credit," I said. "Although I enjoy all designing, Mata's the one whose forte is architecture."

"Oh, he's so modest," said Mata. "We collaborate on almost everything, but it's true. I do love architecture...and kids. I love working with kids. You know what Mike? If I could design my own school, and fill it with bright-eyed bundles of energy, I'd be in seventh heaven. But, judging by the way Daisy Enterprises is growing, I have a feeling my schoolmarm career may soon take a forced hiatus before my very eyes. I can't even concentrate on architecture, for a while, because I don't have time to go back to take the courses I'd like to take."

"Speaking of not going back," said Mike, to divert the conversation, "did we ever move our parents out to the suburbs in time, or what? When was the last time you've been back to Clark and Fulton?"

"Matter of fact," I said, "not too long ago. I had to go to a meeting at the Cleveland Daisy Plant. Jesus, Mike, I kept hearing about how bad the old neighborhood was getting, but I was not prepared for what I saw." I told him about my getting mugged and how Tony Giardello solved the vandalism problems that had been plaguing the plant for years. "All of the old landmarks are gone. Poof! Gone, without a trace."

Mike picked up the thread. "I went back just once. Your mother's house? Gone! So is Costello's Grocery, Miller's Drugstore, Texaco gas station...gone!" Each time he said *gone,* he punctuated the word with a thumbs-down stab at the air, and a denigrating Bronx cheer.

"Without the chain-link fence and Tony Giardello," I said, "ain't no way Daisy Display would still be standing. By the way...do you know that Tony has started a boy's club for those so-called incorrigible street kids? I understand they meet on a regular basis at the 25th Street gym."

"Well, bless...his...courage," said Mata.

"That neighborhood," said Mike to Mata, "now has a new ethnic mix that breeds drugs, squalor and...as Jamie learned... real, serious danger. The only buildings left from our time are Daisy Display and St. Francis's Church. Everything else is fast food places and neon sleaze. No, man, I don't have any desire to ever go back. It was a great place to grow up in, but it's a septic tank now. If Tony can do something with that garbage, more power to him. I sure wish him luck."

"Amen to that," said Mata. There was a pause and she asked, "How far back do you two go?"

"First time I met Jamie I was just about to get my law degree and he came to my rec-room office with his father with the drive-in problem."

"No, Mike. No. You don't remember, but when you were the Garden Theatre manager —"

"Mike!" said Mata. "You were a theatre manager?"

"Was he ever." I said. "Once a week they had what used to be called "grocery night," and one night —"

Mike leapt up and said, "H-o-l-y crow! I just put it together. *I-just-put-it-together!*" He walked around in his stocking feet, and tucked part of his shirt back into his pants. "When your father brought you to my house you looked familiar but I couldn't quite connect you with anything. The goddam chickens! I've told that story a million times but you came up with some cockamamie name...what the hell was it? —"

"Lange," I said, "Jamie Lange who preferred Jamie Languini because it sounded more Anglo Saxon!" We were pointing at each other, convulsed with laughter. I filled Mata in on the events of that memorable night. Halfway through the story she came up to speed and joined the howling.

"Jenny sounds like my kinda person," said Mata. "Whatever happened to her?"

"I don't know. She —"

"Gone!" said Mike, With both thumbs stabbing downward again to the accompaniment of the razzing sound. "Gone with the wind...*razz!* and the neighborhood...*razz!*"

Mike and I decompressed from the exhilaration by walking around the room with our hands on our hips like sprinters returning from the finish line. We eventually collapsed into the stuffed furniture with aching sides and dabbed at our eyes and noses until we recovered from the runaway hilarity.

"Mike, my parents resisted like hell, but we finally dragged them, kicking and screaming, out to North Olmsted, where the whole bunch of 'em are colonized. When I visit, it's a nice short run from the airport."

"By the way, how are your folks doing?"

"Well, Mamma has her diabetes problems and Papa has trouble with his emphysema. He doesn't smoke any more, but he does still carry around that damn unlit pipe like it's his security blanket."

"How 'bout your folks, Mata," asked Mike, still trying to collect himself, "they doing OK?"

"My parents are going to outlive the pyramids," said Mata. "Thank you, Mike, for asking about them."

We finished another round of the soothing liqueur and retreated into our individual reveries. I stoked the log remnants and adjusted the screen so the popping embers were contained. Mata walked to the record player, put on a stack of old 45 rpm discs, and looked out the window.

"Now isn't that just like him?" she said. "Do you know

that Brat is still working out there?"

"That doesn't surprise me," I said. "If you left him alone, that guy would forget to go to bed."

"Two things before *I* go to bed," said Mike. "I haven't been this relaxed in years and...I'd like to extend my stay. Not here, but if you'd allow me to, I'd like to go out to your place in the Hamptons for a couple of days. Alone. Be honest and tell me if that's a good idea."

As Mata drew a map, I described our cottage on Louse Point Road in Springs, just north of Amagansett, on the outskirts of East Hampton. The cottage was in a picturesque setting on Accabonac Harbor with access from Louse Point Road off the Springs-Amagansett main road. She marked hide-aways we'd discovered as well as vital points of interest like Mr. Miller's General Store, where he'd get food, gas, and friendship.

We gave Mike the keys to the cottage and to my Alfa Romeo. Mata said she'd pack a reminder list of where things were located in the cottage, along with some other basics required to survive a vacation on the shore.

"Oh, Mike," I said, "if you're up to it, you might want to see the property we bought for building our Shangri-la. Mata's been working on this for a couple of years. Come 'ere. Take a quick look at this model."

We scattered the house and site plans all over the floor but Mike was most intrigued by the scale model of the house, which took less mental transposing.

We eventually got down on all fours and I pointed out Lookout Lane, our private road which went meandering up 65 feet from the rented cottage and terminated at a bluff called Spy Glass Hill. The bluff overlooked Gardiner's Bay, and the open water to the horizon and Montauk Point.

Spy Glass Hill, our house site, originally got its name from the prohibition bootleggers who used the vantage point to guard against surprise raids by the Feds. The site also overlooked Gardiner's Island, a large, private, tree-covered island where some of the infamous pirate Captain Kidd's gold doubloons were recovered on the wide sandy beach.

"That's pretty funny, isn't it?" said Mike. "You buying an oak forest on a peninsula surrounded by a spectacular beach, overlooking the place where bootleggers beached their boats. Bootleggers! Can you imagine that? I'll bet your father and your brother Ric will appreciate *that* irony."

The logs had reduced to smoking embers and Mata portioned what was left in the bottle, three ways.

"Speaking of ironies," continued Mike, over the soft background music Mata had turned on, "Do you realize that if Vinnie hadn't bopped that guy on the head and stored booze in your barn, I wouldn't be here?"

"Mike," I said, "I know for his own safety you can't talk much about our prodigal son, but he's on my mind a lot, and sometimes I can't stand not knowing where, or how, that s.o.b. is doing. You keep saying he's OK, he's OK, but I worry —"

"Don't worry about Vinnie, Jamie. If you wanna worry, worry about the other guy."

"Mike," said Mata, "you have to give us a tiny little morsel of news... something."

"Jamie," said Mike, "remember what my brother Frankie the Foot's basic premise was for a scam? The fewer people know about how it works, the better the odds of pulling it off. Now...back to where we were. If it wasn't for the irony of Vinnie bopping that guy on the head, I wouldn't be here, and you wouldn't be a big shot on Madison Avenue. OK? Have I made my point? Are we on a new subject now?"

"OK. You made your point. Let's talk ironies, Mike. How do you like this climb up the totem-pole? McCallister boots me out to Siberia to get rid of me. Now *my* Daisy Enterprises is doing the agency work for Vanderlane, *their* Madison Avenue agency. Then *they* pass the work back to McCallister and I get 20 times more for designs that *they* rejected when I worked for them. How's that for irony? Sometimes I think Vinnie is right... 'the whole friggin' world is one big friggin' shell game.'"

"Well," said Mike, "there's no question that image and perception play a major role in the day to day decisions we make. In the courtroom, and I can vouch for this, the name of the game certainly is *illusion*."

"Oh, pooh," said Mata, "You should all join hands and form the local cell of SOCK. That's Society Of Cynical Kinsmen. And Vinnie, as chief cynic, should be president."

"That's our in-house optimist speaking, Mike. She forgets that a pessimist is an optimist with experience. Mata, you and I are above role playing, right? We used to wine and dine our clients at the Four Seasons restaurant in New York, like all the other deal makers. Right? So now I pick them up at the train station in the Model T —"

"You still have the Model T?"

"Yeah, I had it shipped out. It's in the carriage house with 'Old Faithful' and the restored Alfa Romeo. Anyway, I tell these guys to dress casually, pick 'em up in the Model T, take them to our place which looks like I'm livin' in Disney's version of Grandpa's well-maintained house, put them up in the carriage house, and after the deal is consummated, take them on a fishing expedition on Daisy I, a 30' planing Bristol fishing boat that's tied up at the South Ocean Avenue pier. Now, that beats dinner at the Four Seasons, anytime, wouldn't you say?"

"Jamie," said Mata, "the point is, we didn't plan it that way. We didn't stage all this as trappings to snare clients."

"Yeah. Let's blame this all on our guardian angels. Right? Point is, they still see us as just plain folks who developed their values around the kitchen table in Grandpa's homestead, even if that was not our intention. Incidentally, the boat-ride *was* calculated for effect. On that one, I plead guilty, your honor."

"Hey," said Mike, "everytime I see you guys, I feel like I've been on a long vacation...or gone to Grandpa's sheltering arms." He put on his shoes, stretched, and said, "Hey...do you guys know it's 1:15 in the morning? And do you know Brat is still out there, working his ass off?"

I got on the intercom and said, "Brat, we just got a news release. Lincoln has just announced the Emancipation Proclamation. You are free to go home now."

"Yowza, boss man. Thank you. One more cigarette and I'll cancel my underground railroad ticket."

Mata gave Mike an extra large bath towel, last minute instructions about the carriage house light switch locations, night lights and other things to tuck him in for the night.

"One more thing before you turn in, Mike," I said. "We have a great boat moored at the Three Mile Harbor Boatyard for you to use. I'll call and tell them you might be coming. They have the keys and you can tie up to the little pier in front of the cottage. When you're done, they'll come get it."

Two days later, Mike called from the cottage and said, "There's one thing better than owning a boat and that's having a friend who owns a boat. The good news is I've never had so much fun in my life. The Blues are running, your house site is the best I've ever seen, anywhere. It is a veritable paradise and

I've made friends with two local Bonackers who showed me where to fish. The bad news is, I got into shoal water and busted up the prop and bent the shaft on the motor but the guys from the boat yard, who towed me in, said it's no big deal and they'd send me the bill. Are we still friends?"

"Mike. Remember what they used to say around the old neighborhood about friends?"

"What's that?" he asked.

"Each time friends share and survive a common crisis, the bond gets stronger," I said.

"Is this a crisis?"

"It's gonna be...if you don't pay up." We both laughed.

"Jamie...I'm proud to be your friend."

"Ya still gotta pay up."

Chapter XXVIII

100 miles east over Montauk, our TWA Boeing 707 circled clockwise around the Montauk Lighthouse, Amagansett, Block Island, and the open sea, over and over again, waiting for permission to make the final landing approach. We were returning from England to land at Kennedy, but the New York Traffic Control Sector had stacked us.

It had been an exhilarating but frustrating trip. Mike's London office wined and dined us, showed us the "sewers of London," treated us to the best theatre seats, and chauffeured us like royalty to sights generally inadmissible to the average tourist. I got to practice my limp "Duke of Windsor wave" on by-standers. At bedtime, we were tucked into a suite at the Grosvenor House on Park Lane. Just before sleep, in the darkened room, I thought about Vinnie, who was tantalizingly within reach, but strictly off limits. *Strictly*.

Each time we flew over Springs low enough to see the ant-size people, the plane tilted on its starboard wing so that passengers on that side of the plane saw the ground and those of us across the aisle saw open sky.

"Here comes that place again," someone said loudly, and everyone scrambled for a look out of the windows on the side facing the ground.

"God," said someone. "Can you imagine actually living in a place like that?"

"Is that?...No. It can't be," said someone else. "It can't be a natural body of water in that rock formation. Water's too clean. That's gotta be a swimming pool."

"Tennis court...I see a stable but no pasture."

"Not a stable. It's a carriage house. When we turn a little more...there...there...see the cars? Antiques, I think."

Mata squeezed my hand as we listened to the compliments and looked down at what looked exactly like the miniature architectural scale model of our compound and property.

"Oh! Jamie! Look!" said Mata. "Waiting there by the—" she pushed my head closer to the window and put her lips to my ear. "It's Blackie! Waiting patiently in front of the studio door. Oh, dear, dear doggy. I miss him terribly. Just terribly." She touched her temple to mine and we went back to studying the terrain passing beneath us.

"Alas," I said, "into each life some rain must fall. Take a look at what's tucked in the bushes behind the guest house. There it is. The van Vinnie bought Stephanie as an engagement present. We're in for another surprise visit by Stephanie and Rodney. I wish she'd surprise us sometime by leaving the kid with her mother in Connecticut."

Stephanie felt that until the deportation dust settled once and for all, she and Vinnie would have to just sit tight; she in the home they had secretly purchased for their new life in New London, 15 minutes away from her parents, and Vinnie, in a mysterious, strange existence, that ebbed and flowed somewhere between southern Italy and Sicily.

Vinnie was nothing but surprises. He had been deported to a place just outside of an American military base in southern Italy. In typical Vinnie fashion, he soon became a broker for surplus ordnance, and had organized and sold catalogues of available surplus military material. He started advertising with ads in paramilitary magazines, expanded into civilian newspapers, and before they realized they were under attack, was making more money than all the base commanders combined.

Then he disappeared for several years. When he surfaced again, we learned that he had been an undercover agent tracking movements and strength of organized prostitution rings established around U.S. military bases in Europe.

Vinnie was putting all of his ducks in a row. His engagement to Stephanie, with her son from a previous marriage, was probably the most important single event that had occurred in Vinnie's life. The betrothal offered all of the essential life-force needs he'd been searching for in "one swell foop," as he would say. Suddenly the love, the stability, the promise of a family unit he'd longed for, and the born-again feeling, changed his personality dramatically for the better. The love exchange, the allegiance, and the commitment, appeared to be equally distributed in the triad.

In the latest leg of his transformation attempts to normalcy, Vinnie cashed in some powerful political chips and, from what we heard from the meager grapevine, was in line to accept a respectable job as an official of the public-health department of the state of Connecticut.

As Stephanie's van disappeared beyond our range of vision, I said to Mata, "Wouldn't it be ironic if the new job Vinnie's getting when this mess is finally over, turns out to be a whorehouse inspector? That, to me, would be poetic justice."

"Jamie," said Mata, "all of us are blessed...Mike...Vinnie. When you consider what a miraculous change Stephanie and that child have made in Vinnie's life —"

"I like the boy. He's a normal, happy, active child. But

that's the problem. Until we get our guest house childproofed ...remember what it took to put that place back together again after their last surprise visit? And now with her new job and her living only a two-hour ferry-boat trip to Orient Point, I'm gonna have to hire an on-site repair crew."

The plane left our home behind and started to retrace the oval pattern once more. Mata and I wobbled our way back across the aisle to our assigned seats; me against the window, Mata on the aisle, with books and pamphlets piled on the seat between us.

When we first boarded and made our way to the rear of the plane, we had plucked eight copies of the complimentary on-board magazine "The Ambassador," which was tucked into the pocket behind every seat. We had been interviewed for a long article for the magazine describing our successful techniques as co-owners of Daisy Enterprises, Inc.

We looked forward to reading the report but were surprised to find a flattering photo of ourselves on the cover of the magazine. At least one copy, I was determined, would make its way into Mamma's family album.

When we finally landed at Kennedy, the stewardess at the exit held out a copy of the Ambassador magazine with a pen and asked for our autographs. We were both surprised and embarrassed by the novel experience. By the time we followed the porter wheeling our luggage to the VIP Ambassador's Club where we were to meet Mike DaFutte, we were flying higher than the 707 had been.

The porter neatly stacked our luggage inside the cloak alcove, and as he started back out, trailing his dolly, Mike rushed past us without saying a word and intercepted the uniformed young man. As Mike was giving the nodding young skycap instructions, he discreetly slipped some folding money into his hand and helped him reload the hand truck.

"I thought *you* were the last of the big-time tippers," said Mata, as we watched Mike from the middle of the swanky, chandeliered room. "But he's worse than you are, Jamie. You both are enigmas to me." She scanned the elegant room and turned back to me. "You and Mike are the only people I know who tip one-hundred-and-fifty percent of the check amount and then, paradoxically, you insist we ride coach on the plane."

I kept my eyes on Mike who was the only man besides me in the room not wearing a white shirt, dark suit and tie. I had on a conservative sport jacket with a white sport shirt collar turned out. Mike was wearing a sweatshirt that said in bold letters, "Blessed Are the Trouble-makers" on the front and "The Cerberus Group" on his back.

"Mata...Mike once said, 'money is often wasted on the rich.' A guy once gave me a twenty-dollar tip when I was a waiter at a Danish Smorgasbord. That's when coffee was still a nickel a cup. That money came into my life at a very opportune time. It gave me a very important boost and I never forgot it. Mike, Vinnie, and I have *all* been there. We'll *never* forget it." We looked into each other's eyes and it was clear that the message had registered.

Chapter XXIX

Mike swept Mata up in a bear hug and without taking his nose out of her hair, extended a hand for me to shake.

"Your sweat shirt is certainly getting its share of attention," said Mata, as we made our way across the dining room. "The pressed suits are looking at you and exchanging knowing glances like you're wearing white patent-leather shoes after Labor Day."

"You couldn't do better if you were dressed in a gorilla costume or a Santa Claus suit," I added.

Walking between us with his arms around our waists, Mike ushered us through the dining room toward the best table in the place, located against one of the glass panoramic walls on the far side. The empty table next to ours had table settings and was marked "reserved."

"They've been eyeing and evaluating me ever since I got here," said Mike. "They can't get past the 'Blessed' on my sweat shirt and I think they've concluded I must be the spiritual leader of the religious cult that's taking advantage of those robed kids out there with the begging baskets and shaved heads that are scattered throughout the airport."

As we approached our table we could see that a copy of "The Ambassador" magazine had been propped open on the approach side of the table with the cover facing us. A small hand-lettered sign that read "Veni, Vidi, Vici" had been scotch-taped above our cover photograph.

The young beautiful brunette in the formal dress who'd been patiently sitting at our table with her hands folded in her lap, rose gracefully, smiling, and took a step toward us.

"This is Regina," said Mike. "These are my celebrity friends, Jamie and Mata, on the cover and in the flesh, whom, I suppose, we'll have to address as 'Your Excellencies' from now on." Regina curtsied, and Mike graciously seated us around the table which was prepared with magnificent tableware and an incongruous four-candle polished silver candelabra that sported small, alternating Italian and American flags instead of candles. All the other tables had flower centerpieces.

Our dining area was cantilevered over the lower level and through the glass wall we overlooked rows of corporate twin-engined turbo-prop airplanes interspersed with smaller Lear jets. Mike's glistening Grumman, which we would be boarding soon, was parked directly below us. It had the name "The Cerberus Group" stretched on the fuselage over the passenger windows.

With menus at all the tables around us but none at ours, Mike said he'd take charge of the ordering and disappeared into the kitchen.

Regina, Mata, and I utilized the time to get acquainted. Regina was one of those people who can generate instant rapport. When we asked her to tell us about herself, she spread the fingers of her left hand and ticked off vital character descriptions and accomplishments on her fingers like she was counting on an abacus. She spoke five languages fluently, had worked for the American Embassy in Rome, the Italian Embassy in Washington, and sometimes at the UN.

Regina knew Stephanie from the Embassies, where both women were instant-translators. She had seen photographs of Vinnie but they'd never met. She spoke with a British accent, was born in Italy, and now worked full time for Mike. *Whew!* She gracefully made a gesture of supplication to indicate the recital was over and we all giggled. Mata and I lightly applauded her performance.

"So you're Italian?" I asked.

"No," she replied with a smile, "I used to be Italian. Now, I'm a naturalized American. How about you?"

"Me too. I used to be Italian...when I was poor. Now I'm a Republican." Regina laughed.

"I would have thought, The American Party; also referred to by the elitists as The Know Nothings."

"Wow," said Mata, "I'm impressed. You sure know your American history. You must have bowled them over at the naturalization test. No, actually we both register as Independents, so that in any political discussion, we get hammered mercilessly from both sides by our friends in both major parties. Tell Jamie who the *No Nothings* were, and I'll listen in...because I know nothing."

Shortly after Mike returned and sat down, two waiters came to our table and carefully placed steaming, aromatic bowls of soup before us.

"You know," I said, after a few minutes of appraising the soup, "this is the first time I've ever seen escarole soup served in a non-Italian restaurant. And...this is weird...but I've never seen it served with these small meatballs, *anywhere,* except in Mamma's kitchen." Next came delicious platters of Eggplant Parmesan with Braciola and Ziti.

"This is getting too weird," I said, as I gazed from one heaping platter to the next which had by now overflowed onto the end-table. The end-table had been added as an extension, to accept the endless courses being relayed like a bucket brigade from the swinging doors of the kitchen.

"The Braciola have toothpicks stuck in them to hold them together, like Mamma's. What the hell is going on here?"

"I don't know," said Mata, "but this sure beats the TV dinners they served on the plane, doesn't it?" We all laughed as she licked her fingertips with exaggerated ecstasy.

A man had come over from the table next to us and said, "Excuse me, but...ah...are you all ordering from a different menu than we got?"

"No," said Mike, who was enjoying my bewilderment, "No...you can't order this —"

"Mr. DaFutte," broke in the waiter who was standing to one side with an oval platter, "you want me to hold off with this Onion Calzone?"

"Onion Calzone!" I looked at Mike who was rocking with laughter and alternately slapping his thighs and the table edge. Regina was discreetly stifling convulsive guffaws behind the napkin she was holding to her mouth.

"OK, Mike. What the hell is going on here?"

"No," said Mike, when he composed himself enough to answer the man who was still standing at the head of our table trying to make sense, like me, of what was going on. "No, you can't order this stuff here...sorry, but all of this food was flown in from Cleveland!"

The man from the table next to us apologized profusely and excused himself. He took a step toward his seat, turned towards us, puzzled, and mouthed, "*Cleveland?*"

Mike and Regina stood up, beaming, and vigorously applauded a commotion that had erupted in the kitchen behind us. Many of the customers sitting at tables just beyond them spontaneously stood up. The action ignited a wave of standing people and applause that gradually spread throughout the large restaurant until the room reverberated with a cacophony of sporadic shouts, whistles, and scraping chairs.

Mata and I slowly turned to follow the focus of all the grinning faces that seemed to be gazing in the direction of the kitchen. The swinging doors were being held open by two pleased waiters. What they flanked took my breath away.

Standing in the opening, framed by the doors and the sentry waiters, stood Mamma, in a large white apron, holding a candlelit birthday cake. She was smiling sheepishly through the embarrassing central role she had obviously been pressed into playing despite her customary reluctance to be the center of attention in crowds.

"Happy Birthday to you / Happy Birthday to you / Happy Birthday dear Jamie —"

My first reaction to the shock was to leap to my feet. I snapped my body forward, eyes closed, rigid arms extended in the general direction of the table edge, and the base of my right thumb, with my body weight behind it, landed precisely on the edge of a saucer which was supporting a full cup of coffee.

As the catapulted coffee cup and saucer spun their way to the ceiling, coffee sprayed on everyone and everything within a radius of ten feet. The melee that followed could not have been more complete if a live hand grenade had exploded in our midst.

Mamma and the waiter to her left stood frozen where they were, not changing expression, not moving a muscle, except the ones required to move their eyes, which were locked on the upward trajectory of the delicate, imported porcelain cup. It was a perfect launch.

When gravity took over, the saucer crashed first and the waiter to Mamma's right leaped forward with outstretched hands to intercept the falling eggshell-thin cup. The spring-loaded door he left unguarded behind him did what it was supposed to do. It slammed the cake and the fluttering candles Mamma was holding out in front of her hard into her chest, reducing the smashed cake to something you'd see in a food fight. It was a perfect smash.

I made my way through the swinging doors into the kitchen, past the flamenco dancers stomping on the burning candles scattered around the kitchen floor, swept Mamma off her feet in a bear hug, swirling and kissing her face repeatedly before I set her down.

It was when we separated and I held her at arm's length that I noticed most of the cake had been transferred to *my* chest. Then to my father, when I hugged him, then my sister got her share, and finally, Ric got his portion. Their lucky spouses were left in Cleveland with the kids.

"Happy Birthday, Jamie," said my brother George, who towered over the fray from a safe distance. As we shook hands and I transferred some white cake icing onto his finger, he said, "I don't think you'll forget this birthday for a while, bro. This hair will grow cake on your chest."

"You all know how I hate surprise parties, but this has got to be the best family gathering of all time!" I looked around and everyone was wiping someone else's torso with a towel and laughing hysterically like we were playing a successful silly parlor game. Everybody looked disheveled except Mamma. She'd taken off her apron, washed her hands and stood pristine and grinning on the fringe of the spectacle. Everything about her was exactly the same. Even her marcelled hair-do. As I walked toward her with outstretched arms to smoozle some more, she waved me off and stepped away.

"Ma!" I said, with a feigned look of shock, "You shun your favorite, best-looking, smartest son, on the day of his birth?"

"You forget," she said, in her Italian dialect, "that this is also the day you almost killed me. Trying to decide for two days whether you wanted to join our family or not. Eh...h...h, you son of a gun, you!"

I faced her at arms length, leaned forward at an awkward angle, took her face in my hands, and kissed her gently on the lips. "Ma, I sure made the right decision when I decided to join *questa famiglio.*"

We stared into each other's eyes, then she looked down at my cake-smeared chest, back into my eyes, and pulled me into a full squishy embrace. "Thanks to God," she said, into my ear and over my shoulder to the others as we hugged and rocked, "you made the right choice, Jeemie. You have brought much honor to our family, my wonderful son." As we started to get weepy, the room exploded into cheers and applause.

Mike came into the kitchen from the dining room where he had been helping with the clean-up.

"Barry," he said, to one of the waiters, "I don't think we'll need any more of this food here. Pack it into a jumbo doggie bag with the rest of the stuff, the way Mamma wants it. But before you do, would you mind putting two portions of the calzone on a platter and serving it to the table next to us...to the man who was standing at our table just before World War III began. And, oh, Barry, would you please serve the after-dinner drinks in here."

We held up our glasses and Mike said, "Happy Birthday, dear friend. We've come a long way since Clark and Fulton. May you live to be 130. And if you do...and I say this in front of witnesses...I'm gonna see to it that you get a decent burial and

I'm *personally* gonna give you a *great* eulogy."

"You know, Mike," said Mata, "I never knew you and Jamie and Vinnie from the Clark and Fulton days, but I still feel I've known you all of my life. You're all financially secure, even Vinnie and Stephanie with their surplus catalog business that's gonna make them richer than God. But the rarest and most valuable thing you all have...is your friendship."

"Here, here," said Mike, "Here's to us, and to Vinnie, God bless 'im. To quote your Uncle Nick...here's to...friendships that are made with fire."

"Forged! Forged!" corrected the ladies in unison. "...Forged with fire!" There was a hearty round of laughter.

"OK...OK...all right —" said Mike, "Here's to Vinnie...the forger... wherever he is!" He moved his glass in an arc above his head and there was another burst of laughter and applause.

"Oh, I can't tell you where *he* is, that's for sure," I said, "but *Stephanie's* slinking around the bushes behind our guest house, waiting to surprise us."

"How...how the hell did you know that?" asked Mike. "That was supposed to be the best kept secret. Jamie, you will never cease to amaze me. Now tell me, Mr. Sherlock. How did you know she was out there?"

In a Gestapo accent I'd learned from the movies, and with one eye squeezed shut like I was wearing a monocle, I smacked an imaginary baton against my calf and said, "*Heh, heh. Ve haff ow vays.*"

As we were filing across the room on our way to the plane, the man who had been sitting next to us caught up with us and shook our hands.

"I must tell you," he said, "that was the most delicious morsel we have ever eaten. Thank you so much. I hope you don't mind, but I took the coffee-stained copy of the Ambassador magazine you left on your table. I know I'm being a little pushy here...but...may I keep it as a souvenir.?"

"Of course you may," said Mata.

As we walked away, Mata leaned toward my ear and asked, "Is it *may I*, or — *can I*?"

"It's *may I*," I said.

"You're sure?"

"Positive."

"Who's your source of authority?"

"A super English teacher, Jenny's mother. Bless her heart. Wherever she is...at."

Everyone was tucked into the seats of Mike's turbo-prop. Mamma, Papa, and Ann, had never been airborne until Mike flew them to New York from Cleveland, but they looked as comfortable in their buckled seats as they would on a Sunday ride to Brookside Zoo in one of Papa's patched-up cars.

We were in the air for about ten minutes when Mike rejoined us after talking to his pilot and co-pilot. "Everything looks good. We'll be surprising Stephanie...oh, wait a minute...I suppose you already know that little Rodney is up in Connecticut with Stephanie's parents. Right?"

"No, as a matter of fact —" Mike nudged my shoulder and motioned me to the rear of the plane with his eyes. We settled into seats that faced each other over a narrow formica table. "According to Yogi Berra, this is *deja vu* all over again."

"What is?"

"They're gonna deport him again."

I studied his twitching face muscles to determine what my reaction was supposed to be.

"OK. I'll bite, Mike. They're going to deport who again? In

my whole life, the only guy I know who's ever had the honor of being run out on a rail is Vinnie, and what the hell would be the point of the U.S. government deporting him —" I studied Mike's attempt to stifle an explosive laugh. "Son-of-a-bitch. It *is* Vinnie, isn't it? The son of a bitch has accomplished another all-time first, hasn't he?"

Mike exploded with hysterical laughter, buried his face into his arms, which were cradled on the table before him. When he came up for air, he kept nodding and pointing to me, managing to gasp out, "...you... guessed —" He finished the sentence with a squeaking sound.

Even though I didn't know the joke, I found myself laughing with him. I scratched my scalp and looked at the Long Island landscape passing below us, knew the source of the joke was going to be Vinnie, and the story was going to be a beauty.

Chapter XXX

The story *was* a beauty. It seems that greedy Vinnie had expanded his surplus ordnance business internationally to include corrupt Italian government bureaucrats and the Sicilian Mafia. The Italian government officials saw an opportunity to work directly with the U.S. supplier and brushed Vinnie aside by finding a pretext to cancel his visa. They, despite the official arrangements made with the U.S. government, wanted to deport Vinnie back to the United States. The tactic created a problem, but not a serious one. Subordinate bureaucrats, with a face-saving, personal interest to protect, had to work out the solution to unscramble that little mess.

The Sicilian Mafia problem, however, was a very serious one. They wanted him dead.

"Jesus, Christ, Almighty, Mike. They'll have every exit port, every road, every mud path out of Italy covered, with a bounty on his head that could turn Mother Theresa into a snitch. He'll never beat this one."

"He's beat it. So far. Our agents put him in a brown frock, sandals, rope around the waist, a full beard and moved him through customs and the ogling airport surveillance cameras in a crowd of 13 other young traveling monks."

"What about a paper trail? You think these guys aren't practiced enough to sift through even shredded records?"

"Jamie...Jamie. That's what I do for a living. Remember?"

"OK. OK. So you're telling me I'm gonna meet Vinnie in... ah...ah...Mike, if you're putting me through this shit for laughs, I'll never believe you again. So help me Christ."

"I know. I know. Just do what I'm telling you. You just go down to St. Rocco's Church in Little Italy on Broome Street between Mulberry and Mott, on the twenty-first, at 6:00 p.m. One of New York's uniformed finest will be standing in front of the small stone church. He'll be one of ours. He won't acknowledge you. All you need to know is, if he's there, go in and sit near the confessional on the left. When the monk goes into the confessional, you follow."

As a precaution, the cab dropped Mata and me off in front of the "Grotto Azure" restaurant on Mulberry Street and we walked the short distance to the church. It wasn't until I saw the uniformed cop studiously ignoring us in front of St. Rocco's that I started to take this thing seriously. We entered the empty church and sat in the last row pew nearest the confessional, as we had been instructed to do. And waited.

We were a little early, so we fell into the stupor usually reserved for doctor's waiting rooms. I studied the stained glass, the architecture, Mata, then my watch; our rendezvous was now ten minutes late.

As I turned my wristwatch toward Mata, she tapped my thigh with her fingertips and pointed with her chin to the rotund monk in the United-Parcel-brown frock who had just entered from the left vestry and was half-heartedly genuflecting at the altar rail. He was still crossing himself as he turned and started up the aisle toward us. By the time the automatic control closed the door behind him with a *CLACK* that echoed around the interior of the church, the full-bearded monk was most of the way to the confessional. We never made eye contact. His detached expression never changed.

I looked at Mata, squeezed her hand, side-stepped to the confessional directly behind me, and slipped in. When the panel was slid open, I couldn't tell for sure if it was Vinnie or an imposter. There was so much hair on the face and head I saw before me through the caned screen, it could have been an off-season Santa in his leisure clothes.

"Gee-Gee?" he asked.

"Ga —" I couldn't form the response. "Gretchen...Goering.... Son-of-a-bitch. Vinnie? Is that really you?"

"Now, now, son," he whispered with his head tilted against the screen, "this church will tolerate a lot of grisly things in the name of God, but one thing we will not tolerate, and that's swearing. Especially in church. And I personally find swearing very offensive, you asshole. Say 27,303 Our Fathers and 10 Hail Marys before you leave this place."

We got to rocking and stifling laughter so hard, like two children who'd passed a dirty note in school, that we banged off the walls of the confessional loud enough to alarm Mata.

"What's going on in here?" she whispered with her head tucked into the opening on my side of the cubicle. With one hand rearranging the stream of tears dripping down my face, the only response I could muster was a throat-clearing gurgle, a lot of nodding, and a "go-away" waggle with my other hand.

It took a while but with a little experimenting, we discovered we could maintain a fragile level of composure if we both stared at the floor.

"Vin, I know how you always felt about the church, but this surrealistic scene, here, is making me very uncomfortable."

"Good! You're not supposed to feel comfortable in church. You're supposed to feel guilty. Ya wanna feel comfortable, go get laid. That's my official recommendation."

"Ah right. C'mon Vin, grab ahold of yourself —"

"Good idea. It's nice and dark in here. Let's both grab ahold of ourselves." We hyperventilated and coughed repeatedly in an attempt to keep the spasm suppressed, and to return to a semblance of control.

"OK...do you know..." I said between sniffs, "...do you know...that you're probably the first guy ever to be banished by both the host and the hostess countries? I know I'm wasting my breath, but, this is dangerous, dangerous, fire you're playing with here, brother. Why the hell do you do this shit?"

When I looked through the caned screen, he had the back of his head resting against the wall, with a meditative expression that was not unlike the novice itinerant priest I'd encountered as a child in the confessional at St. Francis. I described how I went into confession as a kid with the same tired sins and tried to impress the young priest with, "I coveted my neighbor's wife."

I could see by his expression that Vinnie had launched his mind back into time. There was an interlude of silence and when his tour of the past was over, his blinking eyes signaled that he was back.

"What was your most confessed sin in those days, Jamie?"

"I disobeyed my parents."

"What did your parents tell you to do that you disobeyed?"

"Stay away from troublemakers like you."

"You know what? They may have been right," said Vinnie. "But, on the other hand, me being the arsonist and you being the fireman, has made for a very lively life, ya gotta admit. Jamie, we're both street-smart fighters. We know that if someone's gotcha by the short hairs, you grab 'em by the balls.

345

You took the high road, I took the low road, and both roads took us to where we wanted go...for a while. When you think about it, at any given point in time, everybody is just about where they ought to be."

"...*At any given point in time, everybody is just about where they ought to be*," I repeated. "I like that. I'm gonna have that inscribed on your tombstone...just below the words, 'Blessed are the troublemakers.'"

"There ya go!" said Vinnie. "See...if it wasn't for guys like me, there'd be no need for smartasses like you!" We snickered, there was a long pause, and he went on.

"It's been a helluva wild ride, ole buddy. You came to Yogi Berra's fork in the road first, and took it.... Now it's my turn."

He leaned into the screen and said firmly, "For me, this is it. I'm dropping 30 pounds, going to scoop my wife-and-son-to-be, settle in the Connecticut house, change my name to hers, surprise you and Mata with more visits than you can stand, and become a pillar of ole New London. So whatta ya think? Think the troublemaker's gonna make it, old buddy?"

"Vinnie, I can't wait to find out."

"Me either, Jamie, me either."

THE END

POSTSCRIPTS

The pecking order of life is determined by gene pool, environment, and experience. The proper mix is yet to be formulated.

Jamie V. LaBianca

Each of us will periodically test our mettle against challenging adversaries, real and imagined. The outcome, each time, reinforces or adjusts our perceived position in the pecking order. Those who continually reach beyond their prescribed capabilities or refuse to submit to their bestowed limitations, are the troublemakers. Blessed are the troublemakers.

Michael A. DeFutte
Attorney at law

At any given point in time, everybody's just about where they ought to be.

Vinnie Grosso

Amicizie sono fabbricate dal fuoco.

ITALIAN PROVERB

Friendships are forged in fire.

ITALIAN PROVERB

Each time a family or friends survive a common crisis together, the bond grows stronger. The more catastrophic the crisis, the stronger the bond. War buddies, for instance, are buddies for life.